# CONSTRUCTION PLANT

Management and Investment Decisions

# CONSTRUCTION PLANT

**Management and Investment Decisions**

Frank Harris and Ronald McCaffer

**GRANADA**
London Toronto Sydney New York

Granada Publishing Limited – Technical Books Division
Frogmore, St Albans, Herts AL2 2NF
and
36 Golden Square, London W1R 4AH
866 United Nations Plaza, New York, NY10017, USA
117 York Street, Sydney, NSW 2000, Australia
100 Skyway Avenue, Rexdale, Ontario, Canada M9W 3A6
61 Beach Road, Auckland, New Zealand

British Library Cataloguing in Publication Data
Harris, Frank
Construction plant.
1. Construction equipment
I. Title        II. McCaffer, Ronald
624'.028        TH900

ISBN 0-246-11240-9

First published in Great Britain 1982 by Granada Publishing

Printed in Great Britain by Richard Clay (The Chaucer Press) Ltd, Bungay, Suffolk

D
624·028
HAR

HS

# CONTENTS

# PREFACE

Technical improvements in construction plant and equipment have caused a movement away from manual labour towards mechanisation on construction projects. This has raised the potential productivity of construction workers while also necessitating relatively large capital investments in machinery and equipment on site which must be operated continuously at an economic level of utilisation if the plant is to achieve a sufficient rate of return on the capital employed. The old option of hiring and firing labour to suit the work load is disappearing fast. As a consequence, increasing numbers of firms, especially those engaged in heavy civil engineering or specialised building, are now placing far more emphasis on the selection, monitoring of performance, control and maintenance of their plant fleets.

At the same time independent plant hire businesses have rapidly expanded to satisfy the short-term equipment needs of construction companies. The plant hire sector is still in its formative stages, but already there are over two thousand enterprises in the U.K. alone. Roughly fifty per cent of all equipment used in the construction industry is now hired.

Because the development of large plant fleets and hiring is a relatively recent phenomenon, detailed and documented analyses describing the nature of construction plant management and its associated organisations are few. During the past few years, however, the authors have made a special study of the management of construction plant and the results of their investigations have been incorporated into both undergraduate and postgraduate teaching in the Department of Civil Engineering at Loughborough University of Technology. This has naturally directed attention towards a textbook on the subject, as it is essential that students receive guidance on the management of construction plant at the onset of their careers. This book has therefore evolved to meet the needs of engineers and builders whose roles are expanding to embrace the increasingly important management of construction plant. Specifically the book covers both the management of plant within a construction company and the independent plant hirer, and deals with policies, strategies and organisational structures from the small to the large concern. By necessity, emphasis is placed on the financial aspects of plant acquisition and control, and modern capital investment decision-making techniques are given special consideration. Operational management is dealt with fully, including health and safety, licensing and insurance: in particular, the logistic problems of maintaining construction plant are discussed in detail. Finally, the book brings together the recent developments in computer technology and its applications to improving plant management.

The book will be beneficial to recently qualified engineers and builders, to students studying for the professional examinations of the Institution of Civil Engineers, the Chartered Institute of Building and the Institute of Quantity Surveyors, and others engaged in technician courses. The book will also serve as a useful reference for plant managers in the industry.

F. C. Harris
R. McCaffer

## ACKNOWLEDGEMENTS

The authors are particularly grateful to Tony Kettle, an accountant in private practice, for advice on some aspects of financial management; Michael Ellis, University Safety Officer, for guidance and comments on the Health and Safety at Work Act; Peter Harlow, Head of Information at the Chartered Institute of Building for suggesting many excellent reference sources; and Richard Miles of Granada Publishing for his invaluable advice and editorial corrections. The book has also benefited from the unstinting efforts of Tony Thorpe, research assistant, for locating the diffused published material on the subjects of this book and checking much of the text. Thanks are also extended to accountants and insurance underwriters for their useful contributions but who, for professional reasons, must remain anonymous. The authors are also grateful to former students who have assisted in extending the body of knowledge in the subject of Plant Management. Finally the authors wish to thank Vera Cole and Barbara Macfarlane who cheerfully and intelligently performed the arduous task of typing the manuscript, and friends and colleagues who helped in the preparation of the artwork.

# CHAPTER 1

# INTRODUCTION

For many years there has been an underlying trend towards a greater use of plant in construction. The scale of modern construction work, and the short construction times required, make the extensive use of plant essential. Furthermore, as the costs of labour have increased so have the benefits of using more machinery, and at site level this has provided the opportunity to achieve greater output per employee.

Unlike firms engaged in labour-intensive construction work and with no plant holdings, plant owners require substantial and continuing capital investment to generate turnover. The profit/turnover ratio of construction companies is usually very low, e.g. 1–3%, while the turnover/capital employed ratio is high. The turnover could be 8 to 15 times the capital employed. For example: if the profit/turnover were 3% and the turnover/capital employed were 10, the profit/capital employed would be 30%. A large plant fleet would disturb this relationship by increasing the capital employed, thereby reducing the turnover/capital employed ratio. In these circumstances high plant utilisation is necessary to generate adequate revenue and a sufficient return on capital.

Consequently civil engineering and building contractors who hold large plant fleets must give very careful consideration to plant selection, the method of acquisition, the monitoring of usage and performance, and the maintenance of their plant fleets. Consequently a separate management organisation has developed around the ownership and use of plant.

The independent plant hire sector has expanded as the trend towards using more mechanical equipment for construction has developed. It now comprises some 2000 companies, accounting for about 50% of all the plant used in the U.K. construction industry. Plant hire companies serve two purposes: they not only provide for hire specialised plant which no single construction company could expect to utilise fully, but also hold and hire everyday items of plant, thereby relieving construction companies of the need to own and manage their own plant fleets. Consequently plant hire firms have acquired specific management skills which are peculiar to owning and operating plant. This has stimulated them to operate their equipment more efficiently and perhaps more profitably than a construction company holding a smaller plant fleet. Thus the need for plant management is divided between construction companies who have their own plant department or division and the plant hire companies. The body of knowledge described as plant management comprises management organisation, economic evaluations, budgetary control and costing, cash flow and financial management. It also involves maintenance and control of maintenance costs, the use of computers particularly for financial and costing purposes, and knowledge of health and safety laws, road transport laws and insurance. This book covers these subjects in four sections:

*Section one: objectives, policies and strategies*
This deals with the objectives of external plant hire firms and the internal plant department of a construction company operating in a profit- or service-centre market.

*Section two: investment and procurement*
This section deals with the economic criteria for evaluating investments in plant including the effects of corporation tax, capital allowances and inflation. These economic analyses are also applied to the various forms of ownership. A detailed procedure for selecting the most suitable plant for acquisition from a range of available plant alternatives is described and the calculation of an economic hire rate taking account of ownership costs is given in a detailed example.

*Section three: operational management*
The various strategies available for effective control of plant maintenance and its costs are described in this section. The Health and Safety at Work Act and the requirements for inspections and testing of plant are summarised. Legal and contractual insurance requirements for plant, especially hired plant are dealt with and the various licences for plant operation on the public roads are reviewed.

*Section four: financial and budgetary control*
This deals with budgetary control and costing, cash flow and financial management as applied to plant companies and plant divisions. The use of computers for these applications is explained.

**Section One**

## OBJECTIVES, POLICIES AND STRATEGIES

# CHAPTER 2

# PLANT POLICY

## Introduction

The development of the plant holding in a construction company's organisation is often the natural result of previous construction activities. Plant items are gradually acquired to service contracts until the holding eventually reaches a size where it becomes necessary to organise the fleet into a separate unit. This marks the beginning of a plant division or even subsidiary, which may continue to develop, supplying the needs of the parent company. In some cases it may become a fully independent concern.

Plant ownership is not a fundamental requirement for a construction company as a vast selection of plant is available for hire as an alternative. Many contractors, however, choose to own some of the plant they need for reasons of convenience and prestige. The decision to acquire plant for profit should be considered carefully: unlike construction work itself, plant should be a capital-intensive business and requires a relatively large central organisation to provide all the facilities for maintenance, cost accounting, hiring, etc. Furthermore an appropriate strategy for achieving profitability for a plant division may not always coincide with that of the construction division.

Therefore it is a major management task to lay down principal policies for the supply and organisation of plant holdings associated with a company's construction activities, so that the objectives for all the company's operations may be achieved. The consequence of these policies will stand as a record for later revision as required. If this is not done the plant fleet may become a hidden and ever-increasing drain on financial resources.

**Plant acquisition policy**

Acquisition options (Figure 2.1)

The means of obtaining construction plant may be broadly classified as follows:

(i)   Owning all plant – including hire purchase, straight purchase and leasing
(ii)  Hiring all plant
(iii) Combining owning and hiring plant

Each method will make special demands on the use of the company's capital and resources.

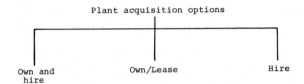

**Fig. 2.1**   Plant acquisition options

*Owning all plant*
The policy practised by many construction companies in Britain before World War II and in most other European countries today is to purchase most of the plant required. Plant availability is maintained thereby at all times with the added advantage of the prestige attached to demonstrating the use of owned plant. However, much capital will be locked up in the plant, which must become capable of generating a sufficient rate of return. A major disadvantage, however, of owning a large plant fleet is the problem of maintaining adequate levels of utilisation. Plant holdings are usually built up to service a growing demand for construction work, and will become a heavy liability when an economic recession occurs. The plant operator could be forced to obtain any work to sustain the plant fleet, since equipment cannot easily be sold in a declining market.

*Hiring all plant*
Many specialist plant hire firms are available in the U.K. for the supply of plant and equipment. The contractor who takes advantage of this facility avoids both the responsibility for maintenance and care of the plant and tying up his capital. The equipment may be hired for a specified period and hire charges minimised by standing off-hire all unwanted plant. In many instances the plant operative is also provided by the plant supplier.

   The main disadvantage of hiring is that hire rates depend on market forces and are largely beyond the control of the contractor, except for limited negotiation between competing firms. This vulnerability to changes in the industry's economic climate could seriously affect a contractor's quoted price for work and the costs incurred later when the work is carried out.

*Combining owning and hiring plant*
A company may prefer a mixed policy of owning and hiring plant. For example, plant that is required for work on most contracts may be purchased and hiring adopted only to smooth out demand.

## Plant policy

### Setting the objectives

*1. The type and quality of service to offer*
The management of a construction company, which has included as one of its main objectives the necessity to own and operate plant rather than hire, must organise itself to either:

(i)  provide plant to service the company's contracts at rates of hire which compare reasonably with those available in the open market; or
(ii)  operate the plant division as a separate entity responsible for generating its own capital and profits, with the freedom to hire plant to clients outside the parent company.

*2. The type and amount of service to offer*
For the provision of plant as a 'service' arrangement, management must decide how much of the firm's capital should be invested in plant, thereby setting indirectly the limits on the proportion of the firm's plant needs that will be self-owned. For the 'profit centre' system of operation, the plant subsidiary is an independent organisation and a specific share of the market for plant hire must be established as a major goal. Both systems will involve taking decisions on the appropriate selections of equipment.

*3. The possible changes and fluctuations in the market for construction work*
The fortunes of the construction industry will fluctuate with the needs of the national economy. There may be, for example, a decline in the road building programme or an expansion of the offshore oil industry. These changes will affect the demand for construction plant and equipment and management should always be looking ahead at the potential consequences.

Finally, whether the plant holdings are organised into a 'profit' or 'service' centre, it must be profitable. Clearly there will be more opportunities for an independent plant company which can set its own objectives and decide on strategies, but even a small service plant department should maintain commercial viability.

## Plant supply policy

The logical way to operate a plant holding is to make it an independent profit centre. This applies particularly to a company trading solely on the basis of hiring plant in the open market. However, many construction companies have plant holdings, some quite large, which are not subject to open competition and it is important that the capital invested is used efficiently. For those firms where the proportion of capital invested in plant is high, it is obligatory to try to maximise the profit on the investment, otherwise the capital would be better used elsewhere in the business. Any other approach will carry with it serious dangers. If, for example, plant is purchased to provide a service to other parts of the construction company and charged below market rates, the resulting low bids must lead ultimately to other parts of the business having to earn excessive profits to generate an acceptable rate of return on the total capital employed.

Several studies[1] have shown that plant operated as a profit centre generally outperforms plant as a service centre as far as profitability is concerned. In the case of the former, the rigours of the market place ensure that only plant which can show a high level of utilisation and/or profit throughout its working life is purchased. In addition, the constraints are such that the costs of maintenance are controlled so that neither too much or too little is undertaken. For the service centre structure, however, operating costs are ultimately met by the company as a whole, and there is a tendency for both maintenance facilities to expand and items of plant to be purchased, with little regard to levels of utilisation. The several organisational arrangements described below have evolved to accommodate the needs of the company, each having consequences which affect the efficient use of resources.

**Alternative options for plant supply** (Figure 2.2)

An independent plant hirer

This type of organisation covers both the independent plant hire company and plant hire subsidiary operating under the umbrella of a holding company which may or may not be a construction firm. The company will supply plant to the market to provide a satisfactory rate of return on the employed capital although sometimes discounts may be offered to a parent company, in accordance with a policy towards a 'favoured' or important client. Decisions on plant purchases and plant holding policy will be taken by the subsidiary board, with only the major objectives set by the parent company.

Normally, the subsidiary company will be given a name which is not associated with the parent firm, so that other construction companies will not be discouraged by advertising a competitor's name on a construction site.

Plant for the hire fleet will be purchased to make a profit based on its utilisation potential and the maintenance record experienced with similar items, together with an assessment of the hire rates likely to prevail in the future.

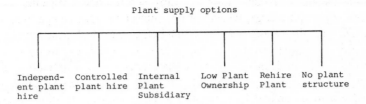

**Fig. 2.2**    Plant supply options.

### Controlled plant

The plant fleet of a construction company may ultimately become so extensive that to maintain effective control, the holdings are incorporated into a subsidiary division. The first priority may be to serve the plant needs of the parent company at a profit, but in order to maintain high levels of plant utilisation and thereby maximise profits, plant items may be hired out to other users. Many construction companies recommend as a rule of thumb that the ratio of 'hiring internally to the parent company' to 'hiring externally to the market', should not be less than two to one.

The tendency with this system, however, is for the plant to be hired out to the market when the rates are attractive, since there will be a demand for such services and the required plant utilisation levels can be more easily achieved this way. Consequently there is a danger that the needs of the parent company may be neglected, and plant items will not be available at the right time for the company's own construction contracts. Furthermore the servicing and maintenance requirements of plant hired internally may have to take second place to that required 'outside'.

### Internal plant subsidiary

The dilemma of servicing two different types of client presented by a controlled plant policy is eliminated when the activities of a plant subsidiary are restricted to internal hire only.

This system often results in plant hire rates which bear little relationship to market rates, as the type of plant items and utilisation levels are dictated by the demands of the construction division. Nominally the plant subsidiary is required to achieve a set rate of return on the capital employed. Sometimes, however, the targets cannot be achieved and the deficits must be covered by the parent company. Such an arrangement may produce a management team which is not held in the same regard as the profit-oriented parts of the company, with a consequent loss of influence and confidence of the plant manager. Decisions on plant purchases and control may increasingly be imposed by the construction side of the business to compound the difficulties of making profits from the plant holdings.

### Low plant ownership

Some construction companies operate very small plant holdings on the grounds that achieving profitability from plant ownership is relatively less rewarding than other construction activities. A small plant depot may be maintained to provide small items only and most of the problems of owning plant are avoided. This system, of course, relies heavily on the facilities provided by plant hire companies. However, the availability of specialist plant items can influence the work load and contract type open to the company and so could affect the success of this sort of policy.

### Rehiring plant company

In order to reduce the administrative duplication of each site or contract, obtaining and then invoicing for payment the plant requirements, some companies operate on a basis similar to the low plant ownership arrangements, but provide a centralised service of hiring-in all plant and passing it on to the sites. The main advantage lies in the ability of a centralised administration to negotiate favourable terms and discounts with regular hire firms. Besides economy, some co-ordination of plant hire requirements across the company can also be achieved and so accommodate the transfer of plant items from one site to another.

### No plant structure

The parent company could take the view that the policy of using an unstructured organisation with respect to plant holding will serve the firm's needs best. Several arrangements are possible: for example, individual contracts may purchase plant and be credited subsequently with nominal resale values when the plant leaves the site. In this case care has to be exercised in assessing equitable sums when purchases and resales are internal transactions. This method is usually confined to special items, such as grouting pumps, cableways, etc. which are usually sold off when a contract has no further use for them. In conjunction with this system more general items may be moved from site to site without a formal charging procedure. Plant is costed as an overhead to the contract on an arbitrary basis but these policies clearly carry the risk of not forcing the plant to make a sound financial contribution to the company's activities.

### Plant structures in practice

The top fifty U.K. construction companies (expressed in turnover terms) operate their plant holdings in the following ways:

| Type of plant organisation | Number of firms |
|---|---|
| (a) Independent plant hirer | 13 |
| (b) Controlled plant hirer | 10 |
| (c) Internal plant subsidiary | 4 |
| (d) Rehiring company | 7 |
| (e) Low plant ownership | 6 |
| (f) No plant structure | 10 |
| | 50 |

It can be seen that almost one half of the firms operate the plant department as a profit centre ((a) and (b)). Only a very small proportion (four firms) have a service system of internal plant hire (c). These latter companies are in fact four of the largest firms in the land and presumably have sufficient work for plant in their own organisations to keep utilisation at levels which are economic and profitable for the firm.

The rehiring and/or low plant options are clearly a favoured option, especially for small firms or those not requiring much plant, such as house building. These firms are turning to the plant hire market for their requirements.

The above list of types of plant organisation covers practically the whole spectrum of the industry. Each method has its own merits and the following questions should be asked before any item of plant is acquired:

(i) Is ownership of that item of equipment fundamental to the operations of the business?

(ii) Will the capital locked up in the plant generate an adequate rate of return compared to other forms of investment?

(iii) Is purchasing the plant for direct ownership the only profitable way of obtaining and operating it?

Unless the reply to these questions is unequivocably positive, then some other sound commerical reason should be established before authorisation to acquire the plant is granted.

## Reading list

1. Green & Co. (Stockbrokers). *Investment in construction*. London, (published annually)
2. Green & Co. (Stockbrokers). *Medium-sized construction*. London, (published annually).
3. Green & Co. (Stockbrokers). *Investment in plant hire*. London, (published annually).
4. Ballard, E.H. *The control of resources required for the construction of a civil engineering project*. Proceedings, Institution of Civil Engineers, November 1972.

5. Knott, S. Subsidiaries can pay their way. *Plant Hire*, supplement to the *New Civil Engineer*, London, 20 November 1975.
6. Davies, W.H. and Warrington, H. Analysing factors − a plant holding policy. *Building Trades Journal*, 17 October 1980.
7. Douglas, J. *Construction equipment policy*. McGraw-Hill, New York, 1978.
8. Chandler, M.J. *Construction plant policy*. Unpublished paper, Department of Civil Engineering, Loughborough University of Technology, 1977.
9. Conquist, J.L. *A review of government policy effects on U.K. construction company plant purchase*. Unpublished paper, Department of Civil Engineering, Loughborough University of Technology, 1979.

# CHAPTER 3

# PLANT HIRE

## Introduction

The hiring of construction plant has developed during the past 30 years and has introduced a new dimension into contracting. A considerable choice is now available in the range of plant for hire, freeing many small contractors from the burden of having to stock and maintain uneconomic items of equipment.

The real birth of the industry occurred in the 1930s during the economic depression, when many companies had an insufficient workload to justify purchasing all the plant they wanted. This presented an ideal opportunity for entrepreneurs to specialise in holding popular items. During the reconstruction which followed World War II hired plant was in great demand, and since then the hire market has continued to grow: today an estimated 60% of all plant used in the United Kingdom is hired.

Independent plant hire firms are a mixture of large and small companies as indicated in Table 3.1.

Table 3.1    Approximate structure of the plant hire market in 1975.

| No. of firms | Percentage of total firms | No. of employees | Percentage of total turnover |
|---|---|---|---|
| 450 | 18 | 0 - 1 | 0.7 |
| 1 000 | 40 | 2 - 7 | 6.6 |
| 350 | 14 | 8-13 | 9.0 |
| 300 | 12 | 14-24 | 11.0 |
| 100 | 4 | 25-34 | 7.4 |
| 150 | 6 | 35-59 | 13.9 |
| 35 ⎫ | 1.6 | 60-79 | 5.9 ⎫ |
| 35 ⎬ 130 | 1.6 | 80-114 | 7.4 ⎬ 51.4 |
| 50 ⎭ | 2.2 | 115-299 | 20.3 ⎭ |
| 10 | 0.6 | 300 or more | 17.8 |
| 2 480 | 100 | | 100 |

It can be seen from the table that the largest 130 firms account for slightly more than 50% of the total value of the plant hire business. The size of the turnover represents about 5% of the total value of work undertaken by the construction industry, or approximately £1 billion in 1980. However, the high proportion of hired plant used by British construction companies is not reflected elsewhere. The figures vary from country to country, but in continental Europe about 5% of the total plant used is hired. The reasons for the plant hire market developing rapidly in the U.K. whilst remaining relatively insignificant elsewhere are difficult to discover, but the need for a hiring facility would seem obvious. The following reasons have possibly been influential.

(i)    Construction companies on the continent tend to take more pride than their British counterparts in displaying the firm's name and livery on plant items used on contracts.

(ii)    In some countries the law protecting firms hiring out plant possibly offers fewer safeguards than in the U.K.

(iii)    The rate of growth of the U.K. economy during the past thirty years has been relatively slow compared to other major industrial economies, with the accompanying lower demand for construction facilities. Thus where economic utilisation levels for many plant items may have been possible, such an advantage has not been available generally in the U.K. Indeed many regions have, in fact, suffered an erosion of their industrial base, with a consequent loss of economic activity. Such a situation has encouraged the pooling of plant resources in a hire market.

(iv)    The U.K. construction industry includes a large proportion of small firms which provides a lucrative market for hired plant.

(v)    Government policies allowing full and immediate depreciation of the cost of plant have encouraged the purchasing of plant to offset tax payments on profits. This is clearly an inducement for firms to buy plant and look for work to maintain profitable levels of utilisation. Such an arrangement would favour the development of a hiring system.

Once a plant market exists, items of equipment cannot readily be disposed of when the economic fortunes of the construction industry deteriorate. Consequently the supply of plant, ably abetted by government tax policies, has generally grown to meet boom conditions, with a subsequent tightening of hire rates during a recession. As a result hire rates have remained relatively low and therefore favourable for the contractor in recent years. Furthermore, severe competition has forced plant hire rate adjustments to fall short of the rate of inflation and in so doing firms have had to extend the life of equipment beyond the original estimates and minimise servicing and maintenance. The net result is that much old plant is hired out at extremely competitive rates. Obviously this situation must eventually correct itself by amalgamations and bankruptcies. Currently hire rates will vary from region to region depending upon the state of the market and the supplier. The Contractors'

Plant Association publish a schedule of hire rates in the CPA Handbook to offer guidance to both the hirer and supplier.

## The plant hire company

The principal purpose of any plant hire firm is to supply the plant needs of construction clients at a profit. The emphasis is therefore market-oriented compared to the 'service' plant division found in a contractor's organisation. The strategy of a single construction company would have relatively little influence as the plant firm should be more concerned at satisfying the demands of the total market. However the market for construction plant hire varies both in the opportunities for specialisation and the quality of service demanded. It is the management's responsibility to define the aims and objectives of the firm, so that a suitable organisation may be assembled to operate in a competitive market.

### Company objectives

The decisions to be taken include defining:

(i)   The kind of goods and services to offer — for example, earthmoving plant, craneage, small general plant or specialist equipment — and the corresponding location and organisation of stockyards and service facilities.
(ii)  The desired share of the market.
(iii) The possible changes and fluctuations of the market in future years.

Once these are established the company's long term plans may be formulated. These will involve the preparation of a market forecast to be matched subsequently with a corresponding corporate analysis to highlight the strengths and weaknesses of the company for coping with the potential market opportunities. (See fig. 3.1)

## The market forecast

This should endeavour to seek out the wants and needs of the market for hired plant. This should be a systematic and continuous process, executed religiously if the firm is to survive and prosper. The task can be taken in separate stages from which information is finally synthesised to produce the new policies and strategies. The main areas for a typical plant hire company are shown below.

### Analysing the competition for plant hire services

A brief survey of other plant hire companies may reveal segments of the market which have not been fully exploited or conversely should be avoided because of fierce competition. An example of the latter is the demand for heavy earthmoving machines. The national motorway construction programme is now almost complete and future opportunities to use road building equipment are therefore likely to decline. The main points to determine are the strong and weak areas of the hire market including the following aspects:

(a) The firms's market share of the different lines of plant and equipment held, together with an analysis of the recent performance of each type with respect to growth and profitability.
(b) The market share, growth in turnover and profitability of the major competitors, noting the areas of interest for each.
(c) The margin of differences between the company's hire rates and those of the competition, to give a guide as to the improvements required.

### Analysing the potential market for plant

Clearly the demands for construction plant will be reflected in the general level of construction activity. The aggressive plant company will research the major areas of the economy to seek out those sectors of potential growth. This should involve investigating both the public and private sectors, including a special analysis of the regions or projects designated by the government for special development and private companies investing heavily in construction facilities.

### Analysing the competition for resources

#### Finance
Plant requires heavy capital investment which is usually provided by the company itself using private resources, retained profit, hire purchase, leasing etc., or by a bank loan. The availability of loan capital is likely to fluctuate according to the fortunes of the national economy with unpredictable changes in the interest rate and lenders may prefer other sectors of the economy to the construction industry. Furthermore, only companies with a sound financial record of profitability, with mortgageable assets, are likely to be favourably considered by the banking and financing sector. Also, before any item of plant is acquired, it should be remembered that plant once purchased often cannot be turned quickly into liquid cash assets to deal with a crisis.

#### Plant, personnel and premises
Few companies possess the resources or expertise to operate in all sectors of the plant hire market. Therefore external factors which would affect the firm's ability to compete must be defined. For example, the reliability of the various manufacturers and supply agents should be assessed, since the quality of back-up services and availability of spares will have a considerable bearing on competitive performance.

Construction plant will usually last longer and be less costly to maintain if the machine operators and servicing staff are well-trained and responsible. There is always competition for such skilled personnel and a company not prepared to train, educate and pay its workforce well should avoid sophisticated and technically complex plant.

New premises may be required to establish a new plant company or area division. Often the depot must be located near the main market, such as a large town. However, sites which can provide room for expansion, good access and security will be in demand from other firms and industries. These aspects are often overlooked when expansion programmes are put into operation.

### Analysing the client

Some clients are 'better payers' than others, which may help to reduce the need for cash or overdrafts maintained by the plant firm. Although there may be an apparently lucrative market, such as a national road programme, for certain plant lines, clients may be so slow and awkward in their attitude to payment that the plant firm would be advised to avoid them.

## Strengths and weaknesses of the company

It is essential to consider the ability of the organisation to cope with a change of direction or expansion. The structure of the firm must be examined both for its overall structure and the strength of each department.

### The corporate analysis

*Organisation structure*
Most companies have a family tree which represents the official structure of the management organisation. In practice, the actual lines of command and communication are likely to be more subtle than those formally recognised. However, this family tree is a good starting point in highlighting potentially weak structural arrangements.

*Management details*
The quality of present managers will be tested when entering new markets. Much information is often held by the personnel department on such matters as salary, qualifications, education, training and experience. This data helps to identify potentially strong management areas and those which have failed to develop a healthy ladder of achievement on which the younger men can gain experience. If the process is repeated for each department, gaps and stagnant areas become apparent.

*Financial and operational control departments*
This review should be extensive and probably should not be undertaken until policies have been made tentatively. The most likely candidates for investigation are the accounts, administration and plant servicing departments, since they tend to be labour-intensive and reluctant to accept rapid changes. Such departments contribute largely to the overheads, which may rapidly increase if the company

expands into new markets. Overheads should also be borne in mind when moving from a fairly low technical market, say small machines, into a specialised market requiring high technical competence and support.

### Engineering experience

Management and operational control surveys may yield much information about the nature of the company and its employees. The plant business requires that good managers should also be good engineers. Any change in policy should spring from a sound base of experience: it is far too risky to rely entirely on imported skills when undergoing change. Therefore a careful analysis is required of the existing skills within the company to see if they will provide an adequate basis on which to build. In particular, staff expertise is likely to be severely tested when policy changes involve the introduction of new plant lines or when the firm decides to decentralise and establish depots sited away from headquarters.

### Physical resources

Putting new objectives into practice may necessitate new depots and storage facilities. However, the acquisition of land and the construction of new facilities take time, are expensive, and demand careful planning of the location. In addition, new and different plant items may require new maintenance equipment which may be costly and beyond the knowledge and experience of the management and work-force.

### Corporate trading analysis

The following financial ratios yield important information in assessing the financial strength of the company and comparing its performance with that of major competitors:

- Return on capital employed
- Profit on turnover
- Turnover of capital
- Growth in capital employed and in net profits
- Current assets to current liabilities
- Stock value to sales ⎫
- Debtors to sales    ⎬ converted to time periods
- Profit per employee ⎭

By comparing figures over the past five years with other companies in similar fields, some judgement is possible on the viability of the firm and its ability to take on new ventures successfully.

### Trading analysis

The trading analysis means looking at individual plant lines in a fair degree of detail. The type of questions to be asked are:

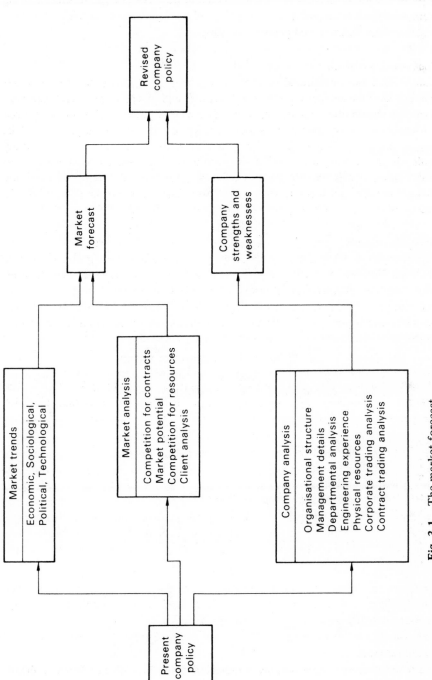

**Fig. 3.1**   The market forecast.

- What trends in profitability, say during the past five years, can be seen in the various plant types and lines?
- How did actual profit compare with estimates?
- How has inflation affected costs and what was the policy towards hire revenues?
- What effect would changing the mark-up included in plant hire rates have had on turnover and overall company profits?
- How did maintenance costs, actual machine life and utilisation levels compare with estimates?

### Trends affecting the forecast

The stage of proposing any changes in company policy, as shown in Figure 3.1, has now been reached. Once the facts are known experienced managers will usually see what changes need to be made. When these tentative proposals have been put forward, managers should realise that new facts will emerge and errors in the forecasts will appear. These are inevitably caused by political changes, shifts in the market outlook, technological developments and economic influences. The effects of these movements are difficult to quantify but should be kept under cautious review and the policies adjusted where necessary. Care should be taken not to over-react to new events as this can cause loss of confidence at middle management level.

### Promoting the company's services and satisfying the customer

Once the company has established the plant lines and the market it desires to service, it becomes vitally important to increase the awareness of the potential customer. This may be achieved by a variety of advertising methods coupled with fostering good public relations. The latter will probably only bring results in the medium to long term and should include providing clean, reliable and well-maintained equipment with an efficient back-up service of spare parts and advice. Co-operation with the client is always helpful. Most construction contracts often involve slight delays and changes to the original requests for plant operation and hire. These are not always detrimental to the operating costs of the plant firm and the goodwill generated will help in the future.

Many clients are impressed by 'added-values' and clearly the firm with back-up services of experienced and well-qualified staff in servicing, maintenance, law, insurance, technical advice, etc. will be a more credible company than one without such facilities.

### Reading list

1. Mead, H.T. Hiring plant for building. *Building Trades Journal*. 23 March 1973.
2. Goodwin, M. Economics of plant ownership. *Contractors Plant Review*. 11 February 1972.
3. When hiring is the best buy. *Illustrated Carpenter and Builder*. 5 December 1969.
4. U.K. Plant Hire Guide. *Contract Journal*, 1978.
5. Drucker, P.F. *The Practice of Management*. Pan Books, London, 1968.
6. Marketing in the Construction Industry. Second report of the working party. Institute of Marketing, 1974.

# CHAPTER 4

# ORGANISATION OF PLANT HIRE COMPANIES AND DEPARTMENTS

## Management Structure

The appropriate management structure will depend upon the nature and size of a firm's business activities. In particular, an independent plant hire firm will require all the management functions of a market-orientated company as shown in Figure 4.1. The internal plant division of a construction company, however, is generally integrated into the parent company's activities and functions such as purchasing and financial accounting may be the responsibility of the parent firm. For both types of business, the need to decentralise into geographical regions, or even major plant types, is a further complication and firms tend to make individual plant depots responsible for their own business activities when faced with this situation although responsibility for overall company policy, major plant purchasing and financial accounts may remain at head office. (see Figure 4.2)

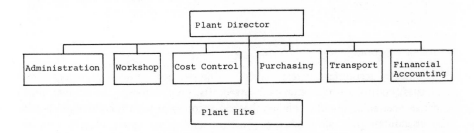

**Fig. 4.1**    Management structure of a plant hire company.

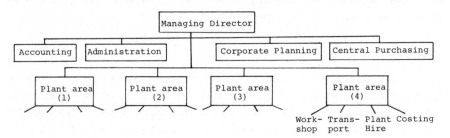

**Fig. 4.2**   Management structure of a regionalised plant holding.

## Typical management functions and departments

### The managing director

The managing director sets the objectives of the business and ensures that necessary strategies are adopted to ensure that the firm will survive and prosper. The managerial functions involved in all but the smallest firms require that much of the day-to-day responsibility for running the various departments is delegated to others, although ultimate responsibility for the success or failure of the business must lie with the managing director. For example, important matters of company policy, expansion plans, development of markets, sources of capital, capital expenditure, purchase and disposal of plant items, are usually decisions taken by the managing director, whose responsibilities may also include liaison with key customers and setting cost and financial budgets for each department.

### Administration

The administrative function will grow with the size of the company and in large firms it is subdivided into separate elements. The list of duties includes health and welfare of personnel, safety regulations, employee training, provision of social facilities, a postal service, legal and insurance advice, the negotiation of wages and salaries, conditions of employment, personnel record keeping, and maintenance of the company's physical assets. Authority is vested with a personnel/administration manager with subordinate heads who are responsible for these duties.

### Financial accounting

The company accountant is responsible for the payment of invoices, receipts from hire sales, control of cash and bank overdrafts, preparation of the trading, profit and loss accounts, and the balance sheet in accordance with the Companies Acts. The accountant has an important function and often works closely with the managing director in controlling the overall financial affairs of the company. He will be involved, for example, in making decisions on the type and source of capital for major purchases, the financial viability of an expansion programme and preparing the company financial budget for the year ahead.

## Purchasing

The buying department is responsible for obtaining quotations for materials supplies and other consumables used at the plant depot and on plant located in the field but maintained and supplied from the central or regional depot. The advantages of centralised purchasing may be realised from:

(i)   the ability to obtain discounts from bulk purchasing;
(ii)  the efficiency generated by adopting standard procedures;
(iii) monitoring the quality of supplies;
(iv)  experience gained from the commercial operations of suppliers and, of course,
(v)   centralised administrative facilities.

However, when a plant department is relatively small and plant items on site are maintained under the responsibility of the construction department, a separate purchasing department is hardly necessary and consumables are purchased as required by site and charged to the workshop maintenance account.

A secondary function of the purchasing department may be participating in the purchase and sale of plant items, especially inviting quotations and assessing the commercial details of a transaction, although, the advice of the heads of other departments will also be involved at this level of plant procurement and disposal.

## Cost accounting

The cost accounts department collects and interprets data from the other departments and its tasks include the preparation of targets in the form of budgets against which costs and revenues may be monitored. This information is used by departmental managers to control and update their operations so that cost targets may be achieved. In particular, the department must record all the data required to prepare hire rates for plant items, and returns are therefore required from all departments, including the hours operated weekly for each plant item.

## Workshop control

The workshop manager is primarily responsible for the maintenance and servicing of the firm's plant. He must provide and maintain a store of consumable materials and spare parts with appropriate stock control procedures although the actual purchasing responsibility usually lies with the buying department. Costs incurred by the workshop include the wages of fitters, mechanics, electricians, and other operatives needed to perform servicing and repair duties, plus the costs of tools, materials, mobile workshops, general overheads, salaries paid to staff and foreman, plant inspection and administration. The budget for the department is allocated from past records of the plant holdings and any additions that can be foreseen. It is therefore essential that maintenance records of each plant item are rigorously updated to facilitate the monitoring of costs against the budget. As a rough guide, maintenance facilities for about 5% of the fleet should be provided.

The workshop manager's function may be augmented by a field manager to provide advice to construction sites on the use, operation and routine maintenance of plant and equipment. In particular, his duties may complement those of the workshop manager, where the company operates a comprehensive system of mobile maintenance to sites. A complaints service may also be provided by the maintenance department.

Transport

Most construction plant is not suitable for travel on public roads and must be transported from site to site on trucks and lorries. The transport supervisor works with the workshop and plant hire departments to co-ordinate the transport needs of the construction sites and other clients. The costs allocated to this department include the running costs of the transport fleet, such as fuel, maintenance, servicing, drivers' wages, supervisors and administration staff salaries, capital cost of the transport fleet and overheads. The responsibility for servicing and maintaining the plant fleet will generally remain with the transport department, but execution of the work may be undertaken by the works department and subsequently charged to the transport account.

Plant hire

The plant hire department provides the selling function and is responsible for generating sufficient revenue from hire of plant to earn a profit for the company. In particular the plant hire manager must work closely with the managing director and cost control department when operating in the open hire market, as it is vital

**Table 4.1**    Example of a company asset register.

| Machine number | Machine description | Purchase date | Purchase price £ | Scrap/ resale value £ | Machine life | Type | Deprecia- tion charge £ | To date £ |
|---|---|---|---|---|---|---|---|---|
| 601 | Terex TS14/70 | 09 1974 | 100 000 | 20 000 | 5 | DBAL | 16 000 | 60 000 |
| 602 | CAT 633C Scraper | 06 1974 | 120 000 | 20 000 | 5 | DBAL | 20 000 | 55 000 |
| 603 | Terex TS14/75 | 11 1975 | 118 000 | 18 000 | 5 | DBAL | 20 000 | 40 000 |
| 604 | Terex IS14 | 11 1975 | 118 000 | 18 000 | 5 | DBAL | 20 000 | 40 000 |

to set flexible and competitive hire rates. The hire manager should be provided with an asset register of records on plant availability and location together with information on plant utilisation levels, plant cost returns and maintenance needs. The costs allocated to this department are those generated by the salaries of the hire staff, marketing, advertising, and overheads.

### The asset register

The efforts of the various departments and functions in the enterprise described above should be directly or indirectly concerned with the profitability, utilisation and performance of the firm's plant. In order that the desired procedures for controlling these functions can be co-ordinated, most firms prefer to record key data on each plant item on an Asset Register as typified by Table 4.1. The recording of the information may be manual, but it is becoming advantageous to store plant data on computer files. The basic information required on the Asset Register should include, for each plant unit, a code number, a registration number, make, model and short description. However, because at some point most departments in the firm will need to refer to the register, additional recorded data is necessary and separate reports must be added. For example, the financial accountant requires data on purchase date and price, planned life, depreciation method, book value, depreciation charge and depreciation to date. The hire department requires the current utilisation factor, hire rate, budgeted earnings, actual earnings and actual costs. In addition an inflation index for the particular plant group is useful in setting new hire rates in times of inflation.

The workshop needs current data on location, base depot, planned operating hours and actual operating hours so that effective maintenance can be monitored. An up-to-date Asset Register can act as a sound programme for carrying out plant safety inspections required for insurance and by law. And not least, the managing director must be constantly aware of a plant item's profitability and utilisation level.

| Written down value | Machine hire rate | Budgeted earnings to date | Actual earnings to date | Total costs to date | % P/L on earnings | % Utilisation Year | Month | Location |
|---|---|---|---|---|---|---|---|---|
| | | | this month | | | | | |
| £ | £ | £ | £ | £ | | | | |
| 40 000 | 45.36 hr | 4 600 | 5 000 | 4 500 | 10% | 82% | 85% | Bristol |
| 45 000 | 47.49 hr | 4 000 | 3 950 | 3 500 | 11.4% | 75% | 76% | Birmingham |
| 60 000 | 48.33 hr | 5 000 | 6 000 | 5 900 | 1.7% | 76% | 73% | Wolverhampton |
| 60 000 | 48.33 hr | 4 900 | 4 000 | 4 100 | - 2.5% | 70% | 67% | Loughborough |

**Reading list**

1. Drucker, P.F. *The Practice of Management.* Pan, 1968.
2. Lemarie, M. Insight on management. *Building Technology and Management.* Vol. 13, No. 6, pp. 5-8, 1975.
3. Koontz, H. and O'Donnell, C. *Principles of Management.* 5th edition, McGraw-Hill, 1972.
4. Hardwick, C.T. and Landuyt, B.F. *Administrative Strategy and Decision Making.* Southwestern, 1966.
5. Barnes, M.C. *et al. Company Organisation, Theory and Practice.* Allen and Unwin, 1970.
6. Brech, E.F.L. (Ed). *The Principles and Practice of Management.* 3rd Edition, Longman, 1975.
7. Calvert, R.E. *Introduction to Building Management.* Newnes-Butterworths, 1970.
8. Dressel, G. *Organisation and Management of a Construction Company.* McLaren, 1968
9. Institute of Cost and Management Accountants. Management by objectives. *Management Accounting,* July 1969.
10. Pugh, D.S. (Ed). *Organisation Theory.* Penguin Books, 1971.
11. Brech, E.F.L. *Construction Management in Principle and Practice.* Longman, 1971.
12. Jayasinghe, D.S. *Managerial structures in plant hire companies and contractors' plant departments.* Unpublished paper, Department of Civil Engineering, Loughborough University of Technology, 1977.

**Section Two**

# INVESTMENT AND PROCUREMENT

# CHAPTER 5

# ECONOMIC COMPARISONS OF PLANT ALTERNATIVES

## Principles of economic comparisons

The basic approach to economic comparisons is to assemble all the costs relating to one course of action and all the costs relating to the alternative course of action and to compare them. The assembling of the costs must be in such a way that the two are comparable. It is the difficulty of ensuring that the assembled 'packages' of costs are comparable that requires the calculation of either present worth, or value, of two proposals or the equivalent annual cost of the two proposals. Of these techniques of comparison present worth is more commonly used. Both present worth and equivalent annual costs require an interest rate which is taken to represent the value of money to the investor. That is, it represents the interest the investor could receive elsewhere.

Comparisons not involving interest rates are very common in short term schemes, that is schemes of less than one year. Construction site staff are continually and almost subconsciously undertaking economic comparisons without interest in the calculations. Such economic comparisons include comparing the hire rate for different cranes, or the hire rate for different excavators, or the hire rate for an excavator from an external plant hire company, with the hire rate from the company's own plant division. Comparing the cost of, say, hand excavation with the cost of using an excavator is another economic comparison. All these comparisons refer to operations with relatively short time periods of a few weeks or a few months and the effect of interest is not significant. Thus, the comparisons are valid and easy to make on an equitable basis. The comparisons become more difficult when the operations or schemes to be compared last a few years or more, when the effect of interest becomes significant and needs to be included in the calculation. The difficulty is assembling the various costs into 'packages' that can be compared for these longer duration operations that require 'present worth' or 'equivalent annual costs'. Some examples of longer duration operations or schemes are plant required for quarrying, open-cast mining or concrete production plant.

All the examples in this section are based on cash flows that have been estimated at present or year zero prices without taking inflation into account. The interest and time relationships used in this chapter are explained later in the Appendix which includes examples of Interest Tables for interest rates of 10% and 15%.

**Present worth**

Present worth comparisons are used to compare two or more schemes where the plant chosen for each scheme leads to different capital investment and different running costs. Essentially, present worth enables the trade-off between capital investment and future running costs to be compared. Example (1) which includes the capital cost of buying plant and the running costs of operating the plant illustrates the comparison. All the estimates used in this comparison are at present day (i.e. year zero) prices.

*Example (1)*
Assuming an interest rate of 15%:

|  | Proposal 1 | Proposal 2 |
|---|---|---|
| Capital cost of plant | £ 8 500 | £ 9 500 |
| Annual running costs | £ 1 750 | £ 1 500 |
| Life | 5 years | 5 years |

The present worth of Proposal 1 is £14 366, and Proposal 2 is £14 528. The calculations are as follows:

*Proposal 1*

$$\text{Present worth} = £8\ 500 + (£1\ 750 \times 3.352)$$
$$= £8\ 500 + £5\ 866$$
$$= £14\ 366$$

*Proposal 2*

$$\text{Present worth} = £9\ 500 + (£1\ 500 \times 3.352)$$
$$= £9\ 500 + £5\ 028$$
$$= £14\ 528$$

The capital sums are already in year zero and need no further manipulation. The running costs of £1 500 and £1 750 each year need to be converted to present worth or capital sums. The factor used for this conversion is the uniform series present worth factor. This factor, 3.352, has been taken from the tables in the Appendix.

The present worth of Proposal 1 is £14 366 and the present worth of Proposal 2 is £14 528. Thus, Proposal 1 is the more economic. The present worth of Proposal 1, £14 366, represents enough money to buy the plant item at a cost of £8 500 and investing the remainder at 15% is enough to produce £1 750 each year for the next five years. Thus, £14 366 is the amount required now to meet all the requirements of Proposal 1. Similarly the present worth of Proposal 2, £14 528, is the amount required now to meet all the requirements of Proposal 2. Since the present worth of

Proposal 1 is the smaller and both proposals would be compared only if the two items of plant were capable of doing the same tasks, then the one with the least cost, i.e. least present worth, is the most economic.

An alternative way of considering this comparison is to examine the differences between the capital costs and the running costs. Proposal 1 has £1 000 less capital but requires £250 more running costs each year. Thus the extra capital of £1 000 involved in Proposal 2 can be seen to be buying £250 of savings in the running costs. The question, which of the two schemes is the more economic, could be re-stated as follows: would the £1 000 of extra investment be better used in saving £250 in running costs or earning 15% if invested elsewhere? £1 000 invested at 15% for five years would give an income of £298.31 calculated as

$$£ 1 000 \times 0.29831 = £ 298.31$$

where 0.29831 is the capital recovery factor, taken from the tables in the Appendix. Thus the return on the investment is better than the saving in the running costs. Therefore Proposal 1, the smaller of the capital investments, is the more economic proposal.

This present worth comparison is valid so long as the lives of the two proposals are the same. This is usually the case in comparing plant items. One exception is comparing the cost of keeping an item of plant for one year, with keeping it for two, three or four years. In such cases the lives are different and require different treatment. This is explained later in the section dealing with replacement.

The example presented is the use of present worth in a simple case where there is only capital and running costs and where the running costs were uniform, that is the same each year. The principles of using present worth are the same even when the cash flow becomes more complicated. The next example shows the running costs varying each year in order to reflect the increasing costs incurred as the equipment grows older. Also included in the next example is a resale value of £4 000 occurring in the last year. The resale value is a return of money to the investor and therefore carries a different sign than the capital and running costs which are outflows of money. Again, all the cash flows are estimated at present prices.

*Example (2)*
Assuming an interest rate of 15%:

| Year | Cash flow for the purchase and resale of an item of plant (£) |
|---|---|
| 0 | −8 500 |
| 1 | −1 750 |
| 2 | −1 850 |
| 3 | −2 000 |
| 4 | −2 200 |
| 5 | −2 500 + £ 4 000 |

The present worth of these cash flows is £13 247.72 calculated as shown below at an interest rate of 15%. This present worth can now be compared to the present worth for an alternative proposal.

| Year | Cash flow (£) | | Present worth factor | | Present worth (£) |
|---|---|---|---|---|---|
| 0 | −8 500 | X | 1.0 | = | −8 500.00 |
| 1 | −1 750 | X | 0.86956 | = | −1 521.73 |
| 2 | −1 850 | X | 0.75614 | = | −1 398.87 |
| 3 | −2 000 | X | 0.65751 | = | −1 315 02 |
| 4 | −2 200 | X | 0.57175 | = | −1 257.85 |
| 5 | −2 500 | X | 0.49717 | = | −1 242.93 |
| 5 | + 4 000 | X | 0.49717 | = | +1 988.68 |
| | | | Total present worth | = | −£13 247.72 |

The present worth factors are taken from the tables in the Appendix. Because the annual sums are varying in this case, the uniform series present worth factor cannot be used and the individual present worth factor for a lump sum, $\frac{1}{(1 + i)^n}$ is used instead, where i is the interest rate and n is the number of years. This increases the arithmetic involved but is unavoidable when dealing with varying annual cash flows.

The treatment of the £4 000 resale value shown here is to simply add it into the present worth, taking account of the different sign. It may be more acceptable to deduct its present worth from the initial capital.

Initial capital invested = £8 500.00
Present worth of resale = £4 000 X 0.49717 = £1 988.68
Adjusted capital invested = £6 511.32

The total present worth calculated after adjusting the capital invested in this way to take account of the resale value will be the same as the example given.

### Equivalent annual costs

An alternative to present worth comparison is comparing proposals on the basis of the equivalent annual costs. Whereas present worth converts all future running costs to a present worth or capital sum, equivalent annual costs convert the capital sums to an annual cost. Equivalent annual cost comparisons achieve the same as present worth comparisons and, like present worth comparisons, are essentially evaluating the trade-off between capital and running costs. Example (3) uses the same cash flows estimated at present prices as Example (1).

*Example (3)*
Assuming an interest rate of 15%:

|  | Proposal 1 | Proposal 2 |
|---|---|---|
| Capital cost of plant | £8 500 | £ 9 500 |
| Annual running costs | £1 750 | £ 1 500 |
| Life | 5 years | 5 years |

The equivalent annual cost of Proposal 1 is £4 285.64 and the equivalent annual cost of Proposal 2 is £4 333.95. The calculations are as follows:

Equivalent annual cost (E.A.C.)
of Proposal 1        $= £1\ 750 + (£8\ 500 \times 0.29831)$
$= £1\ 750 + £2\ 535.64$
$= £4285.64$

Equivalent annual cost (E.A.C.)
of Proposal 2        $= £1\ 500 + (£9\ 500 \times 0.29831)$
$= £1\ 500 + £2\ 833.95$
$= £4\ 333.95$

The annual running costs of £1 750 and £1 500 do not need further manipulation. The capital costs of £8 500 and £9 500 need to be converted to annual costs. The factor used for this conversion is the capital recovery factor, 0.29831, and has been taken from the tables in the Appendix.

The equivalent annual cost of Proposal 1 is £4 285.64 and the equivalent annual cost of Proposal 2 is £4 333.95. Thus, Proposal 1 is the more economic as was found by the present worth comparison. The E.A.C. represents the annual cost of owning and operating the item of plant. This is made up of £1 750, representing the annual running cost, and £2 535.64 representing the annual cost of the capital investment. This is calculated on the basis that if £8 500 were invested at an interest rate of 15% an income of £2 535.64 could be taken each year for the next five years. This income would be made up of the interest earned plus the original capital. At the end of the first year £1 275 of interest would be earned on the £8 500 of capital invested. Thus, if an income of £2 535.64 were taken this would be made up of £1 275 of interest plus £1 260.64 of capital, leaving £7 239.36 of capital. At the end of the second year the £7 239.36 of capital would earn £1 085.90 of interest. The income of £2 535.64 would be made up of the £1 085.90 of interest plus £1 449.74 of capital leaving £5 789.62. The interest earned in the third year would be £868.44 and the income of £2 535.64 would be made up of the £868.44 of interest plus £1 667.19 of capital leaving £4 122.43 capital. In the fourth year the interest earned would be £618.36 and the income of £2 535.64 would be made up of the £618.36 interest plus £1 917.27 of capital leaving £2 205.16. In the fifth year the interest earned would be £330.77 and the income would be made up of the £330.77 interest plus £2 204.86 capital, leaving the account exhausted and no capital (on the basis of the calculations presented here £0.30 of capital would remain but this is due simply to rounding errors in the calculation). Thus if the £8 500 were invested at 15% an income of £2 535.64 could be taken each year for five years. However, since the £8 500 was not invested in such an account but used to purchase the item of plant, the investor is deprived of the income of £2 535.64 and therefore this can be regarded as equivalent to the annual cost of owning the plant item.

This example shows the use of equivalent annual cost where only capital and running costs are considered and the running costs are uniform. The use of equivalent annual costs becomes more difficult when running costs vary from year to year. In such cases it is necessary to convert the varying running costs to a capital cost before converting them back to an equivalent annual cost. The next example, using the same cash flows as Example (2) illustrates this difficulty. As in Example (2) the cash flows are estimated using present prices.

*Example (4)*
Given that the interest rate is 15%:

| Year | Cash flows for the purchase, operating and disposing of an item of plant (£) |
|------|------|
| 0 | − 8 500 |
| 1 | − 1 750 |
| 2 | − 1 850 |
| 3 | − 2 000 |
| 4 | − 2 200 |
| 5 | − 2 500 + £4 000 |

The present worth of the resale is £1 988.68 and the purchase price less resale, i.e. the adjusted capital invested, is £6 511.32 as explained in Example (2).

The equivalent annual cost of the capital invested is £1 942.39, calculated as follows taking the capital recovery factor for 5 years, 0.29831, from tables in the Appendix:

$$\text{E.A.C.} = £6\ 511.32 \times 0.29831 = £1\ 942.39$$

The present worth of the running costs are £6 736.40, summed from the calculations in Example (2) and the equivalent annual cost of the present worth of these running costs is £2 009.54, calculated as follows taking the capital recovery factor for 5 years, 0.29831, from tables in the Appendix:

$$\text{E.A.C.} = £6\ 736.40 \times 0.29831 = £2\ 009.54$$

Thus, the total equivalent annual cost for all the cash flows − the purchase price less resale value and running costs − is £3 951.93. This is made up of £2 009.54 representing the running costs and £1 942.39 representing the purchase price less resale. Thus, the equivalent annual cost of £3 951.93 can be used to compare with similarly calculated equivalent annual costs for alternative proposals.

By converting the varying annual running costs to a present worth and then converting this present worth to an equivalent annual cost the running costs can be distributed uniformly over each year. This procedure overcomes the difficulty with varying running costs. However, this procedure also illustrates why the use of present worth as a basis for comparison is more common. To arrive at an equivalent annual cost, the cash flows had first to be converted to a present worth. Therefore it is easier to perform the comparison on the basis of present worth rather than involve the extra calculation of producing equivalent annual costs.

However, the equivalent annual cost method does not require the lives of proposals under comparison to be equal as is required in a present worth comparison. The reason is that the sum calculated, the equivalent annual cost, refers to one year and the equivalent annual cost of any alternative scheme also refers to one year. The process of calculating equivalent annual costs takes account of the duration of the plant item and produces annual costs which can be compared to annual costs for other proposals. An example of this is comparing the cost of keeping an item of plant for one, two, three, four or five years thereby determining the best replacement age. The costs of keeping an item of plant for different periods are, in effect, different proposals which have different lives and therefore present difficulties in comparing on the basis of present worth.

Another use of equivalent annual costs is to convert the purchase price and running costs to annual costs that can then be compared to the cost of hiring. The same device of converting the capital costs to annual costs is one way of determining the capital element in a hire rate when determining what the economic hire rate should be.

## Economic comparisons and inflation

In the previous section all the examples were based on cash flows that were estimated at present or year zero prices. The effect of inflation was not taken into account. In Examples (2) and (4), the annual costs increased due to incurring increasing running costs as the equipment grew older and not to the effect of inflation. A simple illustration of inflation is that, if in year zero a 'basket of goods' cost £100 and in year one the same basket of goods cost £110, then inflation of 10% has occurred. In other words, inflation causes more money to be paid out for the same goods. As individual items change price, or inflate, at different rates the basket of goods concept is used to create indicators of the average price movements or inflation. The most commonly known 'basket of goods' is that used to calculate the retail price index. Other indices of inflation used in the construction industry are the 'cost of new construction index', 'tender price index' or the NEDO indices used to calculate price adjustments in construction contracts. All these indices refer to different goods or 'baskets of goods' and indicate the variable nature of inflation between different goods over the same time periods. In the United Kingdom, the years since 1973 in particular, have also indicated how volatile inflation can be and how elusively difficult it is to predict. This difficulty in prediction cannot be overcome by adjustments in the calculations supporting economic comparisons but, given assumptions as to the forecast inflation, these assumptions can be incorporated into the comparisons.

The approach of estimating cash flows for purchase price, running costs and re-sale at present or year zero figures and then including the adjustments for inflation is frequently used because it separates the difficulties of estimating the cash flows resulting from the selection of the plant item and its technical capabilities from the vagaries of inflation. This separation also allows different inflation assumptions to be made and evaluated without disturbing the underlying estimates.

The following methods explain the means by which the inflation assumptions can be incorporated into economic comparisons. The explanations are based on the cash flows for Example (1) and Example (2)

### Method 1: Ignore inflation

Example (1) compared the cash flows from two proposals to purchase and operate a piece of equipment for five years. The comparison was made on the basis of present worth. The present worth of Proposal 1 was £14 366, and the present worth of Proposal 2 was £14 528. The cash flows leading to these present worths were based on estimates at year zero prices, the interest rate was taken as 15%, and this comparison which excluded inflation indicated that Proposal 1 was the most economic.

Inflation would increase the running costs of both proposals and so increase the present worths. It should be remembered that the present worth is the sum of money required to be invested now to generate the stated cash flows given a certain interest rate. Thus, if the cash flows are increased, the amount required for investment to generate the cash flows must also increase, given that the interest rate remains the same.

If the purpose of the exercise is simply to *compare* the proposals and select the most economic, and the inflation rate assumed is small, the comparison will not be affected seriously by the inclusion of inflation. That is, if *small* inflation allowances are added into both proposals the difference between them will not be affected enough to change the comparison. This may be sufficient for small inflation rates but is unlikely to be satisfactory for larger inflation rates experienced since 1973.

### Method 2: Adjusting the cash flows

*Example (5)*

The cash flows in Example (1) were:

| Year | Proposal 1 Cash flow | Proposal 2 Cash flow |
|------|----------------------|----------------------|
| 0 | £8 500 | £9 500 |
| 1 | £1 750 | £1 500 |
| 2 | £1 750 | £1 500 |
| 3 | £1 750 | £1 500 |
| 4 | £1 750 | £1 500 |
| 5 | £1 750 | £1 500 |

These cash flows were all estimated at year zero prices. Any cash flow not occurring in year zero would be subject to inflation.

If an inflation rate of 10% per annum were assumed the cash flows would be adjusted as follows:

| Year | Proposal 1<br>Original cash flow +<br>inflation adjustment | Proposal 2<br>Original cash flow +<br>inflation adjustment |
|---|---|---|
| 0 | £8 500 | £9 500 |
| 1 | £1 750 + 10% | £1 500 + 10% |
| 2 | £(1 750 + 10%) + 10% | £(1 500 + 10%) + 10% |
| 3 | £((1 750 + 10%) + 10%) + 10% | £((1 500 + 10%) + 10%) + 10% |
| 4 | £(((1 750 + 10%) + 10%) + 10%)<br>+ 10% | £(((1 500 + 10%) + 10%) + 10%)<br>+ 10% |
| 5 | £((((1 750 + 10%) + 10%) + 10%)<br>+ 10%) + 10% | £((((1 500 + 10%) + 10%) + 10%)<br>+ 10%) + 10% |

When calculated, these figures become:

| Year | Proposal 1<br>Original<br>cash flow | Inflation<br>adjustment | Adjusted<br>cash flow | Proposal 2<br>Original<br>cash flow | Inflation<br>adjustment | Adjusted<br>cash flow |
|---|---|---|---|---|---|---|
| 0 | £8 500 + | 0 = | £8 500.00 | £9 500 + | 0 = | £9 500.00 |
| 1 | £1 750 + | £175.00 = | £1 925.00 | £1 500 + | £150.00 = | £1 650.00 |
| 2 | £1 750 + | £367.50 = | £2 117.50 | £1 500 + | £315.00 = | £1 815.00 |
| 3 | £1 750 + | £579.25 = | £2 329.25 | £1 500 + | £496.50 = | £1 996.50 |
| 4 | £1 750 + | £812.18 = | £2 562.18 | £1 500 + | £696.15 = | £2 196.15 |
| 5 | £1 750 + | £1 068.39 = | £2 818.39 | £1 500 + | £915.77 = | £2 415.77 |

Now that the cash flows have been adjusted for inflation the present worth of both proposals can be calculated as before. Because the cash flows vary from year to year and are not uniform, the present worth factors for each year will have to be used as in Example (2).

The present worth of both proposals are calculated as follows, using an interest rate of 15%:

*Proposal 1*

| Year | Cash flows | Present worth factors | | Present worth |
|------|-----------|:-----:|:-----:|---------------|
| 0 | £8 500.00 | X 1.0 | = | £8 500.00 |
| 1 | £1 925.00 | X 0.86956 | = | £1 673.90 |
| 2 | £2 117.50 | X 0.75614 | = | £1 601.13 |
| 3 | £2 329.25 | X 0.65751 | = | £1 531.51 |
| 4 | £2 562.18 | X 0.57175 | = | £1 464.93 |
| 5 | £2 818.39 | X 0.49717 | = | £1 401.22 |
| | | Total present worth = | | £16 172.69 |

The present worth factors were taken from the tables in the Appendix. The present worth for Proposal 2, similarly calculated, is £16 076.58.

This comparison reverses the choice indicated in Example (1) by indicating that at 10% inflation Proposal 2 becomes the most economic. Proposal 2, having the smaller running costs suffers less from inflation than Proposal 1. At smaller inflation rates the choice would still be Proposal 1, as before. However, with an inflation rate at 10%, Proposal 2 becomes the more economic. Originally, the present worth of £14 366 for Proposal 1 was sufficient to provide for the £8 500 purchase price and the £1 750 running costs each year and the present worth of £14 528 for Proposal 2 was sufficient to provide for the £9 500 purchase price and the £1 500 running costs each year. 10% inflation, however, causes the present worth of Proposal 1 to become £16 172.69 and provides for the £8 500 purchase price, the £1 750 running costs each year and the additional running costs incurred due to inflation. The £16 076.58 present worth of Proposal 2 provides the £9 500 purchase price, the £1 500 running costs each year and smaller additional running costs due to inflation.

### Method 3: Adjusting the interest rate
The previous comparison including inflation could have been achieved by adjusting the interest rate rather than the cash flows.

### Example (6)
In Example (5) the cash flows from Example (1) were adjusted to include an inflation rate of 10% per annum, as follows:

| Year | Proposal 1<br>Original cash flows | Proposal 2<br>Adjusted cash flows |
|:---:|:---:|:---:|
| 0 | £8 500 | £8 500.00 |
| 1 | £1 750 | £1 925.00 |
| 2 | £1 750 | £2 117.50 |
| 3 | £1 750 | £2 329.25 |
| 4 | £1 750 | £2 562.18 |
| 5 | £1 750 | £2 818.39 |

This adjustment was achieved by adding 10% to the first year cash flows and 10% + 10% to the second year cash flows and so on. This can be represented as follows where d represents the inflation rate (0.1 for 10%):

| Year | Proposal 1<br>Original cash flow | | Inflation adjustment |
|:---:|:---:|:---:|:---:|
| 0 | £8 500 | | |
| 1 | £1 750 | $\times$ | $(1 + d)^1$ |
| 2 | £1 750 | $\times$ | $(1 + d)^2$ |
| 3 | £1 750 | $\times$ | $(1 + d)^3$ |
| 4 | £1 750 | $\times$ | $(1 + d)^4$ |
| 5 | £1 750 | $\times$ | $(1 + d)^5$ |

To calculate the present worth of each of these adjusted cash flows multiply each year by the present worth factor as, for example, year 3:

| Year | Cash flow | | Present worth factor |
|:---:|:---:|:---:|:---:|
| 3 | £1 750 $\times (1 + d)^3$ | $\times$ | 0.65751 |

The present worth factor 0.65751 was taken from the tables in the Appendix or calculated from the expression $\dfrac{1}{(1 + i)^n}$ where i is the interest rate and n is the number of years. In this case i = 0.15 (for 15%) and n = 3.

The present worth for year 3 can be calculated, thus:

| Year | Cash flow | | Present worth factor |
|:---:|:---:|:---:|:---:|
| 3 | £1 750.00 $\times (1 + d)^3$ | $\times$ | $\dfrac{1}{(1 + 0.15)^3}$ |

or for any year as:

| Year | Cash flow | | Present worth factor |
|:---:|:---:|:---:|:---:|
| n | £1 750.00 $\times (1 + d)^n$ | $\times$ | $\dfrac{1}{(1 + i)^n}$ |

This calculation can be simplified by the following adjustment: for $(1 + i)^n$, substitute $(1 + d)^n (1 + e)^n$ where d is the inflation rate as before and e is calculated such that:

$$(1 + i)^n = (1 + d)^n (1 + e)^n$$

$$\text{giving } (1 + e) = \frac{(1 + i)}{(1 + d)}$$

$$\text{and} \qquad e = \frac{(1 + i)}{(1 + d)} - 1$$

Using this substitution the calculation of present worth becomes:

| Year | Cash flow | | Present worth factor |
|------|-----------|---|----------------------|
| n | £1 750 $\times (1 + d)^n$ | $\times$ | $\dfrac{1}{(1 + d)^n (1 + e)^n}$ |

The elements $(1 + d)^n$ cancel and the calculation is reduced to:

$$£1\ 750 \times \frac{1}{(1 + e)^n}$$

The present worth in the original example was calculated by multiplying the cash flow by the present worth factor $\frac{1}{(1 + i)^n}$, and so the present worth calculated above differs only in the interest rate used. The inflation adjustment has been transferred from the cash flow to the interest rate.

Given the interest rate i = 0.15 (15%) and the inflation rate d = 0.10 (10%):

$$e = \frac{(1 + 0.15)}{(1 + 0.10)} - 1 = 0.454545 = 4.54\%$$

Therefore, the present worth of Proposal 1 using the interest rate adjusted for inflation is:

| | | Proposal 1 | |
|------|-----------|------------------------|----------------|
| Year | Cash flow | Present worth factors | Present worth |
| 0 | £8 500 | 1 | £8 500.00 |
| 1 | £1 750 | 0.95652 | £1 673.90 |
| 2 | £1 750 | 0.91493 | £1 601.13 |
| 3 | £1 750 | 0.87515 | £1 531.51 |
| 4 | £1 750 | 0.83710 | £1 464.93 |
| 5 | £1 750 | 0.80070 | £1 401.22 |

Total present worth = £16 172.69

The present worth calculated using the original cash flows and the adjusted interest rate gives a present worth of £16 172.69 which is the same as that given by Example (5) where the interest rate was kept at 15% and the cash flows were adjusted for inflation.

The adjusted interest rate of 4.54% is measuring the interest earned in excess of the inflation rate and by taking the effect of inflation away from the interest rate it is possible to calculate present worths which allow for the effect of inflation. Calculating the present worth with the adjusted interest rate involves less work than first adjusting the cash flows and then calculating the present worth. Consequently, the method of adjusting the interest rate to allow for inflation is the most commonly employed.

This technique allows for the effects of inflation by reducing the actual interest earned from the apparent rate to an 'effective' or 'real' rate.

In Example (6) the interest rate was 15%. This would be the rate that the investor would take to represent the value of money and most likely would be equated to an interest rate that could be earned in investments deposited elsewhere. The inflation rate used was 10% and the 'effective' interest was calculated as 4.54% for the following reasons. £100 at present day prices would, at the end of the first year with inflation at 10%, be equivalent to £110 and the amount required for investment today at 15% to produce £110 in one year would be £110 × 0.86956 = £95.65 (0.86956 is the present worth factor for 15%). If the £100 required at the end of one year were left and the effect of inflation subtracted from the interest rate then the amount required to be invested today at 4.54% would be £100 × 0.95652 = £95.65, where 0.95652 is the present worth factor for 4.54%. Thus the amount required for investment today would be the same.

Another example would be to assume an interest rate of 15% and an inflation rate of 15%. Since the inflation rate and the rate at which interest is earned are the same, the effective rate becomes zero as follows:

$$e = \frac{(1+i)}{(1+e)} - 1 = \frac{(1.15)}{(1.15)} - 1 = 0$$

Thus, if £100 at present day prices were due at the end of one year and inflation at 15% made this £115, the amount required to be invested today at 15% to produce £115 in one year would be £115 × 0.86956 = £100 (0.86956 is the present worth factor for 15%). If the £100 required at the end of one year were left and the effect of inflation taken away from the interest rate then the amount required today at 0% would be £100 × 1.0 = £100 where 1.0 is the present worth factor for 0%. The amount required by both calculations is the same.

This example is particularly noteworthy because if inflation rates and interest rates are equal calculating present worths taking account of inflation simply involves summing the cash flows estimated at present prices. The effect of inflation totally eliminates the earned interest.

A final example would be to assume an interest rate of 15%, as before, but an inflation rate of 20% so that the inflation rate is greater than the rate at which interest can be earned. The effective rate then becomes − 4.16% as follows:

$$e = \frac{(1+i)}{(1+e)} - 1 = \frac{(1.15)}{(1.20)} - 1 = -0.0416$$
$$= -4.16\%$$

Thus, if £100 at present day prices were due at the end of one year and inflation at 20% would make this £120, the amount required to be invested today at 15% to produce £120 in one year would be £120 × 0.86956 = £104.34, where 0.86956 is the present worth factor for 15%. If the £100 required at the end of one year were left and the effect of inflation taken away from the interest rate then the amount required today at − 4.16% would be £100 × $\frac{1}{1 - 0.0416)^r}$ = £100 × 1.0434 = £104.34, where 1.0434 is the present worth factor for 4.16%. It is to be noted that the present worth factor had to be calculated from the expression $\frac{1}{(1+i)^n}$ because negative interest rates are not usually tabulated. Again, the amounts required calculated by the two methods are the same.

Thus, this method of adjusting the interest rate is valid for *all* interest and inflation rates and, by producing cash flows estimated using present day prices, the effect of inflation at various rates can be easily assessed using a range of assumed inflation rates.

The following example illustrates the application of this technique to Example (2):

*Example (7)*

| Year | Cash flow for the purchase, operating and resale of an item of plant |
|---|---|
| 0 | − £8 500 |
| 1 | − £1 750 |
| 2 | − £1 850 |
| 3 | − £2 000 |
| 4 | − £2 200 |
| 5 | − £2 500 + £4 000 |

The cash flows estimated at present day prices reflect only the increasing cost of operating the equipment and not increases due to inflation.

The value of money is 15%. The present worth, as shown in Example (2), is £14 366. If inflation over the next five years is estimated at 12% the effective interest rate would be 2.68% calculated as follows:

$$e = \frac{(1+i)}{(1+d)} - 1 = \frac{1.15}{1.12} - 1 = 0.0268 = 2.68\%$$

The present worth of the cash flows allowing for inflation at 12% is £14 471.42, are calculated as follows:

| Year | Cash flow | Present worth factors | Present worth |
|------|-----------|----------------------|---------------|
| 0 | − £8 500 | 1.0 | − £8 500.00 |
| 1 | − £1 750 | 0.9739 | − £1 704.32 |
| 2 | − £1 850 | 0.9485 | − £1 754.73 |
| 3 | − £2 000 | 0.9237 | − £1 847.40 |
| 4 | − £2 200 | 0.8996 | − £1 979.12 |
| 5 | − £2 500 | 0.8761 | − £2 190.25 |
| 5 | + £4 000 | 0.8761 | + £3 504.40 |

Total present worth − £14 471.42

This £14 471.42 is the present worth of the original cash flows plus the present worth of the cash flows that would have to be included for inflation.

### Method 4: Varying inflation rates
Methods 2 and 3 illustrate how uniform inflation rates can be dealt with, but this leaves the difficulty of coping with varying inflation rates. The most commonly adopted approach in these economic comparisons is to take a long-term view of the interest rate to be used to represent the value of money and to ignore short-term variations. The same argument is usually applied to the assumed inflation rates. It is possible, if required, to cope with varying inflation rates but to do this by adjusting the cash flows as illustrated in Method 3 for uniform inflation rates. The following example based on Example (5) demonstrates how cash flows can be adjusted for varying inflation rates. The assumed inflation rates are 10% for years 1 and 2, 12% for year 3 and 14% for years 4 and 5.

*Example (8)*

| | | Proposal 1<br>Inflation adjustments | | | | |
|------|---------------------|-----------------|-----------------|-----------------|-----------------|-----------------|
| Year | Original<br>cash flows | For year<br>1 | For year<br>2 | For year<br>3 | For year<br>4 | For year<br>5 |
| 0 | £8 500.00 | | | | | |
| 1 | (£1 750.00 | + 10%) | | | | |
| 2 | ((£1 750.00 | + 10%) | + 10%) | | | |
| 3 | (((£1 750.00 | + 10%) | + 10%) | + 12%) | | |
| 4 | ((((£1 750.00 | + 10%) | + 10%) | + 12%) | + 14%) | |
| 5 | (((((£1 750.00 | + 10%) | + 10%) | + 12%) | + 14%) | + 14%) |

When calculated, these figures become:

| | Proposal 1 |
| Year | Cash flows including inflation adjustment |
| --- | --- |
| 0 | £8 500.00 |
| 1 | £1 925.00 |
| 2 | £2 117.50 |
| 3 | £2 371.60 |
| 4 | £2 703.62 |
| 5 | £3 082.13 |

Similarly the cash flows for Proposal 2 can be adjusted for inflation as follows:

| | Proposal 2 |
| Year | Cash flows including inflation adjustment |
| --- | --- |
| 0 | £9 500.00 |
| 1 | £1 650.00 |
| 2 | £1 815.00 |
| 3 | £2 032.80 |
| 4 | £2 317.39 |
| 5 | £2 641.83 |

The present worths of both proposals calculated at 15% are £16 412.51 for Proposal 1, and £16 282.16 for Proposal 2. Thus, with this inflation pattern and interest at 15%, Proposal 2 is the more economic.

*Note on all methods*

All the examples shown based the comparison on present worth and did not employ equivalent annual costs. The reason for this is that equivalent annual cost comparisons involve more calculation than present worth when the annual cash flows are not uniform. When inflation is introduced the annual cash flows cannot be uniform and it is easier to use present worth calculations.

**Valuation of a plant item**

The principles of economic comparisons can be employed to place a value on an item of plant. The term value has several definitions such as the accountant's value as recorded in the asset register or the market value as determined by how much the item will sell for on the open market. The market value has the most practical meaning as it is the amount of capital that can be obtained for the plant item. However, the plant item may be worth more to the owner than he can obtain by selling the plant item or the market value may be more than the plant item is worth to the owner. To determine either of these requires the evaluation of worth or value to the owner of the item of plant. Economic comparisons, based on present worth can be used to determine the value of the plant item to the owner.

*Example (9)*
An item of plant whose original purchase price was £10 000, and has been in use for two years, has a remaining useful life of four years and the estimated running costs at present prices for the next four years are £661.25, £766.44, £874.50, and £1 005.68. The estimated resale at the end of the four years is £2 000. Thus the cash flows are:

| Year | Cash flows for existing plant item |
|------|-----------------------------------|
| 0 | — |
| 1 | − £661.25 |
| 2 | − £766.44 |
| 3 | − £874.50 |
| 4 | − £1 005.68 + £2 000 |

Note that there is no cash flow in year zero because the plant item is already owned.

The present worth of these cash flows using an interest rate of 10% is £1 212.45 calculated as follows:

| Year | Cash flows for existing plant item | Present worth factors | Present worth |
|------|-----------------------------------|----------------------|---------------|
| 0 | — | — | — |
| 1 | − £661.25 | 0.90909 | − £601.14 |
| 2 | − £766.44 | 0.82644 | − £633.42 |
| 3 | − £874.50 | 0.75131 | − £657.02 |
| 4 | − £1 005.68 + £2 000 | 0.68301 | + £679.13 |

Total present worth − £1 212.45

If this item of plant were not available to the owner an alternative method of providing the equipment would be necessary and the present worth of the alternative method calculated and compared to that for the equipment already owned.

*Alternative method 1: Hiring*
If the annual hire charge for a similar item of plant were £2 500 each year for four years then the present worth of hiring this equipment for four years, using an interest rate of 10%, would be £7 924.50, calculated as follows:

$$£2\ 500 \times 3.1698 = £7\ 924.50$$

The difference between the two present worths is an estimate of the value of the equipment to the owner. The difference is £7 924.50 − £1 212.45 = £6 712.05 and if the owner were able to sell the plant item for £6 712.05 and to offset this against the cost of hiring then the present worth of cash flows for hiring would be exactly the same as that for already owning the plant item. If the owner were able to sell the plant item for more than £6 712.05 it would be more economic to do so and to hire the equipment. If £6 712.05 could not be realised by selling the existing equipment it would be more economic to retain the existing item of plant.

If the effects of inflation were to be introduced this could be achieved by adjusting the interest rates as explained previously in the section dealing with inflation adjustments.

*Alternative Method 2: Buying new equipment*
If a similar item of equipment were available for purchase then the cash flows for purchase, operating and resale would have to be estimated as in this next example.

*Example (10)*
The cash flows estimated at present prices for purchasing, operating and reselling after four years for a similar item of equipment are:

| Year | Cash flows for purchase, operating and resale for new item of plant |
|:---:|:---:|
| 0 | − £11 000.00 |
| 1 | − £    400.00 |
| 2 | − £    460.00 |
| 3 | − £    529.00 |
| 4 | − £    608.35 + £4 000 |

The present worth of these cash flows using an interest rate of 10% is calculated as follows:

| Year | Cash flows for new item of plant | Present worth factors | Present worth |
|------|----------------------------------|------------------------|---------------|
| 0 | − £11 000.00 | 1.0 | − £11 000.00 |
| 1 | −    £400.00 | 0.90909 | −    £363.64 |
| 2 | −    £460.00 | 0.82644 | −    £380.16 |
| 3 | −    £529.00 | 0.75131 | −    £397.44 |
| 4 | −    £608.35 + £4 000 | 0.68301 | +  £2 316.53 |

Total present worth  −   £9 824.71

The difference between the present worth of keeping the existing plant item and replacing immediately with a new item of plant is:

$$£9 824.71 − £1 212.45 = £8 612.26$$

Thus if the owner could sell the existing plant item for £8 612.26 and offset this against the cost of the new equipment the present worth of acquiring the new equipment would be the same as keeping the existing item of plant. If the owner could sell the item of plant for more than £8 612.26 then it would be more economic to sell and replace: if £8 612.26 could not be realised from the sale of the equipment it would be more economic to retain the equipment.

If the effects of inflation were to be introduced this could be achieved by adjusting the interest rates as explained previously in the section dealing with inflation adjustments.

### Valuations for longer lives

The above valuations have been calculated using the useful life of the existing item of plant. This was estimated at four years, the plant already being two years old and having a total life of six years. If the need for the equipment extended for, say, twenty years the comparison would also need to be extended for that time period. Thus, the cost of keeping the existing plant item and its subsequent replacements must be compared with the cost of immediate replacement and subsequent replacements. The replacements will all be estimated at the same costs as the immediate replacements, as all cash flows are estimated at present prices and the effects of inflation incorporated separately.

*Example (11)*
The cash flows for keeping the existing item of plant and subsequent replacements for twenty years are as follows:

| Year | Running costs existing plant | Resale existing plant | Purchase of replacements | Running costs of replacements | Resale of replacements |
|---|---|---|---|---|---|
| 0 | – | | | | |
| 1 | – £661.25 | | | | |
| 2 | – £766.44 | | | | |
| 3 | – £874.50 | | | | |
| 4 | – £1 005.68 | + £2 000.00 | – £11 000.00 | | |
| 5 | | | | – £400.00 | |
| 6 | | | | – £460.00 | |
| 7 | | | | – £529.00 | |
| 8 | | | | – £608.35 | |
| 9 | | | | – £699.60 | |
| 10 | | | – £11 000.00 | – £804.54 | + £2 000 |
| 11 | | | | – £400.00 | |
| 12 | | | | – £460.00 | |
| 13 | | | | – £529.00 | |
| 14 | | | | – £608.35 | |
| 15 | | | | – £699.60 | |
| 16 | | | – £11 000.00 | – £804.54 | + £2 000 |
| 17 | | | | – £400.00 | |
| 18 | | | | – £460.00 | |
| 19 | | | | – £529.00 | |
| 20 | | | | – £608.35 | + £4 000 |

The cash flows for immediate replacement with a new item of plant and replacements for 20 years are:

| Year | Purchase price | Cash flows Running costs | Resale |
|---|---|---|---|
| 0 | – £11 000 | | |
| 1 | | – £400.00 | |
| 2 | | – £460.00 | |
| 3 | | – £529.00 | |
| 4 | | – £608.35 | |
| 5 | | – £699.60 | |
| 6 | – £11 000 | – £804.54 | + £2 000 |
| 7 | | – £400.00 | |
| 8 | | – £460.00 | |
| 9 | | – £529.00 | |
| 10 | | – £608.35 | |
| 11 | | – £699.60 | |

*Contd*

| Year | Purchase price | Cash flows Running costs | Resale |
|------|----------------|--------------------------|--------|
| 12   | − £11 000      | − £804.54                | + £2 000 |
| 13   |                | − £400.00                |        |
| 14   |                | − £460.00                |        |
| 15   |                | − £529.00                |        |
| 16   |                | − £608.35                |        |
| 17   |                | − £699.60                |        |
| 18   | − £11 000      | − £804.54                | + £2 000 |
| 19   |                | − £400.00                |        |
| 20   |                | − £460.00                | + £8 000 |

To compare these cash flows the present worth of both must be calculated, and the present worth of the immediate replacement can be calculated as follows, using an interest rate of 10%:

| Year | Cash flow | Present worth factor | Present worth |
|------|-----------|----------------------|---------------|
| 0 | − £11 000.00 | 1.0 | − £11 000.00 |
| 1 | − £400.00 | 0.90909 | − £363.64 |
| 2 | − £460.00 | 0.82644 | − £380.16 |
| 3 | − £529.00 | 0.75131 | − £397.44 |
| 4 | − £608.35 | 0.68301 | − £415.51 |
| 5 | − £699.60 | 0.62092 | − £434.40 |
| 6 | − £804.54 + £2 000.00 | 0.56447 | + £674.80 |

Total present worth  − £12 316.35

Thus the cash flows for the immediate and subsequent replacements can be represented as shown below.

| Year | Cash flow |
|------|-----------|
| 0  | − £12 316.35 |
| 6  | − £12 316.35 |
| 12 | − £12 316.35 |
| 18 | − £11 000.00 |
| 19 | − £400.00 |
| 20 | − £460.00 + £8 000 |

The £12 316.35 at years 0, 6 and 12 represents all the cash flows for the replacements purchased in those years and the present worth for the immediate and subsequent replacements up to 20 years is £24 115.92, calculated as follows:

| Year | Cash flow | Present worth factors | Present worth |
|------|-----------|----------------------|---------------|
| 0 | − £12 316.35 | 1.0 | − £12 316.35 |
| 6 | − £12 316.35 | 0.56447 | − £6 952.21 |
| 12 | − £12 316.35 | 0.31863 | − £3 924.36 |
| 18 | − £11 000.00 | 0.17985 | − £1 978.35 |
| 19 | − £400.00 | 0.16350 | − £65.40 |
| 20 | − £460.00 + £8 000 | 0.14864 | + £1 120.75 |
| | | Total present worth | − £24 115.92 |

The present worth of keeping the existing plant item until the end of its useful life and its subsequent replacement can be calculated first by representing the cash flows as shown below:

| Year | Cash flows |
|------|-----------|
| 0 | − £1 212.45 |
| 4 | − £12 316.35 |
| 10 | − £12 316.35 |
| 16 | − £11 000.00 |
| 17 | − £400.00 |
| 18 | − £460.00 |
| 19 | − £529.00 |
| 20 | − £608.35 + £4 000 |

The £1 212.45, taken from Example (9), represents all the cash flows for the existing item of plant.

The £12 316.35 in years 4 and 10 are used to represent all the cash flows for the replacement in those years. Consequently, the present worth for keeping the existing plant item until the end of its useful life and subsequent replacements up to twenty years is £16 511.14, calculated as follows:

| Year | Cash flows | Present worth factors | Present worth |
|------|------------|----------------------|---------------|
| 0  | −  £1 212.45 | 1.0 | −  £1 212.45 |
| 4  | −  £12 316.35 | 0.68301 | −  £8 412.19 |
| 10 | −  £12 316.35 | 0.38554 | −  £4 748.45 |
| 16 | −  £11 000.00 | 0.21762 | −  £2 393.82 |
| 17 | −  £400.00 | 0.19784 | −  £79.14 |
| 18 | −  £460.00 | 0.17985 | −  £82.73 |
| 19 | −  £529.00 | 0.16350 | −  £86.49 |
| 20 | −  £608.35 + £4 000 | 0.14864 | +  £504.13 |

Total present worth − £16 511.14

The difference between these two present worths is £24 115.92 − £16 511.14 = £7 604.78. If the owner could sell the existing plant item for £7 604.78 and this amount offset against the cost of the immediate replacement, the present worth of the immediate and subsequent replacements would be the same as keeping the existing item. If the owner could sell the existing plant item for more than £7 604.78 the acquiring of an immediate replacement would be more economic. If £7 604.78 could not be realised by the sale of the existing plant item then keeping the existing plant item would be more economic.

If the effects of inflation were to be introduced this could be achieved by adjusting the interest rates as explained previously in the section dealing with inflation adjustments.

The above calculation was based on an overall duration of twenty years, and the present worths were comparable because they were calculated for equal periods of time. The fact that the overall duration was not equal multiples of the life of the plant item, which was estimated at six years, was taken into account by adjusting the resale value of the last replacement which was resold before the end of its useful life. Thus when, in the calculation, it was resold at an earlier age than six years the resale value was estimated at a higher value.

*Example (12)*
An alternative to assuming a finite cut-off, of twenty years as in the last example, is to assume that the replacements will go on in perpetuity. The cash flow for immediate and subsequent replacements to infinity can be represented as follows:

| Year | Cash flows representing replacements to infinity |
|------|--------------------------------------------------|
| 0    | − £12 316.35 |
| 6    | − £12 316.35 |
| 12   | − £12 316.35 |
| 18   | − £12 316.35 |
| 24   | − £12 316.35 |
| . | . |
| . | . |
| . | . |
| . | . |
| ∞ | ∞ |

The £12 316.35 is the present worth of purchasing, operating and reselling the new plant item. This present worth was calculated previously as part of Example (11). If this plant item is replaced every six years then this amount recurs every six years to infinity.

The present worth of a sum recurring every one year starting at the end of the first year is given by the factor

$$\frac{(1+i)^n - 1}{i(1+i)^n}$$

which is the uniform series present worth factor given in the Appendix.

The present worth of a sum recurring not every year but every y years starting in y years is given by the factor

$$\frac{1}{(1+i)^y - 1}$$

Thus if the sum recurring every y years was x the present worth would be

$$x \times \left( \frac{1}{(1+i)^y - 1} \right)$$

and if the sum x occurred in year 0 the total present worth of the whole series would be

$$x + x \left( \frac{1}{(1+i)^y - 1} \right)$$

which reduces to

$$\frac{x}{1 - \dfrac{1}{(1+i)^y}}$$

Thus substituting £12 316.35 for x and 6 years for y and 10% for i the present worth of the series starting in year 0 and recurring to infinity is

$$\frac{£12\,316.35}{1 - 0.56447} = £28\,278.99$$

The 0.56447 can be taken from tables since the element $\frac{1}{(1 + i)^y}$ is the expression for the present worth factor.

The amount calculated, £28 278.99, represents the amount that would be required today which if invested at 10% would produce £12 316.35 every six years forever. This can be checked as follows: first take away the initial £12 316.35 and this leaves £15 962.64 for investment. In six years this £15 962.64 would increase to £15 962.64 × 1.77156 = £28 278.99. This £28 278.99 is made up of the original capital £15 962.64 and interest earned in those six years of £12 316.35. The factor 1.77156 is the compound amount factor for 10% and is taken from tables in the Appendix. Thus the sum of £12 316.35 can be used every six years to provide a replacement plant item. This £12 316.35 is the interest earned on the capital of £15 962.64 and is entirely used up every six years. The capital of £15 962.64 remains undepleted and can go on producing £12 316.35 every six years indefinitely.

The £12 316.35 is the present worth of purchasing, operating and reselling the plant item, and £28 278.99 is the present worth of purchasing, operating and reselling every six years in perpetuity. This present worth is sometimes called the capitalised cost.

To arrive at a valuation of the existing plant item it is necessary to calculate the capitalised cost of the cash flows relating to the scheme whereby the existing plant item is retained. That is the present worth of the existing plant item and its replacements to infinity.

Taking the cash flows from Example (11) for keeping the existing plant and its replacements, these can be represented as shown:

| Year | Cash flows for keeping existing plant and its replacements | | |
|---|---|---|---|
| | Running costs existing plant | Resale | Replacements |
| 0 | — | | |
| 1 | − £661.25 | | |
| 2 | − £766.44 | | |
| 3 | − £874.50 | | |
| 4 | − £1 005.68 | + £2 000 | − £12 316.35 |
| 10 | | | − £12 316.35 |
| 16 | | | − £12 316.35 |
| 22 | | | − £12 316.35 |
| 28 | | | − £12 316.35 |
| . | | | . |
| . | | | . |
| . | | | . |
| . | | | . |
| ∞ | | | ∞ |

The cash flows in years 0 to 4 representing the running costs of the existing plant and the resale value have a present worth of £1 212.45 as calculated in Example (9).

The £12 316.35 every six years have a present worth of £28 278.99 as calculated in Example (12). However, in this set of cash flows the first of the £12 316.35 occurs in year 4 and the cash flows for keeping the existing plant item and its replacements to infinity can be represented as follows:

| Year | Cash flows for keeping the existing plant item and its replacements |
|------|--------------------------------------------------------------------|
| 0 | − £1 212.45 |
| 4 | − £28 278.99 |

The present worth of these cash flows is £20 527.28 calculated thus:

$$£1\ 212.45 + (£28\ 278.99 \times 0.68301) = £20\ 527.28$$

Given an interest rate of 10%, £20 527.28 is the amount required for investment today to give £1 212.45 in year 0, enough for the existing plant, and £28 278.99 in year 4, enough for the replacements at £12 316.35 every six years until infinity. Thus £20 527.28 is the capitalised cost of keeping the existing plant and then replacing it in perpetuity.

The difference between the capitalised cost of keeping the existing plant and its immediate replacement is the value to the owner of the existing plant. The difference is £28 278.99 − £20 527.28 = £7 751.71. This £7 751.71 is the amount that could be compared to the market value when considering disposal. The value calculated here is only slightly different from that calculated for replacements up to twenty years because the present worth factors become smaller with increasing time and the effect of cash flows beyond twenty years on such calculations is small.

If the effects of inflation were to be incorporated in this calculation it would be achieved by adjusting the interest rates as explained previously in the section dealing with inflation adjustments

### Determining replacement age

The factors that determine the economic replacement age of a plant item are the purchase price, the operating costs and the resale value. The purchase price is relevant because the plant must be kept long enough to warrant the investment. The operating costs usually increase with ageing plant and it is therefore important not to keep the plant item too long. Also, as these operating costs increase the resale value declines. The purpose of an economic analysis is to find the balance between these. As the comparisons are being made between keeping a plant item for one, two, three or four years etc., the use of present worth presents the difficulty of equalising the lives of the comparisons. This is achieved by considering replacements to infinity. As the operating costs are not usually uniform, the use of equivalent annual costs is not easily applied. Thus, neither present worth nor equivalent annual costs offer any real advantage in this comparison. The method presented here is based on equivalent annual costs.

*Determining replacement age using equivalent annual costs*
The concept of equivalent annual costs is explained in Example (3).

*Example (13)*
The purchase price of a small concrete batching plant is £25 000. The operating costs based on the estimated annual average hours of use are £1 000 in the first year when manufacturers' warranties operate, and £1 500 in the second year rising by £375.00 per year thereafter. The resale values are as follows:

| Year | Predicted resale values |
|------|-------------------------|
| 1 | £22 500 |
| 2 | £20 000 |
| 3 | £18 750 |
| 4 | £15 000 |
| 5 | £10 000 |
| 6 | £6 250 |

The calculations to determine the equivalent annual cost of keeping this plant for one, two, three and four years, etc. are set out in Table 5.1.

Most of the entries in Table 5.1 which calculates the equivalent annual costs for one, two, three, etc. years are self-explanatory.

Column C shows the equivalent annual cost of the purchase price. For example, if the plant were kept for four years, the equivalent annual cost of the purchase price would be £8 750 per year.

Column F is the present worth of the running costs. In year 4 the running costs for that year were £2 250, and the present worth of this amount is £1 284.75: i.e. the amount required to be invested in year 0 to provide £2 250 in year 4 is £1 284.75.

Column G is the running total of the present worths of the running cost, so £3 234.88 is the sum of the present worths for years 1, 2 and 3. Thus, if £3 234.88 were invested in year 0 at 15% it would provide enough to pay for the running costs of years 1, 2 and 3.

Column H is the equivalent annual cost of the present worth of the running costs. Taking the £3 234.88 for year 3 from Column G and converting it to an annual sum using the capital recovery factor gives £1 413.64, and the running costs of £1 000, £1 500 and £1 875 for years 1, 2 and 3 are now converted to a uniform series of £1 413.64 per year. The calculations in Columns F, G and H are devices to convert the varying operating costs to a uniform series.

Table 5.1    Determining replacement age using equivalent annual costs

|  | A | B | C | D | E | F | G |
|---|---|---|---|---|---|---|---|
| Year | Purchase price | Capital recovery factors for 15% | Equiv. annual cost of pur-chase price (A × B) | Running costs | Present worth factors at 15% | Present worth of running costs (D × E) | Sum of P.W. of running costs (Σ F) |
|  | £ |  | £ | £ |  | £ | £ |
| 0 | 25 000 |  |  |  | 1.0 |  |  |
| 1 |  | 1.150 | 28 750 | 1 000 | 0.869 | 869.00 | 869.00 |
| 2 |  | 0.615 | 15 375 | 1 500 | 0.756 | 1 134.00 | 2 003.00 |
| 3 |  | 0.437 | 10 925 | 1 875 | 0.657 | 1 231.88 | 3 234.88 |
| 4 |  | 0.350 | 8 750 | 2 250 | 0.571 | 1 284.75 | 4 519.63 |
| 5 |  | 0.298 | 7 450 | 2 625 | 0.497 | 1 304.63 | 5 824.26 |
| 6 |  | 0.264 | 6 600 | 3 000 | 0.432 | 1 296.00 | 7 120.26 |

Note: The minimum in column N, £6 955.35, is the minimum equivalent annual cost.

Column I is the equivalent annual cost for the purchase price added to the equivalent annual cost for the running costs.

Column L is the present worth of the resale value. £12 318.75 in year 3 is the present worth of the resale value of £18 750 in year 3.

Column M is the equivalent annual cost of the resale value. Thus, £5 383.29 for year 3 is the equivalent annual cost of £12 318.75 from Column L.

Column N is the equivalent annual cost of the resale subtracted from the equivalent annual costs of the purchase price and running cost. This gives the net equivalent annual cost for purchase, operating and resale for years 1 to 6.

Thus the minimum in Column N is the minimum equivalent annual cost and the best replacement age by this economic criterion.

The effects of inflation could be incorporated by adjusting the interest rates that were used to calculate the present worths, but not the interest rate used to calculate the equivalent annual costs.

**Reading List**

See list at end of Chapter 6

| H | I | K | L | M | N |
|---|---|---|---|---|---|
| Equivalent annual cost of P.W. of running costs (B × G) £ | Equivalent annual costs of purchase price and running costs (C + H) £ | Resale value £ | Present worth of resale (E × K) £ | Equivalent annual costs of resale (B × L) £ | Equivalent annual costs of purchase, running and resales (I − M) £ |
| 999.35 | 29 749.35 | 22 500 | 19 552.50 | 22 500.00 | 7 249.35 |
| 1 231.84 | 16 606.84 | 20 000 | 15 120.00 | 9 298.80 | 7 308.04 |
| 1 413.64 | 12 338.64 | 18 750 | 12 318.75 | 5 383.29 | 6 955.35 |
| 1 581 87 | 10 331.87 | 15 000 | 8 565.00 | 2 997.75 | 7 334.12 |
| 1 735.62 | 9 185.62 | 10 000 | 4 970.00 | 1 481.06 | 7 704.56 |
| 1 879.74 | 8 479.74 | 6 250 | 2 700.00 | 712.80 | 7 766.94 |

# CHAPTER 6

# PLANT PROFITABILITY

## Measuring profitability

The economic analyses described previously in Chapter 5 have related to schemes whereby only the expenditure was considered. The purchase price and running or operating costs were not offset in the calculations against any revenue and the only monies returning to the investor were from resale. Thus the previous analyses were confined to determining whether one course of action, say the purchase of one particular plant item, was more economic than another course of action, the purchase of an alternative item. What will be considered now is the situation where the plant generates a revenue. The simplest situation to imagine is where the plant is purchased and hired out so that the owner has capital expenditure, operating costs, revenue and resale value. The analysis required now is not simply whether one item is more economic than another but whether the item is earning an adequate return on the invested capital. That is, whether the return on capital derived from owning and hiring out plant is better than could be obtained from less risky investment elsewhere or, if the capital to buy the equipment were borrowed, whether the return is greater than the cost of capital as measured by the interest on the capital. The capital made available by the company to purchase the equipment should earn at least the minimum return expected by the company. This analysis, therefore, requires that the rate of return is measured and the most widely used method is known as the 'internal rate of return', 'yield' or 'discounted cash flow (d.c.f.) yield'. All these are names for the same measure of profitability.

The interest factors used in this chapter are taken from the Appendix.

## Discounted cash flow (d.c.f.) yield

Calculating the d.c.f. yield requires first that the net cash flows be calculated. The net cash flows are the sum of the cash flows relating to the investment project. It is useful in calculating the net cash flows to construct a cash flow tree or model as shown in Figure 6.1, a cash flow tree for a simple purchase, operating, hire and resale model.

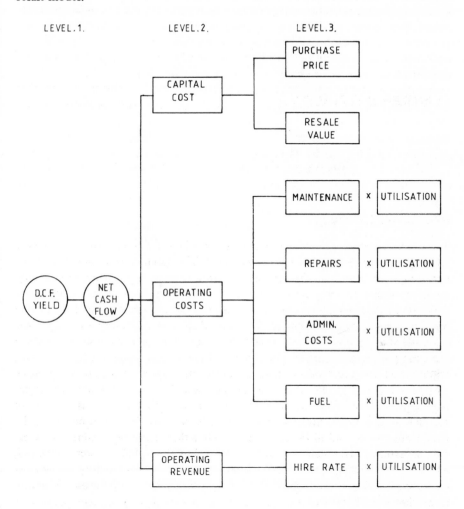

**Fig. 6.1**   Simple cash flow tree for a plant hire operation

This shows the cash flows broken down into three levels. The first level is the net cash flow. It is from this net cash flow that the d.c.f. yield will be calculated. The next level represents the three general categories of 'capital cost', 'operating cost' and 'operating revenue'. These three general categories apply to most cash flow trees. It is the next level, level 3, that determines the unique features of the operation or investment being modelled, and breaks down the capital costs to purchase price and resale. The operating costs are broken down into estimates for 'maintenance', 'repairs', 'administration' and 'fuel'. The estimate for the purchase price is a

single sum occurring in year 0 and the estimate for the resale value is a single sum occurring in the year when the resale takes place. The estimates for the operating costs
are not single sums but estimates of cost for each year of operation. In more detailed
models these estimates of cost may be made for each month. All the operating costs
are shown tied to the utilisation as clearly a relationship exists between the utilisation
and these costs. Similarly the operating revenue which is derived from the hire rate
and the utilisation will be yearly or monthly estimates. If this level is not detailed
enough for producing estimates then each element in level 3 will have to be broken
down further. When a level of detail is achieved such that estimates can be supplied
then the process of aggregation through the cash flow tree will produce the net flows
taking account of the algebraic sign (positive cash flows being income and negative
cash flows being outgoings). The d.c.f. yield is calculated from these net cash flows.

To demonstrate calculating d.c.f. yield and to explain the meaning and importance of d.c.f. yield an example will be used based on the following simple net cash
flows:

| Year | Net cash flows |
|------|----------------|
| 0    | − £1 000.00    |
| 1    | +    £315.47   |
| 2    | +    £315.47   |
| 3    | +    £315.47   |
| 4    | +    £315.47   |

These cash flows are assumed to have been derived from a cash flow tree calculation
similar to that described. These net cash flows show a pattern of negative, outgoing,
cash flows in the beginning followed by positive, incoming, cash flows in the subsequent years. The d.c.f. yield or internal rate of return is a measure of the return
on the capital invested of −£1 000.00 given by the positive cash flows occurring in
years 1 to 4.

D.c.f. yield or internal rate of return has two definitions:

(i)   the d.c.f. yield or rate of return is the *maximum* interest rate that could be
      paid for borrowed capital assuming that all the capital required to fund the
      project is acquired as an overdraft and all the positive cash flows are used to
      repay this overdraft.
(ii)  the d.c.f. yield or rate of return is the interest rate which if used to discount a
      project's cash flows will give a net present value (or worth) of zero.

The second of these definitions is more usually employed in calculating the yield,
and is also the definition that has given rise to the name d.c.f. yield. It is also the
more difficult to understand at first reading so the example will be calculated in the
first instance using the first definition.

Calculation of d.c.f. yield by the first definition is a process of trial and error.
An interest rate is assumed and tested to determine if it is the maximum; if it is
above the maximum a new trial with a smaller interest rate is used. If it is below the

maximum a new trial with a larger interest rate is used until the maximum is found, eventually by interpolation if necessary.

Using an interest rate of 12% as the first trial rate the test as to whether this is the maximum is shown in the following table.

| Year | Net cash flow | Interest paid on borrowed capital at 12% | Borrowing account |
|------|---------------|------------------------------------------|-------------------|
| 0 | − £1 000.00 | | − £1 000.00 |
| 1 | + £315.47 | − £120.00 | − £804.53 |
| 2 | + £315.47 | − £96.54 | − £585.60 |
| 3 | + £315.47 | − £70.27 | − £340.41 |
| 4 | + £315.47 | − £40.85 | − £65.78 |

In year 0 the amount borrowed was −£1 000.00 and the interest on this during year 1 was −£120.00. Thus at the end of year 1 the borrowing account was the original −£1 000.00 together with the interest of −£120.00 offset by the income of +£315.47, leaving −£804.53 in the borrowing account. Repeating this calculation until the end of the project indicates that there is −£65.78 left in the account. Thus this project could not have paid interest at 12% on the borrowed capital because to do so would require £65.78 from other sources. Thus 12% is greater than the maximum interest rate that this project could support and the trial and error process continues with a smaller interest rate. Suppose the second guess is 8%: the test as to whether this is the maximum is shown in the table below.

| Year | Net cash flow | Interest paid on borrowed capital at 8% | Borrowing account |
|------|---------------|-----------------------------------------|-------------------|
| 0 | − £1 000.00 | | − £1 000.00 |
| 1 | + £315.47 | − £80.00 | − £764.53 |
| 2 | + £315.47 | − £61.16 | − £510.22 |
| 3 | + £315.47 | − £40.82 | − £235.57 |
| 4 | + £315.47 | − £18.85 | + £61.05 |

Proceeding through the calculations as before, the amount left in the account at the end of the project is +£61.05. Thus this project could have paid more for its borrowed capital than 8%, which is therefore less than the maximum interest rate.

Given that 12% is greater than the maximum interest rate and 8% is less than the maximum interest rate, the maximum clearly lies between the two. Therefore the next reasonable guess would be 10%. The trial to determine if 10% is the maximum is:

| Year | Net cash flow | Interest paid on borrowed capital at 10% | Borrowing account |
|------|---------------|------------------------------------------|-------------------|
| 0 | − £1 000.00 | | − £1 000.00 |
| 1 | + £315.47 | − £100.00 | − £784.53 |
| 2 | + £315.47 | − £78.45 | − £547.51 |
| 3 | + £315.47 | − £54.75 | − £286.79 |
| 4 | + £315.47 | − £28.68 | 0.00 |

Performing the calculation as before shows that an amount of zero would be left in the borrowing account. Thus 10% is the maximum interest rate that could be paid for the borrowed capital in this project and by definition (i) 10% is the d.c.f. yield.

Measuring this *maximum* that *could* be paid for the borrowed capital is a way of measuring how much the project cash flows are producing. Measuring the amount that can be taken away (by interest charges) shows how much the project is producing. Also this measure (the d.c.f. yield or rate of return) is directly comparable to the cost of capital, the cost of capital being the weighted average of the costs of all sources of capital. If the company were paying more for its capital than 10%, the project would not be satisfactory because it would not be yielding more than borrowing the capital is costing.

The method more commonly employed in calculating the d.c.f. yield is according to definition (ii). Calculating the d.c.f. yield by the second definition is also a trial and error process which also requires an assumed interest rate and a trial to determine if the assumed interest rate gives an N.P.V. (net present value or worth) of zero. If the calculated N.P.V. is negative the assumed interest rate is too large and a smaller one is assumed and the N.P.V. is recalculated. If the calculated N.P.V. is positive the assumed interest is too small. The process is repeated until the interest rate which gives a zero N.P.V. is found, by interpolation if necessary.

| Year | Net cash flow | Present worth factors for 9% (1st trial) | Present worth | Present worth factors for 11% (2nd trial) | Present worth |
|------|---------------|------------------------------------------|---------------|-------------------------------------------|---------------|
| 0 | − £1 000.00 | 1.0 | − £1 000.00 | 1.0 | − £1 000.00 |
| 1 | + £315.47 | 0.91743 | + £289.42 | 0.90090 | + £284.21 |
| 2 | + £315.47 | 0.84168 | + £265.52 | 0.81162 | + £256.04 |
| 3 | + £315.47 | 0.77218 | + £243.60 | 0.73119 | + £230.67 |
| 4 | + £315.47 | 0.70842 | + £223.49 | 0.65873 | + £207.81 |
| | | | + £22.03 | | − £21.27 |

Using 9% as a first trial, the N.P.V. is calculated and found to be positive; a larger interest rate of 11% is then used to produce a negative N.P.V. Interpolation produces the interest rate which gives an N.P.V. of zero and is found to be 10% as before.

By interpolation:

the interest rate which gives an N.P.V. of zero

$$= 9\% + (11\% - 9\%) \times \left(\frac{22.03}{22.03 - (-21.27)}\right)$$
$$= 9\% + 2\% \times 0.508$$
$$= 9\% + 1.01\% = 10.0\%$$

The present worth factors are taken from tables or calculated as $\frac{1}{(1+i)^n}$. This 10.0% has exactly the same meaning as the 10.0% calculated by the first definition. The trial and error process that produces the interest rate that gives an N.P.V. of zero can be understood by examining the graph of N.P.V. versus interest rates as shown in Figure 6.2.

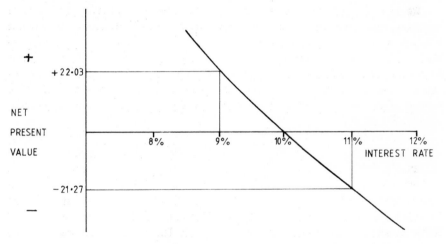

**Figure 6.2**    Graph of net present value v. interest rate

To understand further the meaning of this calculated interest rate which has been given the name d.c.f. yield or internal rate of return, consider this question: if £1 000 were invested at 10%, what regular income could be taken each year for the next four years?

The capital recovery factor for 10% and four years is 0.31547. This is taken from the tables in the Appendix. Thus the income that could be taken each year for four years from £1 000 invested at 10% is:

$$£1\ 000 \times 0.31547 = £315.47$$

This £315.47 is the same as the net cash flow in the example used.

Given a capital sum and an interest rate, the income can be calculated. Also, given the capital sum and the income, the interest rate that would produce that income from that capital sum can be calculated. This interest rate is called the d.c.f. yield or the internal rate of return.

This example was based on uniform revenues but the searching techniques for d.c.f. yield will work equally well for non-uniform revenues as shown in the next example, in which the net cash flows are:

| Year | Net cash flows |
|------|----------------|
| 0 | − £10 000 |
| 1 | + £2 800 |
| 2 | + £3 000 |
| 3 | + £2 500 |
| 4 | + £2 300 |
| 5 | + £2 200 |

The d.c.f. yield is 9.35%, calculated as follows:

| Year | Net cash flow | Present worth factors at 9% (1st trial) | Present worth | Present worth factors at 11% (2nd trial) | Present worth |
|------|---------------|------------------------------------------|---------------|-------------------------------------------|---------------|
| 0 | − £10 000 | 1.0 | − £10 000.00 | 1.0 | − £10 000.00 |
| 1 | + £2 800 | 0.91743 | + £2 568.80 | 0.90090 | + £2 522.52 |
| 2 | + £3 000 | 0.84168 | + £2 525.04 | 0.81162 | + £2 434.86 |
| 3 | + £2 500 | 0.77218 | + £1 930.45 | 0.73119 | + £1 827.97 |
| 4 | + £2 300 | 0.70842 | + £1 629.36 | 0.65873 | + £1 515.07 |
| 5 | + £2 200 | 0.64993 | + £1 429.84 | 0.59345 | + £1 305.59 |
| | | Net present worth + | £83.50 | − | £393.99 |

Interpolation:

$$\text{d.c.f. yield} = 9\% + (11\% - 9\%) \times \left( \frac{83.50}{83.50 - (-393.99)} \right)$$
$$= 9\% + (2\% \times 0.175)$$
$$= 9\% + 0.35\%$$
$$= 9.35\%$$

The yield or rate of return is the most widely used measure of profitability.

## Other measures of profitability

Yield is not the only measure of profitability and others in use are net present value, payback period, and average annual rate of return.

Net present value is used to determine whether a proposed project yields at least the minimum return specified by the company. The N.P.V. is calculated for the net cash flows using the minimum rate of return required, this rate representing the cost of capital. If the N.P.V. is positive it follows that the yield is above the minimum and the project is worthy of further consideration. If the N.P.V. is negative then the yield is less than the minimum and the project can be rejected without further analysis.

The payback period is the time taken to repay the original capital invested. The payback period is not very useful without predetermining what a satisfactory payback period should be. If a company usually expects payback periods of one year or eight months it would clearly by unhappy with proposals that incurred payback periods of three or four years. In general, the shorter the payback period the more profitable the project, provided that the project continues to have positive net revenues for a number of years after the payback period.

The average annual rate of return is all the returns (positive cash flows) for the project averaged over the number of years the project lasts and expressed as a percentage of the invested capital. Like the payback period, the average annual rate of return is not very useful without first determining what a satisfactory rate should be. An average annual rate of return of 33% and a payback period of 3 years are similar. The higher this rate of return the more profitable the project.

The payback period or the average annual rate of return are never used on their own as measures of profitability but always in conjunction with other measures such as N.P.V. or even d.c.f. yield.

### Varying hire rates and yield

If a cash flow tree such as that illustrated in Figure 6.1 is constructed to represent a plant hire operation, then the effects of the key elements in that cash flow tree can be studied by substituting a range of values for the key variables and determining the different net cash flows and hence the different yields. Two major variables in a plant hire operation are the hire rate and the utilisation factor. So, if a range of 5 hire rates is used with a range of 7 utilisation factors from 50% to 110%, different net cash flows can be calculated for each of the combinations, making a total of 35. For each of the net cash flows a yield can be calculated. Results of this type are best presented graphically as shown in Figure 6.3. This graph is known as a sensitivity chart and the analysis performed is known as a sensitivity analysis as it is displaying the sensitivity of yield to both the hire rate and the utilisation factor.

This family of curves illustrates two obvious points: the greater the hire rate, and the greater the utilisation factor the greater the rate of return. But while these points are obvious, this type of graph quantifies the increase in rate of return for any assumed increase in hire rate or utilisation factor. For example, for hire rate number 3, £10 per hour, the graph illustrates that the plant has to be on hire for 77% of the normal maximum usage before it would show a positive return and to record a return equal to the company's minimum at this hire rate, the equipment would need to be on hire all the available normal working time plus some overtime working. Adding the company's minimum return required to the graph reveals the combination of usage rate and hire rate that would produce this return or more.

The hire rate eventually adopted would be chosen for marketing reasons. These sensitivity graphs help to assess whether the market hire rate is likely to produce an adequate return on capital.

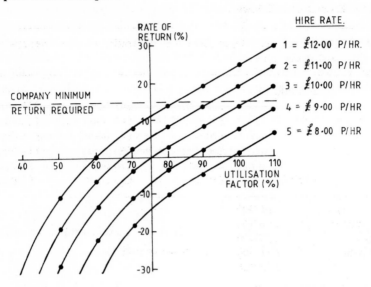

**Fig. 6.3**  Sensitivity of rate of return to the hire rate and the utilisation of an item of plant

### Yield and the effect of corporation tax and capital allowances

If a company trades profitably then it will be subject to corporation tax. Currently, corporation tax rate is 52% except for the smaller companies. There is a delay between the company engaging in trade, declaring a profit and paying tax. This lag in paying tax varies and depends on the relationship between the company's accounting year and the fiscal year. The lag could vary from 9 months to 18 months. In the example which follows and is used to demonstrate the effect of corporation tax on yield, two simplifying assumptions have been made: the first is that we are dealing with a large company, hence the corporation tax rate is 52%, and the second is that a tax lag of one year operates. Neither of these assumptions, although simplifying, is invalid.

A system of capital allowances also exists and must be included in this example. At the time of writing, U.K. tax legislation allows for industrial plant, including construction plant, that 100% of the investment in the plant can be used as a capital allowance in the first year of the plant's life. That is, if £10 000 is invested in a plant item then an allowance of £10 000 can be set against tax.

Thus, in our large company, corporation tax is being paid at 52%, a tax time-lag of one year exists, and capital allowances for investment in plant are at 100% of the investment in the first year.

If the company proposes to invest in a large item of earthmoving plant the net cash flows estimated at present day prices are given in Table 6.1.

Table 6.1    Estimated cash flows

| Year | Purchase price and resale value | Operating costs | Operating revenue | Net revenue |
|------|------------------------------|-----------------|-------------------|-------------|
| 0 | £50 000 | | | |
| 1 | | £20 000 | £45 000 | £25 000 |
| 2 | | £22 000 | £45 000 | £23 000 |
| 3 | | £24 000 | £40 000 | £16 000 |
| 4 | | £26 000 | £40 000 | £14 000 |
| 5 | | £28 000 | £36 000 | £8 000 |
| 6 | (£15 000) | £30 000 | £35 000 | £5 000 |

| | | | |
|---|---|---|---|
| Total net revenue | = | £91 000 | |
| Capital invested | = | £50 000 | |
| Resale value | = | £15 000 | |
| Pre-tax profit | = | £91 000 − £50 000 + £15 000 | |
| | = | £56 000 | |

Corporation tax and capital allowance calculations are shown in Table 6.2.

Table 6.2    Calculation of net-of-tax cash flows

| Year | A Purchase price and resale | B Net revenue | C Corporation tax due on previous year's net revenues | D Capital allowance (100% in year 1) (Balancing allowance) | E Tax saved or owed on allowances | F Tax paid | G Net cash flow after tax |
|------|------|------|------|------|------|------|------|
| 0 | £50 000 | | | | | | − £50 000 |
| 1 | | £25 000 | | £50 000 | £26 000 | (£26 000) | + £51 000 |
| 2 | | £23 000 | £13 000 | | | £13 000 | £10 000 |
| 3 | | £16 000 | £11 960 | | | £11 960 | £4 040 |
| 4 | | £14 000 | £8 320 | | | £8 320 | £5 680 |
| 5 | | £8 000 | £7 280 | | | £7 280 | £720 |
| 6 | (£15 000) | £5 000 | £4 160 | | | £4 160 | £15 840 |
| 7 | | | £2 600 | (£15 000) | (£7 800) | £10 400 | − £10 400 |

Column A shows the original purchase price of £50 000 and the resale value of £15 000.

Column B shows the net revenues.

Column C shows the corporation tax that would be due on these net revenues if no capital allowances were in operation. The corporation tax in Column C is time-shifted by one year to reflect the tax time lag. Thus the £13 000 of calculated corporation tax shown in year 2 is calculated on the net revenues shown in year 1 in Column B. Column D shows the capital allowance of £50 000 calculated at 100% of the purchase price, and a balancing allowance of £15 000 calculated on the resale value. The balancing allowance is to compensate for the £15 000 of capital returning to the company from the resale. Having already received a capital allowance of 100% on the original £50 000, the company now finds that the capital invested was only £50 000 − £15 000, hence the balancing allowance.

Column E is the tax saved by the capital allowance calculated as the capital allowance times the tax rate. The tax due on the balancing allowance is also calculated at the balancing allowance times the tax rate.

Column F is the tax paid, which is Column C less the savings in Column E plus the tax due in Column E.

Column G is the net cash flows after tax. The capital invested is in year 0. Year 1 is the £25 000 net revenue from Column B plus the tax saving from Column F. The explanation for this is that the tax saving can only be taken if the profits and hence the tax due are sufficient to accommodate that saving. If this project were the only project the company had, then the profits and the tax in year 1 would be insufficient and the tax saving would have to be rolled forward to be absorbed in later years. However, it was assumed that this was a large company, and it is further assumed that this large company has sufficient profits to accommodate this saving in year 1 of this project. Because this project has given rise to this saving (cash that would otherwise have left the company), the saving is credited to this project. Years 2 to 5 are the net revenues from Column B less the tax in Column F. Year 6 is the resale value plus the net revenue from Column B less the tax in Column F. Year 7 is the tax from Column F.

The net sum of the net cash flows after tax is £26 880. This could be regarded as the net-of-tax profit and is substantially less than the pretax profit of £56 000 already calculated.

The introduction of corporation tax and capital allowances has therefore greatly reduced the profit but it has also distorted the cash flows. The cash flow in year 1, for example, is much larger than before tax considerations while the others are much smaller. The payback period calculated on the cash flows in Table 6.1 is a little over two years: £25 000 from year 1 plus £23 000 from year 2 plus £2 000 from year 3 making up the original £50 000. The payback period after tax considerations from Table 6.2 is less than one year.

Table 6.3   Calculation of yield before tax

| Year | Cash flow |
|------|-----------|
| 0 | − £50 000 |
| 1 | + £25 000 |
| 2 | + £23 000 |
| 3 | + £16 000 |
| 4 | + £14 000 |
| 5 | +   £8 000 |
| 6 | + £20 000 |

The calculations in Tables 6.3 and 6.4 compare the yield obtained before tax and after tax.

The calculations were performed using the computer program listed in *Modern Construction Management* by McCaffer and Harris (Granada Publishing). The results were:

Payback period    2.13 years
D.c.f. yield      31.43%

Before calculating the yield after tax it is necessary to adjust the cash flows to remove the negative cash flow in year 7. The method of calculation explained previously is known as the single rate calculation and is not suitable for cash flows that have negatives anywhere other than the starting years. If used on cash flows with large negative cash flows at the end it could produce more than one interest rate giving a zero net present value. To overcome this, provision is made for the negative cash flow by taking a suitable amount from the previous year's positive cash flow. The amount set aside is the negative cash amount discounted by one year. The rate used to discount the negative cash flow is called the 'earning rate' and represents the return that can be obtained from a safe investment. Thus, using an earning rate of 10% the negative cash flow of £10 400 in year 7 can be discounted to £9 453.60 (£10 400 $\times$ 0.9090, where 0.9090 is the present worth factor taken from tables). If this £9 453.60 is deducted from the positive cash flow of £15 840.00 in year 6, then year 6's cash flow becomes £6 386.40. Thus the £9 453.60 removed from year 6 provides for the negative cash flow in year 7 and the cash flows are now suitable for a single rate d.c.f. yield calculation as before. For a fuller explanation see *Modern Construction Management*.

Table 6.4    Calculation of yield after tax.

| Year | Cash flow |
| --- | --- |
| 0 | − £50 000 |
| 1 | + £51 000 |
| 2 | + £10 000 |
| 3 | +  £4 040 |
| 4 | +  £5 680 |
| 5 | +   £720 |
| 6 | +  £6 386.40 |

The calculations were performed using the computer program listed in the Investment Appraisal Exercise in *Modern Construction Management*. The results were:

Payback period    0.98 years
D.c.f. yield      30.89%

Thus although the corporation tax removed considerable amounts from this investment project, the yield rate of return was reduced only from 31.43% to 30.89%. The reason for the yield remaining so high is due to the distortion in the cash flows brought about by the 100% capital allowance in the first year. This gave the net cash flows a relatively large positive cash flow in year 1. This occurred only because the tax saving arising from the capital allowance was taken and credited to this project. If the company were unable, due to lack of profit, to take immediately the benefit of the tax savings given by the capital allowance and had to delay taking the savings until enough profits were available, the yield after tax would fall. Thus the benefits of capital allowances are at their greatest when the company is trading profitably enough.

The example shown here was presented in the form of appraising a proposed investment whose cash flows were estimated at present prices. Taxation, of course, would be calculated on the actual cash flows as they occurred. These actual cash flows would be subjected to inflation and would reflect the effects of inflation. The effects of inflation on yield calculations are explained in the next section.

### Yield calculations and inflation

If cash flow estimates are made at present day prices the yield calculated on these cash flows will not reflect the effects of inflation. An example would be the purchase and hiring of an item of plant as shown below.

Table 6.5   Cash flow estimates for purchasing and hiring a plant item

| Year | Cash flows | | | |
|---|---|---|---|---|
| | Investment | Operating costs | Operating revenue | Net cash flows |
| 0 | £10 000 | | | − £10 000 |
| 1 | | £3 000 | £6 000 | + £3 000 |
| 2 | | £3 500 | £7 000 | + £3 500 |
| 3 | | £4 000 | £7 000 | + £3 000 |
| 4 | | £4 500 | £7 000 | + £2 500 |

The yield of this project is 8.0% calculated as shown in Table 6.6.

Table 6.6   Calculation of yield

| Year | Net cash flow | Present worth factors at 9% | Present value | Present value factors at 7% | Present value |
|---|---|---|---|---|---|
| 0 | − £10 000 | 1.0 | − £10 000.00 | 1.0 | − £10 000.00 |
| 1 | + £3 000 | 0.91743 | + £2 752.29 | 0.93457 | + £2 803.71 |
| 2 | + £3 500 | 0.84168 | + £2 945.88 | 0.87343 | + £3 057.00 |
| 3 | + £3 000 | 0.77218 | + £2 316.54 | 0.81629 | + £2 448.87 |
| 4 | + £2 500 | 0.70842 | + £1 771.05 | 0.76289 | + £1 907.23 |
| | | Net present value | − £214.24 | Net present value | + £216.81 |

By interpolation:

$$\text{Yield} = 7\% + \left[(9\% - 7\%) \times \frac{216.81}{216.81 - (-214.24)}\right]$$
$$= 7\% + 1\%$$
$$= 8.00\%$$

As the estimates were based on present day prices this 8.00% yield does not include any effects of inflation.

Including inflation at the uniform rate of 10% per year on both the operating costs and the operating revenues, the cash flows adjusted for inflation are as shown in Table 6.7.

The revised net cash flows are in fact simply the original net cash flows inflated at 10% per year. The yield of these cash flows which now include inflation is calculated as shown in Table 6.8.

By interpolation:

$$\text{Yield} = 18\% + \left[(19\% - 18\%) \times \frac{156.22}{156.22 - (-41.61)}\right]$$
$$= 18\% + 1\% \times 0.79$$
$$= 18.8\%$$

This yield calculated on the revised cash flows is larger than the yield calculated on the original cash flows because the revised positive cash flows themselves were larger. These cash flows were larger due to the inflation included in them. The £3 993 revised net cash flow in year 3 does not buy any more goods than the £3 000 original net cash flow. The difference in the two amounts is cancelled by inflation. The £993 more in the revised cash flows just compensates for the inflation at 10% per year. Thus, although the revised positive net cash flows are larger and hence the yield is larger at 18.8% the investor is no better off because the extra monies acquired are absorbed by inflation. Thus 8% on the original *uninflated* cash flows is equivalent to 18.8% on the revised *inflated* cash flows. To distinguish between these two rates of return the rate of return calculated on the estimates which did not include inflation, the original *uninflated* cash flows, is called the *real rate of return*. The rate of return calculated on the estimates which included inflation, the revised *inflated* cash flows, is called the *apparent rate of return*.

The relationship between these two rates of return is through the inflation rate. The apparent rate of return is the real rate of return increased by the inflation rate as follows:

$$(1 + a) = (1 + r)(1 + d)$$

where a is the apparent rate of return, r is the real rate of return and d is the inflation rate.

Substituting the values calculated from Tables 6.7 and 6.8 for a and r (a = 0.188 (18.8%) and r = 0.08 (8%)) into the expression gives a value for d the inflation rate:

Table 6.7    Cash flows adjusted for inflation.

| Year | | Cash flows | | | | | | |
|---|---|---|---|---|---|---|---|---|
| | Investment | Operating costs | Inflation adjustment | Revised operating cost | Operating revenue | Inflation adjustment | Revised operating revenue | Revised net cash flows |
| 0 | £10 000.00 | | | | | | | − £10 000.00 |
| 1 | | £3 000.00 | £300.00 | £3 300.00 | £6 000.00 | £600.00 | £6 600.00 | + £3 300.00 |
| 2 | | £3 500.00 | £735.00 | £4 235.00 | £7 000.00 | £1 470.00 | £8 470.00 | + £4 235.00 |
| 3 | | £4 000.00 | £1 324.00 | £5 324.00 | £7 000.00 | £2 317.00 | £9 317.00 | + £3 993.00 |
| 4 | | £4 500.00 | £2 088.45 | £6 588.45 | £7 000.00 | £3 248.70 | £10 248.70 | + £3 660.25 |

Table 6.8    Calculation of yield on revised cash flows.

| Year | Revised net cash flows | Present value factors at 19% | Present value | Present value factors at 18% | Present value |
|---|---|---|---|---|---|
| 0 | − £10 000.00 | 1.0 | − £10 000.00 | 1.0 | − £10 000.00 |
| 1 | + £3 300.00 | 0.84033 | + £2 773.09 | 0.84745 | + £2 796.59 |
| 2 | + £4 235.00 | 0.70616 | + £2 990.59 | 0.71818 | + £3 041.49 |
| 3 | + £3 993.00 | 0.59341 | + £2 369.49 | 0.60863 | + £2 430.26 |
| 4 | + £3 660.25 | 0.49866 | + £1 825.22 | 0.51578 | + £1 887.88 |
| | | Net present value: | − £41.61 | Net present value: | + £156.22 |

$$(1 + 0.188) = (1 + 0.08)(1 + d)$$
$$\therefore (1 + d) = \frac{(1.188)}{(1.08)}$$
$$\therefore d = 1.10 - 1 = 0.10 = 10\%$$

Given the value of the calculated real rate of return at 8% and the calculated apparent rate of return at 18.8%, the expression estimates that the inflation rate is 10%. Since the inflation rate included in the estimates was 10% this serves as a check on the above explanation.

As most proposed investments are appraised on estimates based on present day prices the rate of return calculated and used to judge a proposal's viability is normally the real rate of return. Since the cash flows recorded as projects taking place are normally based on the transactions that occur at current prices, the cash flows determined usually have inflation included as a matter of course. Thus, the yield calculated on these recorded cash flows will be the apparent rate of return. It is therefore important to distinguish whether the cash flows are based on constant, year 0, prices or current prices when interpreting the yield calculated.

The situation used to explain the relationship between real rate, apparent rate and the inflation rate was one where the plant owner was allowed to increase his revenue at the same rate as inflation. However if this were not the case then the apparent rate would be less than 18.8% but the inflation would still be 10% and the *achieved* real rate of return would be less than the *estimated* real rate of return of 8%.

The following example illustrates this. If the project originally described in Table 6.5 had been executed and completed, the cash flows could have been recorded. Throughout the duration of the project inflation had been 10% per year. Public spending cuts, high interest rates and a general recession had made it impossible for plant hirers to raise the hire rates in line with inflation, although rates had increased to some extent. Thus the operating revenue, although increasing, had not kept pace with inflation. The recorded cash flows are as shown in Table 6.9.

Table 6.9   Cash flows recorded during the execution of the project.

| Year | Investment | Operating costs | Operating revenue | Net cash flow |
|------|-----------|-----------------|-------------------|---------------|
| 0 | £10 000.00 | | | − £10 000.00 |
| 1 | | £3 300.00 | £6 435.00 | + £3 135.00 |
| 2 | | £4 235.00 | £8 057.09 | + £3 822.09 |
| 3 | | £5 324.00 | £8 747.50 | + £3 423.50 |
| 4 | | £6 588.45 | £9 569.75 | + £2 981.30 |

The apparent rate of return calculated on these recorded cash flows is 12.85% as calculated in Table 6.10.

Table 6.10    Calculated apparent rate of return on recorded cash flows.

| Year | Recorded net cash flows | Present value factors at 13% | Present value | Present value factors at 12% | Present value |
|------|------|------|------|------|------|
| 0 | − £10 000.00 | 1.0 | − £10 000.00 | 1.0 | − £10 000.00 |
| 1 | + £3 135.00 | 0.88495 | + £2 774.32 | 0.89285 | + £2 799.08 |
| 2 | + £3 822.09 | 0.78314 | + £2 993.23 | 0.79719 | + £3 046.93 |
| 3 | + £3 423.50 | 0.69305 | + £2 372.66 | 0.71178 | + £2 436.78 |
| 4 | + £2 981.30 | 0.61331 | + £1 828.46 | 0.63551 | + £1 894.65 |
| | | | − £31.33 | | + £177.44 |

By interpolation:

$$\text{Apparent rate of return} = 12\% + \left(13\% - 12\%\right) \times \frac{177.44}{177.44 - (-31.33)}$$
$$= 12\% + 1\% \times 0.85$$
$$= 12.85\%$$

Thus the achieved apparent rate of return is 12.85% but as inflation during this time was 10% per year then the real rate of return achieved is 2.59% calculated as follows:

$$(1 + a) = (1 + r)(1 + d)$$
$$(1 + 0.1285) = (1 + r)(1 + 0.1)$$
$$\therefore (1 + r) = \frac{(1.1285)}{(1.1)}$$
$$\therefore r = 1.0259 - 1 = 0.0259 = 2.59\%$$

Thus because the income or revenue was restrained from increasing at the rate of inflation but costs were rising at the rate of inflation, the real rate of return was reduced to 2.59%.

Other examples could be apparent rates of return of 10%, inflation rates of 10% and real rates of return of zero, or an apparent rate of 8%, and inflation rate of 10% and a real rate of return of −1.8%.

Inflation evidently reduces the real rate of return unless prices are allowed to rise to compensate for its effects. This reduction in the real rate of return could drag the achieved real rate of return below the cost of capital. In other words, the capital could well be costing more than the project is yielding. In such a case the project is uneconomic and if such projects are sustained the company will become bankrupt. The first noticeable effect probably will be that the company cannot replace its plant and will either go on using ageing equipment or reduce its fleet.

The construction plant hire industry is particularly vulnerable to the effects of inflation. This is because the construction industry is largely an industry that does not create its own demand and is dependent on public works and public spending for a substantial portion of its workload. The rest of the industry's workload depends on the private sector being willing to invest. If the cost of money, i.e. interest rates, is high, the private sector is discouraged from investing and the demand for construction work declines. Since in times of rising inflation governments cut public spending while also increasing interest rates, the demand for construction declines accordingly. As the demand declines, prices for construction work fall and the plant hire industry cannot raise prices in line with inflation. As a result, the gap between operating costs and revenue is squeezed with a consequential fall in the return on capital invested in the plant.

## Reading list

1. Harris F.C. and McCaffer, R. *Modern Construction Management*. Second edition. Granada, 1982.
2. Merret, A.J. and Sykes, A. *The Finance and Analysis of Capital Projects*. Longman, 1963.
3. Merret, A.J. and Sykes, A. *Capital Budgeting and Company Finance*. Longman, 1966.
4. Alfred, A.M. and Evans, J.B. *Discounted Cash Flow – Principles and Short-Cut Techniques*. Chapman and Hall, 1965.
5. Wright, M.G. *Discounted cash flow*. McGraw-Hill, 1967.
6. Institution of Civil Engineers. *An Introduction to Engineering Economics*. ICE, 1969.
7. Pilcher, R. *Appraisal and Control of Project Costs*. McGraw-Hill, 1973.
8. Savage, C.I. and Small, J.R. *Introduction to Managerial Economics*. Hutchinson, 1970.
9. Pace, M. *A cost reporting system for construction plant management*. MSc. project report, Department of Civil Engineering, Loughborough University of Technology, 1972.
10. Samuels, J.M. and Wilkes, F.M. *Management of Company Finance*. Third edition. Nelson, 1980.

# CHAPTER 7

# PLANT ACQUISITION

## Methods of acquisition

Much of Chapters 5 and 6 dealt with the economic analyses that help decide whether or not to acquire a plant item, based mainly on the question: 'does this proposed acquisition offer the opportunity to earn an adequate rate of return and which of the possible plant items is the most economic?' So far the question of how the plant item should be acquired has not been considered. There is a tendency in very large companies for the two decisions of whether to acquire and how to acquire to be taken by separate people, the specialist or technical directors being responsible for the decision whether to acquire, and the finance directors responsible for the decision how to acquire. In smaller companies these two decisions often get merged. Major methods of acquisition are reviewed in this chapter and the relative advantages of each method are highlighted.

The decision to acquire an asset should be made for both technical and economic reasons. The profitability of the proposal should be evaluated by calculating the expected rate of return and comparing it with the cost of capital. The decision of how to acquire the asset can then be regarded as a financial one.

The major methods of acquisition can be classified as purchase, leasing or hiring. The major factors that influence the decision as to which is the more advantageous are:

(a) tax legislation which allows 100% capital allowances against the purchase of construction plant,

(b) the profit flows of the acquiring company which determine whether these allowances can be turned into tax savings benefiting the company immediately or rolled forward until later years, thus becoming devalued,

(c) the acquiring company's cash flows which determine what money is available for plant acquisition, and finally

(d) the acquiring company's gearing ratio (borrowed capital/equity capital) which influences the amount of further borrowing possible.

## Purchase

Outright purchase is simply payment of the purchase price by the acquiring company to the supplier. This involves the acquiring company in a large cash payment very early, before the equipment acquired has earned any revenue. However, outright purchase provides the acquiring company with capital allowances of 100% of the purchase price of the equipment in the first year. If the acquiring company's profit flows are sufficient these allowances can produce a saving of 52% of the purchase price in the first year. Thus an item of plant worth £10 000 would produce capital allowances of £10 000 in the first year and tax savings of £5 200 (£10 000 × 52%, 52% being the corporation tax rate). This tax saving is most valuable but it is only available if the profit flows in the company are £10 000 or more.

If the cash is available from within the company's own resources or even from an overdraft this form of acquisition is probably the cheapest, provided the capital allowances can be used to produce the tax saving immediately. If the capital allowances cannot be used immediately because the company's profit flows are inadequate then the capital allowances can be rolled forward until sufficient profit flows are available. In this situation the benefit of the capital allowances and derived tax savings become devalued, in simple present worth (or value) terms, and in these circumstances outright purchase may not be the cheapest method of acquisition.

Outright purchase places the title of the equipment immediately with the acquiring company. This means that it becomes an asset over which the company has full control, can use it in negotiating finance, use the equipment anywhere including overseas, and dispose of it to produce cash from its resale value.

Other methods of purchase include credit sale and hire purchase.

A *credit sale* is a sale in which the acquiring company takes the ownership or title of the plant item immediately but the purchase price is paid in instalments. These instalments include the purchase price plus any financing charges the vendor makes. Credit sales, like outright purchase, attract capital allowances immediately and can be used in the same way as in outright purchase.

*Hire purchase* and *leasing* are significantly different in the treatment of tax and therefore must be considered quite separately. Hire purchase is a contract whereby the acquiring company pays a regular hire charge and at some predetermined point after payment of a proportion of the agreed hire charges the acquiring company buys the plant item for a nominal sum. This facility to purchase distinguishes the hire purchase contract from leasing which under U.K. tax legislation does not permit the acquiring company to purchase the leased equipment. Hire purchase also attracts the capital allowances as if the plant item were purchased outright. Thus in terms of tax savings, hire purchase has the same advantages as outright purchase.

Both hire purchase and credit sales are likely to require deposits but these deposits are much less than the whole purchase price and therefore in cash flow considerations these forms of acquisitions are less demanding than outright purchase. However, the interest charges included in hire purchase contracts are likely to be greater than the acquiring company would pay on an overdraft. Thus if the hire purchase method of acquisition is compared to outright purchase, outright purchase would be cheaper in most cases, the capital allowances available in both cases being the same.

## Leasing

The leasing method of acquisition is different in concept from the previous methods outlined. The difference is that the ownership or title of the plant item remains the property of the leasing company (the lessor), and the acquiring company (the lessee) never becomes the owner. The acquiring company (the lessee) only acquires the *use* of the plant item in return for payments or rentals but never becomes the owner. While this is more common in the leasing of property it is also used in the acquisition of the use of capital equipment such as construction plant. Although there is a plethora of leasing arrangements, they all adhere to the basic principle that the lessor is the owner and the lessee is the user of the plant. There are two broad categories of lease, the finance lease and the operating lease.

The *finance lease* is normally arranged through leasing companies who have no particular interest in the equipment, offer no technical support, but merely arrange the lease. The lessee pays the lessor payments or rentals for the use of the plant acquired. The plant is usually supplied by a third party, the plant manufacturer or manufacturers' agent from whom the plant will be bought by the leasing company. The payments or rentals for this type of lease will be divided into two parts, the primary period and the secondary period. The duration of the primary period is dependent on the useful life of the plant but is two to five years for most construction plant. Payments during this primary period are calculated by the leasing company to include the capital cost of the plant item less any allowance for the resale value, plus the leasing company's additions for their own overheads, interest charges and profit. The capital cost will also reflect the capital allowances that the leasing company will be able to claim against the leasing company's tax. Thus the capital allowances due do not go to the acquiring company using the plant as in purchasing because the lessee is not the owner. The capital allowances are claimed by the owner who purchased the plant, and that is the leasing company. The advantages the lessee gains are from the amount of this benefit that is passed on by the leasing company through the payments or rentals. Payments for any secondary period are negotiated but could be relatively small as the leasing company has already recovered all costs and profit during the primary period. The using company is not permitted by tax legislation in the U.K. to buy the plant or to sell it although the leasing company, which is unlikely to have any interest or ability to use the plant, is free to sell it and may share the proceeds with the user company who had leased the plant. The conditions of such a lease agreement tend to prevent the company that leases the plant from cancelling the agreement during the primary period. The contract is also likely to specify responsibility for insurance, maintenance, servicing and repairs. All these are designed to protect the owner's property for the duration of the primary period. The leasing company's contribution is simply that of providing finance.

The outgoings of the lease to the user company, the lessee, are the lease payments or rentals: the lessee does not have to find the purchase price, or deposits as in hire purchase or credit sales but may have to pay about three months' rental in advance. Thus the cash flow for leasing is less difficult to arrange. Some leasing companies have been known to arrange uneven lease payments which are negotiated to match the cyclical use of equipment. Thus the leasing of earthmoving equipment which may be idle during December, January and February could well benefit from such uneven repayment schemes.

As described, the lessee does not receive the capital allowances directly: these go to the owner, the leasing company, and the benefit is passed on via the lease payments. This benefit is available to the lessee regardless of his profit flows. Thus whether the lessee (the construction company) has large profits able to benefit from capital allowances or small profits unable to benefit from capital allowances is no longer relevant as it is in purchasing. Thus leasing in terms of costs when compared to the purchasing option is more advantageous to a company when its profit flows are small and it is unable to use the capital allowances to generate tax savings immediately; or when the company is rapidly expanding and its investment programme has created such a total of capital allowances that even although it is profitable it is unable to use all these capital allowances. In addition to the capital allowances, the lease payments themselves are normal trading expenses and therefore deductible from revenue before calculating tax due. Thus there is some tax saving on the lease payments as well as any benefit from the capital allowances the leasing company may have passed on when calculating the lease payment.

Another feature of finance leases is that the security of the lease may well be only the asset itself and the rest of the company's borrowings against the company's owned assets may not be affected by a leasing arrangement. Therefore a company that is already 'highly geared', i.e. has high borrowings in relation to equity or shareholders' capital, may find leasing attractive. Although the leased asset may not show on the balance sheet the company has nevertheless committed itself to payments and in practical terms is just as vulnerable as if it had increased its borrowings.

Thus a finance lease is likely to be more advantageous to a construction company when its profit flows do not allow the full benefit of capital allowances from purchasing and/or when the company cash flow situation is unable to provide funds for purchase, or when the company is unable to undertake further borrowings to purchase equipment.

The *operating lease* is normally arranged with manufacturers or suppliers who offer such a service as part of the marketing of their products. Again, such leases are likely to have a non-cancellable primary period but the duration and costs may be quite different from finance leases because the leasing company, being the manufacturer, has a different interest in the plant. For example, the supplying company may have use for the plant itself or a well-developed secondhand leasing market. In these circumstances an operating lease may be cheaper than a finance lease. The capital allowances would, as with finance leases, go to the leasing company who own the plant.

### Hiring

Hiring and leasing are sometimes regarded as similar and for plant items that are on hire for long periods the difference may be unclear. An example of such a long-term hire is the contract hire arrangement for vehicles. The payments are similar to leases and the owner of the vehicles, the hire company, claims the capital allowances. However, contract hire arrangements can involve the hire company supplying the vehicles and providing repair and maintenance whereas finance leases do not involve the leasing company in providing these services. Thus there are distinctions. Short-term hire of construction plant is not usually regarded as leasing and the company hiring the plant pays an hourly, weekly or monthly rate for the plant. The period of hire may well be as short as one week or one month and therefore the construction company is not committed to a long primary period as it would be in a finance lease. The use of such short-term hire is, of course, widespread in the construction industry and within the industry there exists a very well-developed plant hire industry to serve this market. Many construction companies who own their own plant run the plant division as a subsidiary offering external hire to other companies and internal hire to their own construction division which may be the parent company or another company within the same holding group. Thus the construction companies, themselves the users of the plant, are well used to hiring either internally or externally. This conveniently separates the problems of plant acquisition, determining adequate hire rates and marketing of plant to ensure adequate utilisation from the work of construction. All these costs are simply reflected in the hire rate to the construction company.

It is worth noting, however, that if a subsidiary plant hire company sets its internal hire rates at strictly economic levels the construction division may be able to find ostensibly better external hire rates from outside companies. These external rates may not have been chosen for economic reasons, or the external hire company may have lower fixed costs and overheads and thereby be able to offer cheaper hire rates. If the external hire is chosen in preference to an apparently more expensive internal hire rate, the parent company may be damaged by the loss of hire income and by the unrecovered part of the fixed costs which still must be met even while the plant is idle.

Thus most of the acquisition of construction plant, whether by purchase or lease, is by the plant hire companies, which are either companies specifically set up to provide the hire service to construction companies or plant subsidiaries of construction companies.

## Comparison of leasing and purchasing

The key to deciding whether leasing is more advantageous than purchasing in cost terms is the use companies can make of the capital allowances. For example, ignoring tax considerations, if the purchase price of an item of plant were £12 000 and the lease payments were £1 360 per quarter for three years, the cost of these two cash flows could be compared on present worth terms using an interest rate that represented the value of money to the company. Table 7.1 illustrates this using an interest rate of 15%.

The leasing v. purchasing comparison is a financial appraisal and usually the discount rate used in these comparisons represents the cost of borrowing. The cost of borrowing is the nominal interest rate less tax for the profitable company.

Table 7.1    Comparison of leasing v. purchasing, ignoring tax considerations.

| Year | Quarter | Period | Purchasing | Leasing |
|---|---|---|---|---|
| 0 | | 0 | − £12 000 | |
| 1 | 1 | 1 | | − £1 360 |
| | 2 | 2 | | − £1 360 |
| | 3 | 3 | | − £1 360 |
| | 4 | 4 | | − £1 360 |
| 2 | 1 | 5 | | − £1 360 |
| | 2 | 6 | | − £1 360 |
| | 3 | 7 | | − £1 360 |
| | 4 | 8 | | − £1 360 |
| 3 | 1 | 9 | | − £1 360 |
| | 2 | 10 | | − £1 360 |
| | 3 | 11 | | − £1 360 |
| | 4 | 12 | | − £1 360 |

Present worth of purchasing = −£12 000
Present worth = −£1 360 × 9.63496
$\qquad$ = −£13 103.54

N.B. The factor 9.63496 is the present worth factor for a uniform series calculated as

$$\frac{(1 + i)^n - 1}{i (1 + i)^n}$$

where n is the number of periods, 12, and i is the interest rate per quarter. The interest rate per annum was given as 15%. Thus the interest rate per quarter is calculated using the compound relationship as

$$(1 + i_{quarter})^4 = (1 + i_{year})^1$$
$$\therefore (1 + i_{quarter})^4 = (1.15)^1$$
$$\therefore i_{quarter} = \sqrt[4]{(1.15)} - 1 = 0.0355 = 3.55\%$$

Thus, at an interest rate of 15% the purchase alternative is cheaper. In fact the interest rate in this example would need to be 21.9% per year or 5.08% per quarter before the leasing costs would just equal the purchase price. The situation is influenced, however, when tax considerations are included.

Table 7.2 shows the cash flows for outright purchase using the 100% capital allowance immediately and assuming a tax lag of one year to represent the delay in meeting a tax liability or, as in this case, recording a tax saving. The tax saving is treated the same as an inward cash flow since this has the same effect as a saving that prevents an outward cash flow. The tax saving is calculated on a tax rate of 52%. The net present value at 15% is −£6 573.95 as shown in Table 7.2

Table 7.2   Cash flows and N.P.V. calculation for outright purchase including tax saving from capital allowances used in year 1.

| Year | Purchase price | Tax saving | Net cash flow | Present worth factor (15%) | Present worth |
|------|----------------|------------|---------------|----------------------------|----------------|
| 0 | − £12 000 | | − £12 000 | 1.0 | − £12 000.00 |
| 1 | | £6 240 | + £6 240 | 0.86956 | + £5 426.05 |

Net present value: − £6 573.95

Table 7.3 shows the net cash flows for the leasing alternative. No tax savings from capital allowances are shown as these would already be reflected in the lease payment charged to the acquiring company. However, tax savings derived from the lease payments are shown as these are normal trading expenses and are deducted from revenue before tax. A tax lag of one year is assumed before the tax reductions are included. The tax rate is 52%. The net present value calculated at 15% is −£7 487.24.

Table 7.3   Net cash flow for the leasing alternative including tax considerations.

| Year | Quarter | Period | Lease payment | Tax reduction | Present worth factors (15%) | Present worth of tax reduction |
|------|---------|--------|---------------|---------------|------------------------------|--------------------------------|
| 1 | 1 | 1 | − £1 360 | | | |
|   | 2 | 2 | − £1 360 | | | |
|   | 3 | 3 | − £1 360 | | | |
|   | 4 | 4 | − £1 360 | | | |
| 2 | 1 | 5 | − £1 360 | | | |
|   | 2 | 6 | − £1 360 | | | |
|   | 3 | 7 | − £1 360 | | | |
|   | 4 | 8 | − £1 360 | + £2 828.80 | 0.75614 | + £2 138.97 |

*Table 7.3 continued*

| Year | Quarter | Period | Lease payment | Tax reduction | Present worth factors (15%) | Present worth of tax reduction |
|------|---------|--------|---------------|---------------|------------------------------|-------------------------------|
|   | 1 | 9 | − £1 360 | | | |
|   | 2 | 10 | − £1 360 | | | |
| 3 | 3 | 11 | − £1 360 | | | |
|   | 4 | 12 | − £1 360 | + £2 828.80 | 0.65751 | + £1 859.96 |
| 4 | 4 | 16 | | + £2 828.80 | 0.57175 | + £1 617.37 |

N.B.  The tax reduction is calculated as
52% of a year's lease payments
and delayed one year (4 × £1 360.00 × 52%).

| | |
|---|---:|
| Present value of tax reductions | + £5 616.30 |
| Present value of lease payments from Table 7.1 | − £13 103.54 |

Net present value: −£7 487.24

Thus, as with the case of Table 7.1, ignoring tax considerations, when tax considerations are excluded but the capital allowances available in outright purchase are used immediately, the outright purchase option is cheaper than the lease option as the net present values of −£6 573.95 for outright purchase and −£7 487.24 for leasing illustrates.

However, this situation changes if there is a delay in taking the tax savings from the capital allowances created by the purchase.

Table 7.4 calculates the net present value for a delay of one year beyond the initial lag of the year in taking the tax savings. This delay could be caused by profit flows being insufficient to use the capital allowances immediately.

Table 7.4    N.P.V. of outright purchase with a 1 year delay in using capital allowances

| Year | Purchase | Tax saving | Net cash flow | Present worth factors (15%) | Present worth |
|------|----------|------------|---------------|------------------------------|----------------|
| 0 | − £12 000 | | − £12 000 | 1.0 | − £12 000.00 |
| 2 | | + £6 240 | + £6 240 | 0.75614 | + £4 718.31 |

Net present value: − £7 281.69

With a two year, rather than one year delay before the tax savings become effective, the difference between purchasing and leasing narrows, and the net present value of leasing remains at −£7 487.24 whereas the net present value of purchasing becomes −£7 281.69. Any further delay in taking the tax savings will make leasing a cheaper alternative as Table 7.5 illustrates by adding a further one year delay before taking the tax saving.

Table 7.5   N.P.V. of outright purchase with a 2-year delay in using capital allowances.

| Year | Purchase | Tax saving | Net cash flow | Present worth factors (15%) | Present worth |
|------|----------|-----------|---------------|-----------------------------|---------------|
| 0 | − £12 000 | | − £12 000 | 1.0 | − £12 000.00 |
| 3 | | + £6 240 | + £6 240 | 0.65751 | + £4 102.86 |
| | | | | Net present value: | − £7 897.14 |

Thus, with a three year delay before the tax savings become effective rather than the initial one year, the leasing option becomes more economic as the net present value of purchasing becomes −£7 897.14 whereas the net present value of leasing remains at −£7 487.24.

A final illustration shows the capital allowances spread over years two and three to represent the ability to take some tax savings in year two and the remainder in year three. This is shown in Table 7.6.

Table 7.6   N.P.V. of outright purchase with the capital allowances used in years 2 and 3.

| Year | Purchase | Tax saving | Net cash flow | Present worth factors (15%) | Present worth |
|------|----------|-----------|---------------|-----------------------------|---------------|
| 0 | − £12 000 | | − £12 000 | 1.0 | − £12 000.00 |
| 2 | | + £3 120 | + £3 120 | 0.75614 | + £2 359.16 |
| 3 | | + £3 120 | + £3 120 | 0.65751 | + £2 051.43 |
| | | | | Net present value: | − £7 589.41 |

Again this illustrates that delays in taking the tax savings can lead to the leasing option becoming more economic as the net present value for outright purchase is −£7 589.41 while the net present value for leasing is −£7 487.24.

In all the lease v. purchase examples shown above a tax lag of one year was adopted to represent the delay in meeting a tax liability. This one year lag could vary and the lag itself influences this lease v. purchase comparison. However, the point is made in these examples that any delay in using the capital allowances that are created by purchasing shifts the balance of the economic comparison in favour of leasing. Thus, the cost comparison of leasing v. buying is determined by the company's profit flows.

The other factors to be considered are:

 (i)   the company's cash flow since leasing makes less demands than purchasing;
 (ii)  the company's ability to raise the capital to purchase since this depends on the extent of the company's existing borrowings;
(iii)  the availability of alternative uses for the investment funds available;
(iv)   the loss of flexibility, due to commitments, to make lease payments annually;
 (v)   the restrictions placed on the using company in using the equipment.

Thus, the resolution of the lease v. purchase issue is not simply an economic comparison but involves these other factors as well.

## Reading list

1. Harris, F.C. and McCaffer, R. *Modern Construction Management*. Second edition. Granada, 1982.
2. Samuels, J.M. and Wilkes, F.M. *Management of Company Finance*. Third edition. Nelson, 1980.
3. Coombs, W. *Construction Accounting and Financial Management*. McGraw-Hill, 1958.
4. Forman, M. and Gilbert, J. *Factoring and Finance*. Heinemann, 1976.
5. Mead, H.T. and Mitchell, G.L. *Plant Hire for Building and Construction*. Newnes-Butterworths, 1972.
6. Sykes, A. The Lease-buy Decision. *Management Survey, Report No. 29.* British Institute of Management, 1976.
7. Smith, T. Plant Finance. *Construction News Magazine*, 2 November 1976.
8. Byrne, P. Today's Plant with Tomorrow's Money. *Contract Journal*, 15 July 1976.
9. George, I. Right Kind of Finance Can Always be Found. *New Civil Engineer*, 6 October 1977.

# CHAPTER 8

# SYSTEMATIC PLANT SELECTION

## Technical evaluation

The purchase of an item of construction equipment requires a high capital outlay, and the consequences of misjudging the potential earnings of the machine over a number of years could have a dire effect on future profits. Thus, unless it can be shown that the plant will yield a rate of return at least as good as making an alternative investment then it should not be purchased at all. In this event either leasing or hiring may be more economical options.

However, even when the financial and other economic factors have been adequately satisfied regarding the purchase, because of the many alternative choices of manufacturer now available for many items of equipment the final decision is likely to be influenced by the merits of small but important differences offered with each make. It is this aspect of the purchase, namely the technical evaluation which is dealt with in this chapter.

The decision process follows a systematic approach originally developed by U.S. consultants, Kepner and Tregoe[1]. The method forces the manager into a sequence of actions and helps to highlight the relevant factors. In this way the many separate judgements needed for an examination of many facts can be weighted and ranked accordingly, and the best buy for the least cost can be chosen.

## The main features of decision making

Dixon[2] describes decision as follows:

'Decision making is compromise. The decision maker must weigh value judgements that involve economic factors, technical practicabilities, scientific necessities, human and social considerations, etc. To make a 'correct' decision is to choose the one alternative from among those that are available which best balances or optimises the total value, considering all the various factors.'

Using this definition, Kepner and Tregoe established seven essential factors in decision making (Figure 8.1).

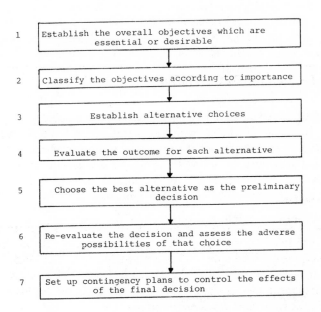

1    Establish the overall objectives which are essential or desirable

2    Classify the objectives according to importance

3    Establish alternative choices

4    Evaluate the outcome for each alternative

5    Choose the best alternative as the preliminary decision

6    Re-evaluate the decision and assess the adverse possibilities of that choice

7    Set up contingency plans to control the effects of the final decision

**Fig. 8.1**    Seven essential factors in decision making

**Example: Crane evaluation**

A company has recently obtained a construction contract which will involve the use of a 40 tonnes capacity, strut-jib, crawler mounted crane. A 9-year working life can be assumed which indicates that an attractive rate of return may be achieved by purchasing the crane. The crane must be capable of conversion to a dragline/grabbing crane and cost less than £41 000.

The plant manager is required to undertake a technical evaluation of the alternative makes of crane available in the market.

The method

*Step 1: Set objectives which are essential and desirable*
The problem as defined is far too vague to establish the precise requirements and some discussion with the site manager, planning engineer and even the operator is required. From these further enquiries the precise features of the machine may be ascertained: these will be called the 'objectives' and examples are listed A–G, 1–18 on the Decision Analysis Sheet shown in Table 8.2 at the end of this chapter.

*Step 2: Classify objectives according to importance*
A careful examination of the listed objectives will reveal that some are mandatory, some are important but not essential, while others would be desirable and useful if available.

From this list of objectives, the mandatory objectives are set aside and called *musts*. The *musts* set the limits which cannot be violated, so makes of machine which do not meet the fundamental requirements are quickly recognised and eliminated early in the analysis.

The remaining objectives are labelled *wants*, and some may be more important than others. The next step therefore is to rank the importance of the *want* objectives. This is achieved by attaching a ranking expressed on a suitable scale. In practice, a 1–5 or 1–10 system is suitable, with the importance of the objective increasing with numerical value. This part of the procedure usually requires much subjective assessment and may vary according to an individual's preference, but at least a record stands for future reference and reconciliation.

The *want* objectives are classified into two groupings:

(i)   the performance results expected from the machine – here called the *technical element*;
(ii)  the demands made upon resources of labour, money, materials, time – here called the *economic element* as associated with costs and servicing.

*Step 3: Develop the alternative choices*
In this arbitrary example, three (entirely fictitious) manufacturers are located making a crane which may be suitable for the specified duties. These are:

(i)   Harris 46T;
(ii)  HFC 416;
(iii) Sirac Highlift.

At this stage only the *musts* are considered. Consequently the field of choice may be narrowed to a small number, saving much time and money.

*Step 4: Evaluate the alternatives against the objectives*
The stage is now reached where it is necessary to consider in detail the specification of the selected machines. Difficulties will now begin to emerge: for instance, there is rarely a unique price for a large item of construction equipment as each manufacturer will offer features slightly different to its competitors' machines.

In this example the quotations received for the three cranes are shown in Table 8.1.

It can be seen that the information assembled for each crane varies in its detail and any decision on price can be only a compromise. However within the limits imposed by these variations the relative prices of the machines can be compared. But it must be remembered that discounts and payment arrangements may influence the final decision. Also the cost and availability of spare parts and maintenance should not be overlooked at this stage, especially from foreign suppliers affected by exchange rate fluctuations.

Table 8.1

| Component | Harris | HFC | Sirac |
|---|---|---|---|
| Base machine | £32 809 | £26 833 | £34 070 |
| Cat head boom | (30') inc | N/A | N/A |
| Taper top boom | (27') £756 | (50') £3 915 | inc. |
| Boom inserts to max. | £1 469 | £2 524 | inc. |
| Fly jib | (30') £573 | (30') £561 | (40') £1 482 |
| Power lowering equipment | inc. | £2 135 | inc. |
| Safe load indicator and tests | £1 830 | £969 | £902 |
| Cab heater | inc. | £90 | £80 |
| Hook block | £213 | £181 | inc. |
| Parts to convert to dragline | £2 500 | £968 | N/A |
| 2½ y$^3$ dragline bucket | inc. | £1 306 | N/A |
| Total cost | £40 150 | £39 482 | £36 534 |

Table 8.1 reveals that the Sirac Highlift was not quoted with dragline equipment and that, as it is a new model, it can only be used as a lift crane at present. Therefore, although this machine slipped through the preliminary screening of the *must* objectives, it is now marked *no go* against objective C shown in Table 8.2 and is eliminated from further consideration. The Harris and HFC cranes comply with all the *must* objectives and effort can now be concentrated upon the *want* objectives of these two machines.

The *want* objectives are now separated into two groups, those which can be evaluated from the manufacturer's specifications and those which cannot, as follows:

CAN
1. Purchase price
2. Safe working loads
8. Weight of machine
9. Bearing pressure under tracks
3. Dragline range
10. Power unit and size
11. Slewing action
12. Hoist system
13. Travelling speed
6. Method of assembly
7. Safety features

CANNOT
4. Maintenance requirements
5. Running costs
15. Manoeuvrability
17. Assembly time
18. Driver comfort

For those *wants* which are not readily available from manufacturers' information, more subtle sources must be found — for example — site demonstrations, visits to the manufacturer, records of data on experiences with similar machines, personnel contacts with other plant users, and discussions with machine operators.

When satisfied that sufficient information on all the *wants* objectives is available, the two remaining crane alternatives namely Harris 46T and HFC 416, are compared for performance. Each *want* objective is considered in turn and rated on a 0–10 scale. The technical element and economic element ratings are separated in order that the importance of each can be ascertained.

To obtain the relative worth of each *want* objective the *rating* value is multipled by the previously given *rank* number. The resulting weighted score represents the performance of the crane against its objective.

The weighted scores for each objective are subsequently added to give totals for each crane alternative and the totals for each provide an indication of the relative position with respect to the specified objectives. In this example the total weighted scores shown in Table 8.2 are summarised as follows:

|  | Percentage of total | Harris | HFC |
|---|---|---|---|
| Cost and service element (S) | 39 | 291 | 348 |
| Technical element (T) | 61 | 607 | 618 |
|  | 100 | 898 | 966 |

Note: It must be emphasised that these numbers are determined largely by subjective judgement, albeit based on careful analysis of the available facts, and as such do not make the selection of the best alternative a routine procedure. However, the values do make it possible to deal systematically with many factors which otherwise could not easily be related for importance.

### Step 5: Choose the best alternative as the preliminary decision

The alternative that receives the highest weighted score is presumably the best course of action to take, in this case HFC 416. It is, of course, not a perfect choice — for instance, one would probably prefer a machine with a Rolls-Royce engine. But the choice is at least one which draws a reasonable balance between the good and bad features of the machine. Fortunately both the technical and cost element totals are greater for the HFC 416. The decision would be far more difficult if one of the elements were larger for the Harris 46T crane. Some further balance would then be needed between economic resources and the technical benefits coming to the company.

The preliminary choice is the one which best satisfies the objectives overall. It is thus a compromise, as undoubtedly the alternatives have some superior features. But the method used shows the manager how he arrived at this decision and therefore where the possible pitfalls may lie.

### Step 6: Re-evaluate the decision and assess the adverse possibilities of that choice

When many alternatives are available, the weighted scores of one or two are sometimes quite close, so, before the manager makes the final decision, any adverse consequences must be considered. He must look for snags, potential shortcomings or anything else that could go wrong. The probability (P) of the adverse consequences should be assessed and a seriousness weighting (I) given to its possible effect. An expression of the total degree of threat may be obtained by multiplying the seriousness weighting by the probability estimate.

In this example the plant and site managers arrange a meeting to discuss the implications of the proposals, and the following points are raised:

(i)  The discarded Sirac Highlift appeared to be a fairly good crane on prelimi-
     nary inspection and perhaps the *must* objective necessitating dragline con-
     version could have been reduced to a major *want* objective. A further check
     on the records reveals that only 20% of the time was spent on such duties.
     Thus, unless the plant manager insists that this facility is essential this crane
     should be reconsidered. But the *must* objective should only be waived in
     very exceptional circumstances.

(ii) Possible adverse consequences of choosing the Harris 46T, such as the effects
     of a strike at the factory can be assessed from past experience. It may be
     that on the past ten occasions when a new wage agreement has been under
     negotiation between the Harris company and its workforce, a strike resulted
     on three occasions. So the probability (P) of a strike at this time is judged to
     be 30%. If a strike did occur which would last more than a few weeks, then
     the delivery of this machine would exceed the specified time on the order,
     in which case the crane should not be considered at all. However, should a
     strike occur lasting four weeks, the cost of hiring a crane would be about
     £300 per week, therefore the degree of threat is $(4 \times 300) \times 0.3 = £360$.

(iii) One possible adverse consequence of the HFC 416 has come to light. A
     serious accident has just revealed a major design fault in the clutch mechan-
     ism of the winch. A temporary modification will be made to all existing
     models and stocks held. But a completely new part is not available for six
     months and will require taking the crane out of service for one week at that
     time. The probability that this service is required is 90% and the cost of hire
     for another crane is £300 per week, thereby directly increasing the contract
     cost at this rate. The degree of threat is $(1 \times 300) \times 0.9 = £270$. The choice
     therefore is still the HFC 416. Had the consequences been reversed, then a
     much closer examination of the advantages and disadvantages would be
     necessary, making the decision much more difficult.

### Step 7: Set up contingency plans to control the effects of the final decision

The adverse consequences represent potential problems, and they must be prevented from causing too much inconvenience. This is done either by taking preventative action to remove the cause or deciding upon a contingency action if the
potential problem occurs. In our case, the simple remedy is to ensure that alternative machines are available for hire at suitable times or to arrange work on site so
that interruption is minimal.

Table 8.2   Decision analysis sheet
Purpose of decision: evaluation of cranes for possible purchase and addition to company fleet

| Objectives | | | | Alternatives | | | |
|---|---|---|---|---|---|---|---|
| **Ref** | **Musts** | | | **Harris 46T** | | **Go/No** | |
| A | Crawler mounted machine | | | Yes | | ✓ | |
| B | At least 150′ boom as lift crane | | | 160′ max main | | ✓ | |
| C | Capable of conversion to dragline/ excavator | | | Yes | | ✓ | |
| D | Delivery less than 10 weeks | | | 6/8 weeks | | ✓ | |
| E | Max purchase price £41 000 | | | Yes | | ✓ | |
| F | Conform to B.S. and statutory regulations | | | Yes | | ✓ | |
| G | 40 tonnes minimum lifting capacity | | | Yes | | ✓ | |

| No. | Wants | Element | Ranking | | Information | Rating | Weighted score = Ranking × Rating | |
|---|---|---|---|---|---|---|---|---|
| 1 | Low purchase price | S | 10 | | £40 150 | 9 | 90 | |
| 2 | Good lifting capacities | T | | 10 | Max 46.0T | 7 | | 70 |
| 3 | Good dragline capacities | T | | 7 | Max 6T | 10 | | 70 |
| 4 | Good service facilities/ technical backing | S | 7 | | | 7 | 49 | |
| 5 | Low running costs | S | 8 | | No information | – | – | – |
| 6 | Low upkeep cost/robust construction | S/T | 4 | 4 | | 7 | 28 | 28 |
| 7 | Good safety features. Reliable safe load indicator | T | | 8 | Weightload | 10 | | 80 |
| 8 | Low machine weight/cost of transport between sites | S | 2 | | 55T | 10 | 20 | |
| 9 | Low ground bearing pressure | T | | 3 | 9.06 psi (ave) | 10 | | 30 |
| 10 | Reliable power unit/smooth operation | T | | 7 | Rolls-Royce diesel | 10 | | 70 |
| 11 | Fast slewing speed | T | | 5 | 3.18 rpm | 10 | | 50 |
| 12 | Fast hoist speed (single line) | T | | 6 | 150 ft/min | 10 | | 60 |
| 13 | Fast travel around site | T | | 4 | 0.750 mph | 9 | | 36 |
| 14 | Familiarity with machine | S | 4 | | | 6 | 24 | |
| 15 | Manoeuvrability/compact Geometry/travel on inclines | T | | 5 | Max grad 1 in 4 | 10 | | 50 |
| 16 | Long working life/good trade-in price | S | 8 | | 9 years – £3 000 | 10 | 80 | |
| 17 | Short rigging time/ease of conversion to dragline | T | | 4 | | 7 | | 28 |
| 18 | Operator view and comfort/ good layout of controls | T | | 5 | | 7 | | 35 |
| S | Cost and service element | 39% | 43 | | | | 291 | |
| T | Technical element | 61% | | 68 | | | | 607 |
| | Totals | 100% | 111 | | | | 898 | |

| | Alternatives | | | Adverse consequences | | | |
|---|---|---|---|---|---|---|---|
| HFC 416 | Go/No | Sirac Highlift | Go/No | Harris 46T | P | I | P×I |
| Yes | ✓ | Yes | ✓ | Strike may | | £ | £ |
| 150′ max main | ✓ | 160′ max main | ✓ | delay | 0.3 | 1200 | 360 |
| Yes | ✓ | Only released as lifting crane at present | ✗ | delivery | | | |
| 6/8 weeks | ✓ | 8 weeks | ✓ | | | | |
| Yes | ✓ | Yes | ✓ | | | | |
| Yes | ✓ | Yes | ✓ | | | | |
| Yes | ✓ | Yes | ✓ | | | | |

| Information | Rat-ing | Weighted score | Information | | | | |
|---|---|---|---|---|---|---|---|
| £39 482 | 10 | 100 | £36 534 | | P | I | P×I |
| Max 53.6T | 10 | 100 | Max 45T | | | | |
| Max 6T | 8 | 56 | | HFC 416 | | | |
| | 10 | 70 | | As a result | | | |
| No information | – | – | – | No information | of a design | | |
| | 10 | 40 | 40 | | fault on the | | |
| | | | | | clutch some | | |
| Wylie | 9 | 72 | Wylie | down-time | | | |
| | | | | may be | | | |
| 66T | 9 | 18 | 50T | necessary | | | |
| | | | | to effect | | £ | £ |
| 9.50 psi (ave) | 9 | 27 | 8.50 psi (ave) | a repair | 0.9 | 300 | 270 |
| Dorman diesel | 7 | 49 | Dorman diesel | | | | |
| 3.00 rpm | 9 | 45 | 4.00 rpm | | | | |
| 140 ft/min | 9 | 54 | 156 ft/min | | | | |
| 0.818 mph | 10 | 40 | 0.907 mph | | | | |
| | 10 | 40 | | | | | |
| Max grad 1 in 4 | 9 | 45 | Max grad 1 in 4 | | | | |
| 9 years – £3 000 | 10 | 80 | | | | | |
| | 10 | 40 | | | | | |
| | 10 | 50 | | | | | |
| | | 348 | This crane is removed from the analysis as *must* C is violated | | | | |
| | | 618 | | | | | |
| | | 966 | | | | | |

*Comments*

A decision has been reached to buy the HFC 416 and this is the best choice based on the judgement of the plant manager concerned. For someone else with different experience the assessment of the objectives might be quite different and would possibly produce a different result. But even accepting this obvious weakness, the method at least forces the manager to consider most of the facts. It provides a record of his thought processes and will help him to sort out points of confusion. For it is almost impossible for him to store all the facts and relationships in his head, except for the very simple choices. In such cases the decision process can be adequately carried out mentally without the need for the elaborate method described. Finally, the decision process is written down on paper and is available for all to see.

**Reading list**

1. Kepner, C.H. and Tregoe, B.B. *The Rational Manager*, McGraw-Hill, 1965.
2. Dixon, J.R. *Design Engineering – Inventiveness, Analysis and Decision Making*. McGraw-Hill, 1966.
3. Willetts, M.D. *A systematic approach to problem solving and decision making*. Unpublished paper, Department of Civil Engineering, Loughborough University of Technology, 1973.
4. Harris, F.C. and McCaffer, R. *Modern Construction Management*. Second edition. Granada, 1982.
5. Harris, F.C. and McCaffer, R. *Worked Examples in Construction Management*. pp. 34, 35 and 90-95. Granada, 1978.

# CHAPTER 9

# CALCULATING A PLANT HIRE RATE

Revenues from plant hired out to the market or owned and operated for internal use by a construction company should not only recover the owning and operating costs, but also achieve an additional profit.

Ownership costs are fixed costs arising indirectly, such as company overheads. Such costs are incurred throughout the period of ownership and are a fixed charge. They include:

(a) cost of capital,
(b) plant depreciation,
(c) insurances and licences,
(d) corporation tax and capital allowances,
(e) establishment charges.

The operating costs are direct costs of material, labour and expenses which vary according to the usage of the machine and include:

(a) servicing costs, e.g. oil, grease and other consumables,
(b) maintenance costs,
(c) transport charges,
(d) fuel,
(e) operators wages.

### Cost of capital

Capital to purchase the machine is generally obtained from borrowing or retained profits. In either case the interest charge on the loan or an acceptable rate of return on private funds should be incorporated into the hire rate.

### Depreciation

Most items of plant wear out and deteriorate with usage or become obsolete with time. Thus, at the end of the plant's economic life sufficient revenues should have been generated to cancel out the capital part of a loan or to replace the machine when internal funds are used. In calculating depreciation it is necessary to estimate the resale or scrap value of the machine and the useful life.

Estimation of the useful life is mostly done by intuition based on experience of operating a similar item of plant, e.g. when the utilisation level shows a clear downward trend accompanied by increased maintenance costs and loss of profit, the machine has probably reached the end of its useful life for the company.

There are several methods of calculating the annual depreciation charge, but the choice will depend largely upon the type of plant and its operation. In principle, depreciation is deducted from profits (since it represents a cost on the business activities) before tax is paid. It is therefore necessary to obtain approval of the method and depreciation period from the Inspector of Taxes before a suitable policy can be adopted. However, capital allowances which are discussed fully in chapters 6 and 15 have superseded depreciation for profit calculation purposes.

Straight line depreciation

*Example*

It is decided to purchase a mechancial excavator costing £42 000 to work on average 2 000 hours per year. The life of the machine is expected to be 10 years, after which time the salvage value will be £2 000.

| | | |
|---|---|---|
| Purchase price | = | £42 000 |
| Residual value | = | £2 000 |
| ∴ Total depreciation | = | £40 000 |
| ∴ Annual depreciation | = | £4 000 |
| ∴ Hourly depreciation | = | £2 |

Declining balance depreciation

Table 9.1   Declining balance depreciation example (at 26.2%).

| End of year | Depreciation (%) | Depreciation for year (£) | Book value (£) |
|---|---|---|---|
| 0 | 26.2 | 0 | 42 000 |
| 1 | ,, | 11 004 | 30 996 |
| 2 | ,, | 8 121 | 22 875 |
| 3 | ,, | 5 994 | 16 881 |
| 4 | ,, | 4 423 | 12 458 |
| 5 | ,, | 3 264 | 9 194 |
| 6 | ,, | 2 409 | 6 785 |
| 7 | ,, | 1 778 | 5 007 |
| 8 | ,, | 1 312 | 3 695 |
| 9 | ,, | 968 | 2 727 |
| 10 | ,, | 727 | 2 000 |

Total   £40 000

Using the example on page 96, suppose that this time the depreciation is made on a fixed percentage basis rather than a fixed sum.

The figures in Table 9.1 can more easily be calculated from the formula:

$$d = (1 - \sqrt[n]{\tfrac{L}{P}}) \times 100$$

where L = salvage value, P = purchase price, $n$ = life of asset and $d$ = percentage depreciation.

### Sinking fund method of depreciation

A fixed sum is put aside from revenue each year and invested with compound interest throughout the life of the asset. After successive instalments the sum accumulates to produce the original purchase price less the scrap value.

Taking the given example and assuming 6% interest is earned on savings, the annual amount required is £3 034, thus:

Uniform series factor that amounts to 1 over 10 years = 0.07586
Therefore annual payment = 0.07586 × (42 000 − 2 000) = £3 034.

Table 9.2 gives a detailed breakdown of the analysis.

Table 9.2    Sinking fund example (6% interest on savings).

| Year | Payment (£) | Interest (£) | Depreciation (£) | Book value (£) |
|---|---|---|---|---|
| 1 | 3 034 | 0 | 3 034 | 38 966 |
| 2 | 3 034 | 182 | 3 216 | 35 750 |
| 3 | 3 034 | 375 | 3 409 | 32 341 |
| 4 | 3 034 | 581 | 3 615 | 28 726 |
| 5 | 3 034 | 798 | 3 832 | 24 894 |
| 6 | 3 034 | 1 028 | 4 062 | 20 832 |
| 7 | 3 034 | 1 271 | 4 305 | 16 527 |
| 8 | 3 034 | 1 529 | 4 563 | 11 964 |
| 9 | 3 034 | 1 803 | 4 837 | 7 127 |
| 10 | 3 034 | 2 093 | 5 127 | 2 000 |

Total: £40 000

### Sum of digits method

Life   = 10 years
Digits = 1 + 2 + 3 + 4 + 5 + 6 + 7 + 8 + 9 + 10 = 55

Table 9.3   Sum of digits depreciation example.

| Year | Factor | Depreciation (£) | Book value (£) |
|------|--------|------------------|----------------|
| 1 | 10/55 | 7 273 | 34 727 |
| 2 | 9/55 | 6 545 | 28 182 |
| 3 | 8/66 | 5 818 | 22 364 |
| 4 | 7/55 | 5 091 | 17 273 |
| 5 | 6/55 | 4 364 | 12 909 |
| 6 | 5/55 | 3 636 | 9 273 |
| 7 | 4/55 | 2 909 | 6 364 |
| 8 | 3/55 | 2 182 | 4 182 |
| 9 | 2/55 | 1 454 | 2 728 |
| 10 | 1/55 | 728 | 2 000 |

Total:  £40 000

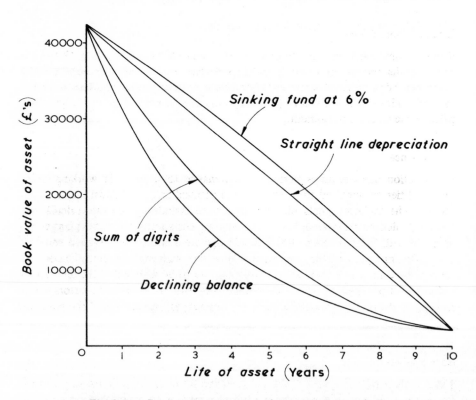

Fig. 9.1   Graphical comparison of depreciation methods.

### Free depreciation

The asset is totally depreciated initially by this method. For example, the item of plant purchased for £42 000 would be depreciated by £40 000 immediately on acquisition, leaving only the £2 000 salvage value.

### *Graphical comparison of the depreciation methods*

Figure 9.1 demonstrates the main features of the declining balance method and the straight line method. In the early years the asset is heavily written down, which is particularly helpful in the case of construction plant as the repair and maintenance costs are likely to be low when new, but increase with age and usage.

### Licences and insurances

The costs for licences and insurance depend upon whether the equipment is to be used on the public roads or otherwise. In general, the amount of insurance cover recommended depends upon the degree of risk to third parties, adjacent property or public utilities. These aspects are fully discussed in Chapter 12.

### Establishment charges

The company must recover the cost of its overheads in the hire rate. Overheads relate to the central organisation and include the offices and workshops and the associated administrative facilities. These fixed costs may be apportioned on the basis of budgeted annual plant operating hours or as a percentage of the purchase price of the machine per annum.

### Maintenance

Construction plant requires periodic maintenance to keep it in working order and facilities are required to provide both a planned and breakdown maintenance service. The budgeted costs of maintenance to include in hire rate calculations should be derived from records of the operating costs incurred by the plant workshop. Indeed, the workshop iteself should operate a cost control system for each item of plant to record the expenditure on spares, maintenance, etc. The costs of maintenance are direct costs and ought therefore to be included in the hire rate as a direct cost per hour operated. In practice, however, many plant operators prefer to express the costs of maintenance in the hire rate as a percentage of the purchase price of the machine.

### Consumables

These include oil and grease, tyres and fuel, and are direct costs which vary according to the condition of the machine, work done and hours operated. Such costs are difficult to estimate unless records have been kept from operating similar equipment in the past. However, manufacturers provide guidelines on the consumption of these materials, but care should be exercised as the data is likely to relate to new equipment operating under ideal conditions.

The inclusion of the cost of fuel in the hire rate will, of course, depend upon the hire contract conditions.

### Operators' wages

These are not usually included in the hire rate, as many items of plant are hired exclusive of the operator. But, when required, costs based on the driver's hourly rate must be recovered with allowances for overtime, bonus, travelling subsistence, national insurance premiums, holiday pay, sick pay, pensions, etc.

## The effect of corporation tax and capital allowances

These are treated more fully in Chapters 6 and 15 but, briefly, government investment incentives encourage companies to account for free depreciation on plant, so that an item of equipment is allowed the full purchase price to be deducted from company profits in the year of purchase and thereby the amount of corporation tax due is reduced in that year. The tax, however, will of course be recovered in full from profits in subsequent years, since there is no allowance to set aside thereafter. The effect of this arrangement is to alter the sequence of cash flows for the business which may produce a more favourable return on capital employed and also encourage other investment.

It is emphasised that capital allowances are basically a feature of the profit and loss account for the whole enterprise for the calculation of corporation tax payments. Clearly to allow full initial depreciation in the hire rate would be nonsensical as the rate would be uncompetitive during that year. Thus, internal depreciation should be based on a realistic assessment of the life of the asset.

The effect of the 100% capital allowance has been to encourage firms to purchase plant to set against profits as a popular tax avoidance device. Consequently, the market has become grossly over-supplied with plant for hire with the unfortunate result that hire rates have now fallen below levels which can earn a healthy rate of return on capital employed. Thus, although over the short term customers and both home and overseas manufacturers have benefited, it is doubtful that the market can remain buoyant with such a low profitability.

## Calculating the economic hire rate

There are several acceptable methods of calculating an economic hire rate. The most favoured is the simple calculation to allow for ownership and operating costs with a contribution for profit. However, a more satisfactory method for investments extending over a few years is the Discounted Cash Flow Yield (d.c.f.), which takes into account the timing of cash flows.

Example: the conventional method

An excavator, crawler mounted, 1½ m$^3$ capacity, is purchased new for £46 000. Its estimated life is 10 years, with a resale value of £4 000.

| | |
|---|---|
| Capital cost | £46 000 |
| Resale value | £4 000 |
| Anticipated life | 10 years |
| Insurance premium | £200 per year |
| Road tax and licences | £100 per year |
| Maintenance | 10% of capital cost |
| Consumables | £400 per year |
| Overheads of business | £2 per hour |
| Required rate of return on investment | 15% per year |
| Budgeted operating time | 2 000 hours per year |
| Transport charges | Say £100 |

| *Item* | *£ per year* |
|---|---|
| Depreciation (straight line) = $\dfrac{42\ 000}{10}$ | 4 200 |
| Interest on finance, calculated using a capital recovery factor from interest tables (CRF = 0.199 at 15% pa for 10 years) $\dfrac{46\ 000 \times 0.199 \times 10 - 46\ 000}{10}$ | 4 554 |
| Fixed overheads = 2 × 2000 | 4 000 |
| Road tax and licences | 100 |
| Insurance premium | 200 |
| Ownership (fixed) cost | 13 054 |

| Item | £ per year |
|---|---|
| Consumables | 400 |
| Maintenance — 10% × 46 000 | 4 600 |
| Operating cost (variable) | 5 000 |
| Total cost | 18 054 |

Hire charge = $\dfrac{18\ 054}{2\ 000}$ = £9.03 per hour (or £361 per 40 hour week).

The cost of transport and any additional profit should be added to this figure.

Finally, the hire rate is based on a utilisation period of 2 000 hours and should this target not be reached then the ownership (fixed) costs will be under-recovered and budgeted profit not achieved.

Alternative analysis using d.c.f. (See Chapter 6)

D.c.f. takes into account the timing of cash flows, whereby income and outgoings are balanced to yield a satisfactory return. The problem is thus restructured as shown in Table 9.4

Information:
 (i) 4.7715 is the net present worth factor of 1 per period for 9 years at 15% interest rate.
 (ii) 0.2472 is the net present worth factor of 1 at year 10 for a 15% interest rate.

Table 9.4    D.c.f. analysis of a hire rate.

| Year | Capital cost £ | Resale value £ | Operating costs £ | Ownership costs £ | Cash out £ | Cash in £ | Total £ |
|------|------|------|------|------|------|------|------|
| (a) | (b) | (c) | (d) | (e) | (b+c+d+e=f) | Revenue (g) | (g+f) |
| 0 | – 46 000 | | – 0 | – 4 300 | – 50 300 | 0 | – 50 300 |
| 1 | | | – 5 000 | – 4 300 | – 9 300 | x | x – 9 300 |
| 2 | | | – 5 000 | – 4 300 | – 9 300 | x | x – 9 300 |
| 3 | | | – 5 000 | – 4 300 | – 9 300 | x | x – 9 300 |
| 4 | | | – 5 000 | – 4 300 | – 9 300 | x | x – 9 300 |
| 5 | | | – 5 000 | – 4 300 | – 9 300 | x | x – 9 300 |
| 6 | | | – 5 000 | – 4 300 | – 9 300 | x | x – 9 300 |
| 7 | | | – 5 000 | – 4 300 | – 9 300 | x | x – 9 300 |
| 8 | | | – 5 000 | – 4 300 | – 9 300 | x | x – 9 300 |
| 9 | | | – 5 000 | – 4 300 | – 9 300 | x | x – 9 300 |
| 10 | | + 4 000 | – 5 000 | 0 | + 1 000 | x | x – 1 000 |

To return 15% on the investment over 10 years the total cash flows reduced to net present worth at time zero must equate to:

$$0 = -50\,300 + ((x-9\,300) \times 4.7715 + (x-1\,000) \times 0.24718)$$
$$0 = -51\,300 + 4.7715x - 25\,289 + 0.2472x - 247$$
$$5.02x = 94\,922$$
$$x = 18\,913$$
$$\therefore \text{Hire charge} = \frac{18\,913}{2\,000} = £9.45 \text{ per hour}$$

It can be seen that the d.c.f. method automatically accounts for the depreciation over the life of the asset.

## The effect of inflation

The two methods outlined above have not considered the effects of inflation on the value of the investment, the consequences of which are emphasised by the following example.

*Example*

(a)  Purchase price                          £46 000
     Resale value after 10 years            £4 000
                                             ─────────
                                             £42 000

     Annual depreciation      $\dfrac{£42\ 000}{10}$      =      £4 200

(b)  Inflation at 10% per year
     Purchase price after 10 years    £4 600 × 2.60  =   £119 646
     Resale value after 10 years      £4 000 × 2.60  =    £10 400
                                                         ─────────
                                                          £109 246

     Average annual depreciation             =    $\dfrac{£109\ 246}{10}$  =  £10 924

The shortfall = £67 246

Depreciation is the most vulnerable element in the hire rate calculation because most other items are the result of obvious cost movements, e.g. materials, wages, interest rates. The hire rate should therefore be revised frequently to keep up with inflation. In fact it may even be necessary to provide for 'backlog' depreciation to allow for the period prior to an under-estimated price rise. Assessments can be made from the Baxter special price indices for construction plant or alternatively for the small operator replacement prices should be obtained from plant dealers and manufacturers.

Inflation has other severe effects by causing trading profits to be overstated. As a result corporation tax is paid on the inflated rather than real profit.

Adjustment of a hire rate for inflation

If the capital to purchase an item of plant is either borrowed or alternatively acquired by hire purchase, then the hire rate would simply be adjusted in line with the terms imposed on the loan, as the total capital sum remains fixed irrespective of the level of inflation. Only the level of interest may fluctuate. However, when the item is to be purchased from internal funds the value of the asset must be periodically revised to keep up with inflation, if the consequences of a shortfall in depreciation provision and in real terms a negative rate of return on capital are to be avoided. The effect of using a 10% inflation price index on the original example is shown below.

*Example*

Inflation is 10% per annum over 10 years. The purchase price is £46 000 and the historical resale value is £4 000.

| Year | Index | (£) Replacement price | (£) Accumulated historical depreciation | (£) Accumulated inflated depreciation | (£) Book value |
|------|-------|------------------------|------------------------------------------|----------------------------------------|----------------|
| 0  | 100.0 | 46 000  | 0      | 0       | 46 000 |
| 1  | 110.0 | 50 600  | 4 200  | 4 620   | 45 980 |
| 2  | 121.0 | 55 660  | 8 400  | 10 164  | 45 496 |
| 3  | 133.1 | 61 226  | 12 600 | 16 771  | 44 455 |
| 4  | 146.4 | 67 344  | 16 800 | 24 595  | 42 749 |
| 5  | 160.7 | 73 922  | 21 000 | 33 749  | 40 173 |
| 6  | 176.8 | 81 328  | 25 200 | 44 554  | 36 774 |
| 7  | 194.5 | 89 470  | 29 400 | 57 183  | 32 287 |
| 8  | 214.9 | 98 854  | 33 600 | 77 206  | 21 648 |
| 9  | 236.4 | 108 744 | 37 800 | 89 359  | 19 385 |
| 10 | 260.1 | 119 646 | 42 000 | 109 242 | 10 400 |

The depreciation in, say, the first year of inflation is £4 620.

*Interest on finance*
With inflation at 10% the apparent rate of return must be used in the calculations

$$(1 + i_a) = (1 + i_r)(1 + i_d) \text{ where:}$$
$$i_a = \text{apparent rate of return}$$
$$i_r = \text{real rate of return}$$
$$i_d = \text{rate of inflation}$$

Therefore,

$$(1 + i_a) = (1 + 0.15)(1 + 0.1) = 1.265$$
$$i_a = 0.265 = 26.5\%$$

Thus interest on finance using a capital recovery factor of 26.5% from interest tables

$$= \frac{46\ 000 \times 0.2929 \times 10 - 46\ 000}{10} = £8\ 873$$

*Other items*

| | |
|---|---|
| Fixed overhead | £4 000 |
| Road tax and licences | £100 |
| Insurance premium | £200 |
| Consumables | £400 |
| Maintenance | £4 600 |
| | £9 300 |

Multiplying the total figure by the first year index $= \dfrac{9\ 300 \times 110}{100} = £10\ 230$

Therefore, the hire charge =    £4 620
£8 873
£10 230

£23 723 ÷ 2 000 = £11.86 per hour
(or £474.46 per week).

If inflation continued as shown by the indices then the hire rate for year 5 should be:

Depreciation for year 5 = 33 749 − 24 595    =    £9 154
Interest on finance                                        =    £8 873
Other items = 9 300 × $\frac{160.7}{100}$           =    £15 531

£33 558

i.e. £16.78 per hour

It can be seen that during periods of inflation the hire rate should be revised at least annually. When inflation exceeds about 10% the period may need to be at quarterly intervals depending upon the demands for payment by suppliers of materials etc. But this is not always possible when the market for hired plant is slack and competitors are willing to undercut hire rates.

The entrenchment of high levels of inflation during the past ten years has attracted the attention of several research workers. In particular Trimble and Neale[4] at Loughborough University of Technology have used simulation modelling to examine a wide range of consequences. Their primary conclusion was that when inflation exceeds the net rate of interest on borrowed capital (i.e. interest on borrowings is deducted from company profits before corporation tax is paid, which in effect produces a lower rate of interest), a three-year replacement cycle for plant is best. Below that rate of inflation a longer cycle is preferable. Also they concluded that the cross-over point in the choice of the method of financing is when inflation is equal to the net of tax interest rate on capital. Below this rate of inflation self-finance is more attractive than borrowed money and vice versa.

### Method of calculating hire rates adopted in practice

Grant[12] working at Loughborough University of Technology undertook a study into methods adopted by a sample of plant hire firms for calculating a hire rate. His research discovered some interesting differences to the principles set out previously.

### Small companies

The firms he considered were those operating only a few popular items of plant with the minimum of office facilities and maintenance provided on an *ad hoc* basis. Such companies tended to set the hire rate in accordance with the market levels and were on average similar to those recommended in publications by the Contractors' Plant Association.

All users were well aware of the prevailing market rate for a machine and each hire was negotiated at around this figure. In addition, the experienced plant hirer was generally well informed of the availability of machines locally and was thus able to negotiate very competitively. Grant noticed, however, that there appeared to be a minimum rate below which most firms would not hire. This seemed to be related to payments needed for repayment of the loan on the piece of equipment plus a sum to cover running costs and the operators' overheads, the latter being perhaps as minimal as providing the owner's salary.

### Medium to large companies

Grant ascertained that the large companies with comprehensive central and regional plant depots carry out detailed analyses into the economics of owning and operating plant. The hire rates were based on collected cost data of the firm's operations and calculated along the principles established earlier but few companies had as yet adopted d.c.f. techniques.

### The effects of economic recession on plant hire

During the period following the oil crisis of 1973 the volume of home-based construction work has steadily declined with an attendant reduction in the need for construction plant. Faced with a declining demand, many owners of plant fleets have had to cut back the size of their fleets in order to survive. However, good maintenance ensured acceptable resale values to the booming markets in the oil-rich countries and fortunately many machines which have been retained were purchased in the days of low interest rates. Therefore many firms could continue to hire out plant at competitive yet economic rates, all aided by government incentives and a wide choice of manufacturers offering generous cash discounts of up to 20% on new purchases. Now that interest levels are extremely high and the prospects for continuing buoyant markets for construction work are poor, however, competition has become very keen. As a consequence machines are being 'run into the ground' as the current rates of hire are often insufficient to cover adequate maintenance and servicing. Unless there is a quick return to growth conditions for construction work, some restructuring of the market for plant hire must take place, perhaps by some mergers and concentration on specialised needs in the construction industry for the medium to large plant owner, leaving the more general market for the small competitive local enterprise.

### Reading list

1. Harris, F.C. and McCaffer, R. *Modern Construction Management*. Second edition. Granada, 1982.
2. American Society of Civil Engineers. Equipment costs by current methods. *Journal of the Construction Division*. New York, June 1978.

3. Mead, H.T. and Mitchell, G.L. *Plant Hire for Building and Construction*. Newnes-Butterworths, 1972.
4. Trimble, E.G.T. and Neale, R.H. *The effect of inflation on plant costs and replacement policies*. Paper presented to Institute of Building Seminar, London, January 1976.
5. Pace, M. *A cost reporting system for construction plant management*. MSc Project Report, Department of Civil Engineering, Loughborough University of Technology, 1972.
6. Merrett, A.J. and Sykes, A. *The Finance and Analysis of Capital Projects*. Longman, 1965.
7. *CPA Handbook*. Contractors Plant Association, London.
8. Knight, P. Economics of plant usage. *Construction Supervisor*, 10 February 1976.
9. Mitchell, B.R. Establishing plant rates. *National Builder*, April 1970.
10. Leon, G. Construction plant economics. *Plant Engineer*, 14(1), 1970.
11. Neale, R.H. Inflation accounting. *Construction News Supplement*, 16 October 1980.
12. Grant, P. Plant hire. Unpublished paper, Department of Civil Engineering, Loughborough University of Technology, 1979.
13. Wheeler, D. The detrimental effect of capital allowances on the U.K. plant hire industry. Unpublished paper, Department of Civil Engineering, Loughborough University of Technology, 1979.

**Section Three**

## OPERATIONAL MANAGEMENT

# CHAPTER 10

# PLANT MAINTENANCE

## Plant maintenance objectives

Construction equipment like any other plant item can be expected to break down during its working life. This may be due to normal wear and tear, or a sudden failure of a component part.

The primary purpose of providing maintenance is to reduce the incidence of failure, either by replacement, repair or servicing in order to achieve an economical level of utilisation during the working life of the machine. A reduction in plant 'down-time' will minimise costly stoppages on the construction site and the disruptive effect on labour and the programme of work. However, whilst the purpose of maintenance is to keep the plant in service, this must not be achieved at the expense of safety. The costs of maintenance must be balanced against the benefits and at some stage a plant item will require complete replacement by a new machine.

## Plant maintenance policy

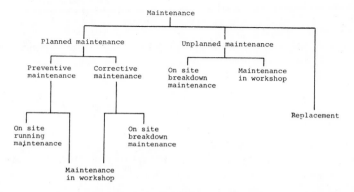

**Fig. 10.1**    Maintenance options.

The alternative plant maintenance policy options are shown in Figure 10.1. The extent to which a company applies one or other of the alternatives will depend upon the type of plant holding and the firm's attitude to maintenance in general and the safety regulations. However, a policy directed towards ensuring controlled, regular and disciplined maintenance procedures is essential if basic maintenance objectives are to succeed. In theory, therefore, planned maintenance should be the backbone of the system, but the practical difficulties arising from the dispersed nature of construction work generally requires aspects of planned, unplanned and replacement maintenance policies to be combined.

### Planned preventive maintenance

This system requires the implementation of planned regular procedures directed towards ensuring the efficient use of a plant item by reducing the incidence of breakdowns. The maintenance actions required are:

(i) Daily servicing and superficial inspection. This aspect is often adequately achieved by allowing the machine operator half an hour before and after normal working hours to carry out the tasks.
(ii) Regular full maintenance and inspection, including periodic overhaul.
(iii) Replacement or repair of component parts within a working period based on the expected duties and conditions.

Clearly this is a very comprehensive service and can be operated only by those firms with extensive holdings of plant, where 'down-time' can be avoided by substituting other machines and where workshop facilities are available.

### Planned corrective maintenance

Adequate maintenance is performed to enable the plant to operate whilst on site, but a major overhaul should be undertaken after its duties are completed. The procedures are therefore slightly less systematic compared with preventive maintenance as components are usually replaced only during the full inspection and servicing period or when a breakdown occurs or is anticipated. This policy does not ensure that the highest safety standards are upheld, but is often favoured by construction companies which hold few items of plant, where full maintenance resources and personnel are available only at central workshops.

### Unplanned maintenance

This system is adopted when the costs of regular maintenance are likely to exceed the cost of complete replacement of the plant item or where it is not economically justifiable to carry out maintenance until the machine either breaks down or the operating efficiency becomes unacceptable. Clearly this would be appropriate only for equipment which is not essential to the production process and whose failure would neither cause considerable disruption nor constitute a safety hazard. As a consequence, unplanned maintenance is rarely appropriate for construction machinery, except for small tools, punctures, etc. although in practice all too many firms adopt this policy for major plant items, with disastrous consequences for production efficiency.

### Replacement

Most items of construction equipment have a life exceeding the point when a major overhaul is required, and the question of replacement should therefore arise only when the costs of maintenance exceed the benefits of operating the item. However, the state of the second-hand market can fluctuate over the short-term to provide a profitable opportunity for selling a machine before its planned replacement period. Alternatively, superior equipment may become available to outweigh the advantages of holding outdated machinery.

### *The merits of planned maintenance*
These are:

 (i) Improved utilisation levels of plant.
 (ii) Maintenance periods can be co-ordinated with site production requirements.
 (iii) Spare parts can be obtained in good time and stock maintained at adequate levels.
 (iv) Regular work schedules for maintenance personnel can be programmed, facilitating fitters and mechanics to be allocated to plant items requiring specialist skills and experience.
 (v) The overall result enhances the awareness and importance of maintenance in the well-being of the company.

Planned maintenance is expensive and is used to maximum advantage where the effects of breakdowns would be extremely damaging. The opportunities for carrying out effective inspection and overhaul for many items of construction equipment often occurs during the transfer from one site to the next and a policy of corrective rather than preventive maintenance is sometimes preferred. Both systems require a comprehensive maintenance organisation, but the costs can be recovered from the improved working efficiency of the plant, unlike the alternative unplanned arrangement.

### Factors affecting plant maintenance policy

Planned maintenance offers the most reliable policy, but involves the setting up of workshops, offices and stores, coupled with a significant investment in tools and trained staff. Also the operational problems imposed by the nature of construction work severely restrict the quality and amount of maintenance provision which may be achieved.

In a large national construction company a centralised maintenance facility is often too expensive to operate for servicing plant items spread over a wide location. The alternative of establishing workshop facilities on individual sites may be justified on the larger and/or more remote contracts, but is generally prohibitively expensive on the typically small site. Regionalisation offers a suitable compromise, whereby individual maintenance facilities may be set up on the large, plant-intensive sites, perhaps co-ordinated from the regional depot, with a mobile workshop operating from the regional facility to serve the smaller sites. This system is popular with plant hire companies and is being adopted increasingly by construction companies. The mobile workshop can be equipped to carry out major servicing and repairs, using a vehicle such as a Land Rover to cope with most of the adverse conditions found on construction sites. A complete overhaul may be performed later at the regional depot.

### Manufacturer's contribution

The assistance offered to plant owners by individual manufacturers or their agents varies. Research carried out by Jones[19] revealed that some manufacturers viewed after-sales service as being entirely the responsibility of their appointed distributor. Others considered maintenance in particular to be a major consideration and provided extensive services both directly and through distributors. There was no apparent correlation between manufacturers' attitudes to maintenance and their size and nature of product.

The services provided generally fall within the following alternatives:

1. The manufacturer or distributor of the plant provides a full maintenance service as part of the purchase contract.
2. The manufacturer or distributor makes available a back-up service in respect of field inspection, field component replacements and workshop overhauls, e.g. for more specialised maintenance needs such as transmissions and engines.
3. Provision of spare parts only by the manufacturer.

The more efficient manufacturer or distributor would tend to have the capability to provide the first alternative and would often include the following facilities:

(i) A nationwide distribution network capable of undertaking maintenance, repairs and overhauls, and stocking a full complement of spare parts.
(ii) Technical support facilities including mobile breakdown units.
(iii) Training programmes designed for distributor's and client's operators and maintenance personnel, including a mobile unit which can visit customers to provide training courses.
(iv) Fully detailed and planned preventive maintenance programme for each type of machine.
(v) Firm guarantees concerning the maintenance commitment required from distributors.

(vi) Supply by the manufacturer of reconditioned parts to reduce major overhaul costs.

(vii) The provision of specially designed tools to aid maintenance work.

(viii) The standardisation of components in different machines to reduce the stock level of spare parts.

## Strategy for plant maintenance

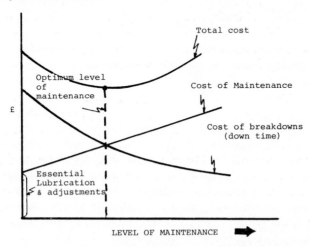

**Fig. 10.2**   Optimum maintenance provision.

The essential aim of all the maintenance policies described is to keep the plant in working order and so increase its productivity. The strategy required to achieve this objective, however, demands the implementation of technical and administrative procedures which inevitably incur costs, and for any organisation, depending upon its maintenance efficiency, there is an optimum level of maintenance provision as shown in Figure 10.2. This implies that at some level the cost of providing the maintenance service will exceed the costs of plant 'down-time'. Thus, it is not only important to install the correct maintenance procedures, but the costs must also be maintained and controlled. These can be considered in two parts — direct and indirect costs.

### Direct maintenance costs

The first step is to prepare a maintenance budget based on the needs of the plant holding and any items to be added during the life of the budget. Reference should be made to historical records of:

(i) breakdown maintenance labour costs;

(ii) planned maintenance labour costs;

(iii) materials costs and fuel consumption;
(iv) spares costs;
 (v) administrative, technical, equipment and other overhead costs.

The budget provides the basis for monitoring the trend in overall maintenance effectiveness. In order to collect costing information each item of plant is identified with a cost centre, which might be a single important piece of plant or alternatively a group of similar machines. The extent and depth of the information will vary between plant firms but as a basis for information flow, a cost and maintenance control system should contain the following features:

 (i) *A register of all plant assets* detailing the type, classification, purchase price, location, life, age, value and condition of each.
 (ii) A schedule of the exact *maintenance tasks* required on each item of plant on a routine basis, together with the extent, details and methods to be employed.
(iii) A *programme of events* defining the frequency of these maintenance tasks.
(iv) An effective *history record* for each plant item to ensure that the maintenance has been performed on schedule and in the correct manner. This will include a weekly return of hours operated or miles travelled and fuel consumed by each plant item coupled with a record of maintenance work carried out and the cost including the materials used and spare parts supplied. The history record card is updated regularly with maintenance information each time a job report card has been completed.
 (v) A cost recording system to facilitate monitoring the effectiveness of the maintenance effort measured against the budget.

The effectiveness of this procedure depends upon a disciplined application of the checking system and should ideally follow the stages indicated in Figure 10.3.

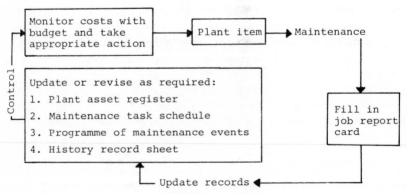

**Fig. 10.3**    Maintenance control cycle.

*Job report card*
The job report card should be completed by the mechanic after work has been carried out on a plant item, and should contain a statement of the work done,

materials used and the condition of the unit. Subsequently, this information is used to update the history record card. See Figures 10.4 and 10.5.

| Job Report Card No. | Date |
|---|---|
| Name & details of mechanic | |
| Plant Item | Location |
| Defects<br>Action taken<br>Spares/materials used<br>Condition/Observations<br>Remarks<br>Time taken<br>Remaining defects | |

**Fig. 10.4**    A job report card.

| History Record Card | | Date    From    to | | Page No. | |
|---|---|---|---|---|---|
| Date | Job Report No. | Summary of Details<br>Hours operated<br>Fuel & lubricants used<br>Maintenance or breakdown cause<br>Action taken<br>Spares/materials<br>Condition<br>Remarks | | Time | Cost |
| Plant item | | | | | |
| Location data | | | | | |

**Fig. 10.5**    A history record card.

### Indirect costs

When plant breaks down there is a loss of production while waiting for repair and during the repair itself. For a plant hire firm this may cause a reduction of the budgeted utilisation period and a loss in revenue, but for the owner-contractor the idle time of the construction work force must also be considered. It is important to consider these costs when preparing an overall budget for owning and operating the plant, including the cost of maintenance. Clearly it is essential to decide upon realistic levels of utilisation time over, say, a yearly budget.

**Safety inspections**

The various safety regulations (see Chapters 11 and 12) require the inspection and testing of equipment. All lifting tackle and most other items of equipment, when first acquired and before use, should be tested and examined by a competent person who should certify that the equipment is suitable for use and issue a certificate stating so. In most cases this certificate will be provided by the manufacturers but, if not, an insurance engineer can issue such a certificate. Once the plant item is in use the regulations also call for period testing by a competent person, the time interval depending upon the type of equipment, and a certificate issued by that person.

Because the various regulations stipulate different inspection periods, the recommended procedures to adopt should consist of a combination of self-inspection by the owner or hirer at say three-monthly intervals, and then externally examined within the legally stated testing period. This latter inspection could be performed by a qualified engineer from the engineering inspection department of an insurance company. The services of the insurance company, however, do not relieve the owner of the plant from the legal responsibility for periodic examination. Although most insurance companies have their own methods to try to ensure that the statutory periods are met, they are not legally bound to do this. Also the insurance engineer, having arrived at the premises will not necessarily search for equipment to test or get it ready for examination, and if the items are not to hand, then the inspection will most likely be missed. Clearly, therefore, it is in the interests of the plant owner to install his own control procedure for inspections.

Control procedures for testing and examination

Whenever possible, responsibility for arranging testing and examination should be given to a single individual. In this context, the asset register can assist in the timetabling of inspections for major plant items, but for small items, such as lifting tackle, a physical audit may be required, since individual employees and machine operators often hoard items like slings etc. in tool boxes, lockers and cabs. To minimise this location problem, all equipment should be issued only through the stores under the control of a storekeeper and records maintained at least to the standard demanded by the legal statutes. The law requires that records be kept of the following details for each item of equipment:

(a)   an identification mark code or number;
(b)   the date and reference of maker's original test certificate;
(c)   date of commissioning;
(d)   dates of statutory tests, inspections and examinations;
(e)   details of defects and subsequent actions required;
(f)   copies of test certificates.

Thus, co-ordinated and well-documented procedures are obviously of paramount importance if items are not to escape inspection. The coding system as used in other contexts to identify a piece of equipment can be adopted for the inspection control purposes and should be painted on to the item itself, to aid identification. In addition a colour coding for each period of statutory inspection helps to ensure that equipment meets the stipulated periods. Notwithstanding the voluntary or insurance company inspection procedures installed by a machine user or owner, the Health and Safety Executive may inspect equipment at any time and suspend its usage if defects are present and/or certificates are not up to date.

## Stock control and spare parts policy

Stock control can play an important role in securing the effectiveness of a plant maintenance system. Manufacturers, suppliers and transport systems are rarely able to deliver goods at the exact time required for the maintenance operation and it is therefore necessary to carry sufficient stock to act as a buffer between supply and demand for a component. However, since the level of stock is only a buffer it is important to keep levels to the minimum needed to service the maintenance needs and so limit the locked-up capital, which otherwise could be more usefully employed elsewhere in the business.

The extent to which component types and stock levels are held will often depend upon the nature of the maintenance policy and the proximity of the manufacturers' distributors. For example, the fleet operator hiring out to the market would probably carry a sophisticated range of spare parts whereas the company with a low plant ownership would hold only those items in frequent demand. Thus the extent to which stock control is made effective is dependent upon:

  (i) defining a realistic stock objective in relation to the firm's activities;
 (ii) using stock as a buffer only to aid production continuity;
(iii) setting economic levels of stock to service the needs of the enterprise.

It is not possible to offer firm advice in setting the correct stock control objectives, without having detailed information for a particular concern. However, the following techniques are available for dealing with the problems arising in items (ii) and (iii) above:

(a)  The ABC method of stock control.
(b)  Inventory control.

### The ABC method

The ABC technique directs effort towards an ordering of stock priorities with the primary objective of avoiding stock-outs of critical items and keeping capital lock-up as low as possible. To operate the technique, stock is classified into three groupings:

*'A' items* are those which are most frequently demanded or expensive or would have a significant impact if not provided.
*'C' items* are those not commonly requested, or are inexpensive or would have the least effect if not provided.
*'B' items* are those which do not fall into categories 'A' or 'C'.

Clearly for the stock control system to be effective, sophisticated information including forecasts of requirements, and lead times for ordering, will be required on 'A' type items. 'B' items will require vigorous stock checking and frequent inspection, with more effort given to the high priority items than for those of low priority. 'C' class items need only routine checking since the effect of a stock-out or miscalculation of the stock requirement will be relatively small.

Typically stock items replenished over a common period could fall into the following categories:

*Class 'A' items*: 10% in number, making up 70% of the value of stock.
*Class 'B' items*: 20% in number, making up 20% of the value of stock.
*Class 'C' items*: 70% in number, making up 10% of the value of stock.

### ABC stock control example
The spare parts department of a plant hire company currently replenishes all stock items every three months as follows:

| Class | Number of items | Value of stock | ABC value of stock |
|---|---|---|---|
| A | 50 | £21 000 | £3 500 |
| B | 100 | £6 000 | £4 000 |
| C | 350 | £3 000 | £3 000 |
| | 500 | £30 000 | £10 500 |

The total cost of maintaining a uniform quantity of three months' minimum stock of all items is £30 000. However, with the items now clearly ranked into an order of stock priorities, decisions can be taken regarding more economic replenishing periods. For example, by keeping two weeks' stock of Class 'A' items, two months' stock of Class 'B' items, and three months' stock of Class 'C' items, the stock value reduces to £10 500. In this way capital is made available for other purposes.

It can be seen that the ABC method principally identifies the critical items and so emphasis may be concentrated on checking Class 'A' items to avoid stock-outs or supporting too much stock.

Inventory control

While the ABC technique of stock control provides a simple checking method, it is usually also necessary to know when to order and the order quantity. In its simplest form, stock is ordered when the current level of stock minus the immediate stock demand equals the forecast demand before the next delivery arrives plus safety stock, thus:

Current stock − immediate stock demand = forecast demand + safety stock
order quantity

The safety stock for a given lead time may be determined from past observations of differences between forecast demand and actual demand. The size of the forecast error, which may only be exceeded within a specified limit defines the size of each safety stock to provide against a stock-out. Unfortunately this method requires information on each stock item, which for a complex inventory would be too tedious to collect and so only Class 'A' items might be considered in this way.

*Method of determining the safety stock level*

1. For each stock item calculate the forecast error by subtracting forecast demand from actual demand over a past time period. A positive difference represents a shortage, whilst a negative value indicates a surplus.
2. Rank the range of forecast errors into 10 to 20 equal divisions, e.g.:

| Range of errors | Forecast error frequency |
|---|---|
| −24 to −20 (items, quantity, etc.) | 5 (occurrences) |
| −19 to −15 | 20 |
| −14 to −10 | 40 |
| − 9 to − 5 | 60 |
| − 4 to   0 | 75 |
| 0 to + 4 | 80 |
| + 5 to + 9 | 65 |
| +10 to +14 | 40 |
| +15 to +19 | 15 |
| +20 to +24 | 5 |
| | 405 |

3. A plot of the forecast errors against the frequency will tend to approximate to the normal distribution and the use of simple statistics can be used to determine the probability of stock-outs and surpluses.

*Example*: The forecast errors shown above were recorded for a particular stock item. Management wishes to know with 95% confidence the level of safety stock required to avoid a stock-out.

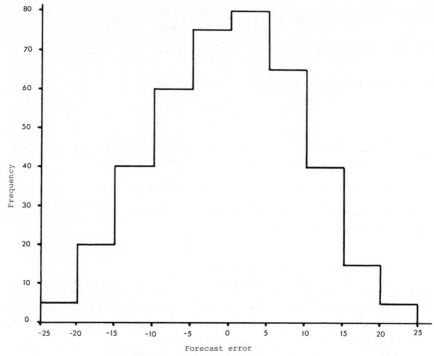

**Fig. 10.6**    Distribution of forecast errors.

*Solution*: A plot of the forecast errors is shown in Figure 10.6. The sample is large and therefore approximates to a normal distribution and the mean and standard deviation are calculated in the following table.

| Range of errors | Mid-point of range x | $x - \bar{x}$ | Frequency (f) | $f \times x$ | $f \times (x - \bar{x})^2$ |
|---|---|---|---|---|---|
| −24 to −20 | −22 | −22.1 | 5 | −110 | 2 442 |
| −19 to −15 | −17 | −17.1 | 20 | −340 | 5 848 |
| −14 to −10 | −12 | −12.1 | 40 | −480 | 5 856 |
| − 9 to − 5 | −7 | −7.1 | 60 | −420 | 3 024 |
| − 4 to   0 | −2 | −2.1 | 75 | −150 | 331 |
| 0 to + 4 | +2 | +1.9 | 80 | +160 | 289 |
| + 5 to + 9 | +7 | +6.9 | 65 | +455 | 3 094 |
| +10 to +14 | +12 | +11.9 | 40 | +480 | 5 664 |
| +15 to +19 | +17 | +16.9 | 15 | +255 | 4 284 |
| +20 to +24 | +22 | +21.9 | 5 | +110 | 2 352 |
|  |  |  | 405 | −40 | 33 184 |

$$\text{Mean stock error } (\mu) = \frac{\Sigma fx}{\Sigma f} = \frac{-40}{405} = -0.099$$

$$\text{Standard deviation } (\sigma) = \sqrt{\frac{\Sigma f(x - \overline{x})^2}{\Sigma f - 1}} = \sqrt{\frac{33\,184}{404}} = 9.06$$

The data described by the normal distribution is governed by

$$Z = \frac{x \pm \mu}{\sigma} = \frac{\text{safety stock}}{\sigma}$$

From statistical tables, for a given error value x to lie within 95% of the area under the graph, Z = 1.96, i.e. within 1.96 standard deviations of the mean.

$$\therefore \text{ The safety stock} = 1.96 \times 9.06 = 17.76 \text{ (say, 18)}$$

If stock were ordered in four week cycles, the probability is that a stock-out will occur every 80 weeks, i.e. 5% chance.

## Economic order quantity (How much to order?)

While the order quantity formula already given is appropriate for simple situations, for more complex stockholdings the costs of procurement and storage can be high. In such circumstances a more general formula is necessary relating order quantity, order period and costs. Two costs must be considered:

1. *Cost of procurement.* Administration costs are incurred whenever an order is placed. This will include (a) purchase enquiries, requisitions and ordering (b) acceptance, inspection and legal requirements (c) preparation of drawings and design details etc.
2. *Cost of storage.* This includes (a) interest to be paid on working capital (b) insurance (c) storage and handling (d) maintenance records (e) wastage, theft, deterioration, etc.

The most economical ordering quantity involves balancing these costs against the rate of usage.

*Example (1)*
Stocks of a component are allowed to run down to a level of three units before being replenished. The components are used steadily at 50 items per week. The component costs £15 per unit and the cost of storage and deterioration per week is 10% of the cost price. Each time a component is ordered there is a cost of processing this order of £1.

(a) How many items should be ordered each time?
(b) What is the cost of ordering and storing each item?

*Solution (1)*
Let *B* = minimum stock level i.e. safety stock

Let $Q$ = number of components delivered with each order, $D$ = rate of usage in units per week, $S$ = cost of processing an order, $h$ = cost of storing an item per week as a percentage of cost price, $P$ = cost of an item, $t$ = time in weeks between orders.

The cycle of usage and replenishment is shown in Figure 10.7.

Average number of items stored in time $t$ is $\frac{1}{2}Q + B$.

Therefore the storing cost per cycle of length $t = \frac{1}{2}QthP + BthP$.

Total cost per cycle of length $t = \frac{1}{2}QthP + BthP + S$.

Total cost per week $= \frac{1}{2}QthP + BhP + \dfrac{S}{t}$.

But $t = \dfrac{Q}{D}$

$\therefore$ Total cost (TC) per week $= \frac{1}{2}QhP + BhP + \dfrac{SD}{Q}$ \hfill (1)

To obtain optimum order size, differentiate with respect to $Q$:

$$\frac{\mathrm{d}TC}{\mathrm{d}Q} = \frac{1}{2}hP - \frac{SD}{Q^2}$$

$$= 0 \text{ for a maximum}$$

$$\text{Therefore } Q^2 = \frac{2SD}{hP}$$

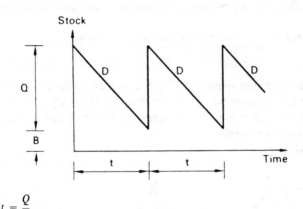

Stock

Q

B

D    D    D

t    t

Time

$t = \dfrac{Q}{D}$

**Fig. 10.7**

(a)

$$Q = \sqrt{\frac{2SD}{hP}}$$

$$= \sqrt{\left[\frac{2 \times 1 \times 50}{(1/10) \times 15}\right]}$$ \hfill (2)

$$= 8.16 \text{ components}$$

(b) Substituting $Q$ in equation (1)

$$TC = hPB + \frac{Q^2hP + 2SD}{2Q}$$

$$= hPB + \frac{2SD + 2SD}{2 \times \sqrt{\frac{2SD}{hP}}}$$

$$= hPB + \sqrt{2SDhP} \tag{3}$$

$$= (1/10) \times 15 \times 3 + \sqrt{[2 \times 1 \times 50 \times (\frac{1}{10}) \times 15]}$$

$$= £16.75 \text{ per week.}$$

*Example (2): Stock control and shortages*
A plant department calls for the steady supply of 50 components each week; the price of the component is £30. The supplier usually keeps sufficient stocks to meet demand and the cost of holding a component per week is 10% of cost price. The cost to the supplier each time a new order is processed is £10. However, sometimes the delivery date cannot be met so to make up the backlog there are special deliveries to the customer as soon as the supplier is able to continue with the order. The extra cost incurred by the supplier in this situation is £10 per component.

(a) Calculate the economic order quantity for the supplier.
(b) Calculate the total cost per week to the supplier of stockholding and processing orders.
(c) Calculate the level to which stock on site is topped up.

*Solution (2)*
$Z$ = cost of shortage per component, $Q$ = economic order quantity, $A$ = top-up quantity, $D$ = rate of usage per week, $h$ = storage cost as a percentage of the cost price of component, $P$ = cost of component, $S$ = cost of processing an order, $t$ = time in weeks between supplies.
From Figure 10.8

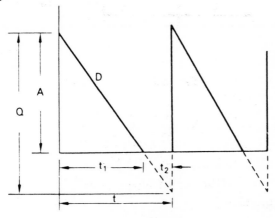

**Fig. 10.8**

(i) Storing cost $= \frac{1}{2}Dt_1t_1hP$ per cycle and $A = Dt_1$

Storing cost per week $= \dfrac{Dt_1^2hP}{2t}$

$$= \frac{At_1hP}{2(t_1 + t_2)}$$

Now from similar triangles

$$\frac{Q}{t_1 + t_2} = \frac{A}{t_1}$$

Therefore

$$t_1 = \frac{At_2}{Q-A}$$

Substituting $t_1$ in equation (1)

Storing cost per week $\qquad = \dfrac{A^2hP}{2Q}$ \hfill (2)

(ii) Cost of shortage per cycle $\qquad = \frac{1}{2}Dt_2^2Z.$

Shortage cost per week $\qquad = \dfrac{Dt_2^2Z}{2t}$

$$= \frac{Dt_2^2Z}{2(t_1 + t_2)} \hfill (3)$$

Substituting $t_1$ in equation (3)

Shortage cost per week $\qquad = \dfrac{(Q-A)^2Z}{2Q}$ \hfill (4)

(iii) Total cost per week $\qquad = \dfrac{A^2hP}{Q} + \dfrac{(Q-A)^2Z}{2Q} + \dfrac{SD}{Q}$

To obtain optimum order size differentiate with respect to $Q$ and $A$ and maximise.

$$Q = \sqrt{\frac{2SD}{hP}} \cdot \sqrt{\frac{Z + hP}{Z}} \text{ units}$$

$$A = \sqrt{\frac{2SD}{hP}} \cdot \sqrt{\frac{Z}{Z + hP}} \text{ units}$$

$$TC = \sqrt{2SDhP} \cdot \sqrt{\frac{Z}{Z + hP}} \text{ per week.}$$

(a)
$$Q = \sqrt{\left[\frac{2 \times 10 \times 50}{(1/10) \times 30}\right]} \times \sqrt{\left[\frac{10 + (\frac{1}{10}) \times 30}{10}\right]}$$
$$= 20.8 \text{ components}$$

(b)
$$TC = \sqrt{[2 \times 10 \times 50 \times (\tfrac{1}{10}) \times 30]} \times \sqrt{\frac{10}{10 + (\tfrac{1}{10}) \times 30}}$$

$$= \text{£48.04 per week.}$$

(c)
$$A = \sqrt{\left[\frac{2 \times 10 \times 50}{(\tfrac{1}{10}) \times 30}\right]} \times \sqrt{\left[\frac{10}{(10) + (\tfrac{1}{10}) \times 30}\right]}$$
$$= 16.01 \text{ components.}$$

*Example (3): Stock control and discounts*
Components are required at the rate of 2 000 per month. The cost of ordering is £20 and the cost of storing the material is 50% of its purchase cost. The cost per item depends on the total quantity ordered as follows: (a) less than 500 items @ £1.21 per item (b) 500–999 items @ £1.00 per item (c) 1 000 or more @ £0.81 per item.

Calculate the optimum order quantity and the optimum total cost per month of purchasing, storing and ordering the material.

*Solution (3)*

$$Q = \sqrt{\frac{2SD}{hP}}$$

$$= \sqrt{\frac{2 \times 20 \times 2000}{\tfrac{1}{2}P}}$$

$$= \frac{400}{\sqrt{P}}$$

Without discounts only the costs of storage have been involved in the calculation and not the cost of the material itself. This may result in a false situation as follows:

(a)

$$Q = \frac{400}{\sqrt{1.21}}$$

$$= \frac{400}{1.1}$$

$$= 363 < 500 \text{ items (i.e. within range).}$$

(b)

$$Q = \frac{400}{\sqrt{1}}$$

$$= 400 \text{ (i.e. outside range 500–999 items).}$$

(c)

$$Q = \frac{400}{\sqrt{0.81}}$$

$$= \frac{400}{0.9}$$

$$= 444 \text{ (i.e. outside range 1000 items or more).}$$

On first inspection the optimum order quantity would be 363 units, but the calculation so far does not take into account the cost of the material itself, which in this instance varies according to the quantity ordered. Therefore, looking at total costs:

$$TC = \text{cost of material} + \text{storage cost} + \text{order cost}$$

Therefore

$$TC \text{ per month} = DP + \tfrac{1}{2}QhP + \frac{SD}{Q}$$

Overall discount situation:

(a)

(i)
$$TC = 2\ 000 \times 1.21 + \tfrac{1}{2} \times 363 \times 0.5 \times 1.21 + \frac{20 \times 2\ 000}{363}$$

$$= £2\ 640 \text{ per month}$$

(b)

(i)
$$TC = 2\ 000 \times 1.0 + \tfrac{1}{2} \times 500 \times 0.5 \times 1.0 + \frac{20 \times 2\ 000}{500}$$

$$= £2\ 205 \text{ per month}$$

(ii)
$$TC = 2\ 000 \times 1.0 + \tfrac{1}{2} \times 999 \times 0.5 \times 1.0 + \frac{20 \times 2\ 000}{999}$$

$$= £2\ 289 \text{ per month}$$

(c)

(i)
$$TC = 2\ 000 \times 0.81 + \tfrac{1}{2} \times 1\ 000 \times 0.5 \times 0.81 + \frac{20 \times 2\ 000}{1\ 000}$$

$$= £1\ 862 \text{ per month}$$

(ii)
$$TC = 2\ 000 \times 0.81 + \tfrac{1}{2} \times 2\ 000 \times 0.5 \times 0.81 + \frac{20 \times 2\ 000}{2\ 000}$$

$$= £2\ 045 \text{ per month}$$

The optimum order quantity, therefore, is 1 000 items per month and the total monthly purchase, storage and ordering cost is £1 862.

*Example (4): Stock control and continuous usage*

A manufacturer is required to supply 1 000 units each week to a large plant store. The store has very little storage space on site and thus requires the units to be delivered at the rate at which they can be used. The manufacturer has the capacity to produce 2 500 units per week. The cost of storing a unit per week is 1p and the cost of setting up the equipment for a production run is £50.

(a)  What is the optimum number of units to produce in a production run?
(b)  What is the total cost of producing and storing the plant department's requirements?
(c)  How frequently should production runs be made?

*Solution (4)*

$Q$ = number of units made per production run, $D$ = number of units required by contractor each week, $k$ = number of units produced per week, $H$ = cost of storing one item per week, $S$ = cost of setting up a production run, $t$ = time interval in weeks between production runs.

From Figure 10.9, the length of the production run $t_1 = \dfrac{Q}{k}$

Length of production and usage cycle $t = \dfrac{Q}{D}$, $AC = Q - Dt_1$

Storage cost per cycle $= \tfrac{1}{2}(Q - Dt_1) \times H \times t = \tfrac{1}{2}Qt \left(1 - \dfrac{D}{k}\right)H$

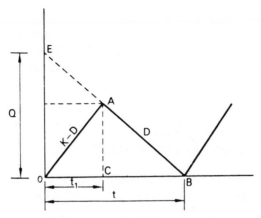

**Fig. 10.9**

Total cost per cycle $= \frac{1}{2}QtH(1 - \frac{D}{k}) + S$

Therefore total cost (TC) per week $= \frac{S}{t} + \frac{1}{2}QH(1 - \frac{D}{k})$

$$TC = \frac{SD}{Q} + \frac{1}{2}QH(1 - \frac{D}{k}) \tag{1}$$

To obtain optimum run size differentiate with respect to Q:

$$\frac{dTC}{dQ} = -\frac{SD}{Q^2} + \frac{1}{2}H(1 - \frac{D}{k})$$

$$= 0 \text{ or a maximum.}$$

$$Q = \sqrt{\frac{2SD}{H\,1 - (D/k)}} \text{ units}$$

$$t = \sqrt{(\frac{2S}{DH\,[1 - (D/k)]})} \text{ weeks,}$$

$$TC = \frac{2SD + Q^2H\,[1 - (D/K)]}{2Q} \text{ per week}$$

or substituting for $Q$

$$TC = \sqrt{[2SDH\,1 - (D/k)]} \text{ per week} \tag{2}$$

$$Q = \sqrt{\left[\frac{2 \times 50 \times 1\,000}{0.01 \times [1 - (1\,000/2\,500)]}\right]}$$

$$= 4\,083 \text{ units per run}$$

(b)

$$TC = \sqrt{(2 \times 50 \times 1\,000 \times 0.01\,[1 - (1\,000/2\,500)])}$$

$$= £24.50 \text{ per week}$$

(c)

$$t = \sqrt{\frac{2 \times 50}{1\,000 \times 0.01\,[1 - (1\,000/2\,500)]}}$$

$$= 4.08 \text{ weeks.}$$

These examples clearly involve a refined level of stock control, necessitating detailed information gathering. For many plant stores departments the type and usage of stocks and spare parts are too few to demand such sophistication. In that circumstance, adoption of the 'ABC' technique coupled with rigorous checking of both stock and order processing should suffice.

**Reading list**

1. Parker, E.J. *Accounting for maintenance.* Mechanical Engineering Publications Ltd., 1974.
2. Clifton, R.H. *Principles of planned maintenance.* Edward Arnold, 1974.
3. Priel, V.F. *Systematic maintenance organisation.* MacDonald and Evans, London, 1974.
4. Corder, A.S. *Maintenance management techniques.* McGraw-Hill, London, 1976.
5. Connor, J. and Evans, J.B. *Replacement Investment.* Gower Press, 1972.
6. Kelly, A. *The control of industrial maintenance (Parts 1 & 2).* The Plant Engineer, 1974.
7. Herbaty, F. Maintenance management systems. *Plant Engineering.* September, November, December 1976; January 1977.
8. Battersby, A. *A guide to stock control.* Pitman, London, 1962.
9. Boodman, D.M. and Magee, J.F. *Production planning and inventory control.* McGraw-Hill, New York, 1967.
10. Churchman, C.W., Ackoff, R.L. and Aruoff, E.L. *Introduction to Operations Research.* John Wiley, New York, 1957.
11. *Health and Safety at Work Act 1974.* HMSO.
12. *Construction Regulations, 1961 and 1966.* HMSO.
13. Higgins, L.R. *Handbook of equipment maintenance.* McGraw-Hill, New York, USA, 1979.
14. Hamburg, M. *Statistical analysis for decision making.* Harcourt, Brace and World, New York, 1970.
15. Sykes, A. The lease-buy decision. *Management Survey Report No. 29.* British Institute of Management, 1976.
16. Barber, G. *Builder's plant and equipment.* Newnes-Butterworths, London, 2nd Edition, 1973.
17. Jurecka, W. Repair costs and preventive maintenance of heavy earthmoving equipment. *Proceedings to CIB 2nd Symposium on Organisation and Management of Construction.* Haifa, October 1978.
18. Whysall, N. Cutting your losses — when to ditch repair-ridden plant. *New Civil Engineer,* 6 October 1977.
19. Jones, D. *The servicing and maintenance of plant.* Unpublished paper. Department of Civil Engineering, Loughborough University of Technology, 1978.
20. Hadfield, D.B. *Servicing, maintaining and replacing construction plant.*

Unpublished paper, Department of Civil Engineering, Loughborough University of Technology, 1978.

21. *Construction Equipment Maintenance*. (Monthly). Cahners Publishing Co. Chicago.

# CHAPTER 11

## HEALTH AND SAFETY AT WORK: REGULATIONS AND REQUIREMENTS

### Basic provisions of the Health and Safety at Work Act

The Health and Safety at Work Act introduced in 1974 provided a legislative frame-work designed to encourage high standards of health and safety at work. The Act is described as an enabling measure superimposed over existing health and safety legislation contained in some 31 Acts. The existing legislation mainly under the Factories, Offices, Shops and Railway Premises and Mines and Quarries Acts remain in force but the Health and Safety at Work Act provides one comprehensive and integrated system of law relating to health and safety at work. The Act consists of four parts:

*Part I*, relating to health, safety and welfare in relation to work;
*Part II*, relating to an Employment Medical Advisory Service;
*Part III*, relating to amendments in the law relating to building regulations; and
*Part IV*, containing a number of miscellaneous and general provisions.

The Health and Safety at Work Act, superimposed over some 31 relevant Acts, was intended to provide for the gradual replacement of the then existing health and safety requirements by revised and updated provisions. These new provisions would be in the form of regulations and codes of practice prepared in consultation with industry.

The regulations are made by the appropriate Minister and where appropriate these are supplemented by codes of practice which although not statutory can be used as evidence that the statutory requirements have been contravened.

The Act provided for the establishment of a Health and Safety Commission and a Health and Safety Executive.

### Health and Safety Commission

The Health and Safety Commission has a full-time chairman and nine lay members. It is responsible for developing the policies in Health and Safety. The Commission consists of representatives of industry, unions and local authorities and is ultimately responsible to the Minister for Employment.

### Health and Safety Executive

The Health and Safety Executive is a separate statutory body appointed by the Commission to work within the direction and guidance of the Commission. The main duty of the Executive is to enforce the legal requirements and to provide an advisory service. The Executive is responsible for the Health and Safety Inspectorates (i.e. Factories, Mines, Quarries, Construction, etc).

### Health and Safety Inspectorate

The Act's major legal requirements are enforced through the work of the inspectors. If an inspector discovers a contravention then he is empowered to issue a prohibition notice, an improvement notice, to prosecute or to seize, render harmless and destroy a dangerous article.

A prohibition notice is issued if there is a serious risk to health or a risk of serious injury and the activity giving rise to that risk must be stopped until remedial action can be taken. The prohibition notice is served on the person undertaking the activity or on the person in control.

An improvement notice is issued so that a fault or contravention of a statutory requirement can be remedied within a specified time. The notice would be served on the person who is not satisfying the legal requirement or on any person on whom the responsibility has been placed and this could be an employer, an employed person or even a supplier of equipment.

There is the right of appeal to an independent tribunal against both a prohibition and improvement notice. Prosecution can take place instead of or in addition to serving a notice. Failure to comply with a notice is also an offence against the law. The inspector can also seize, render harmless and destroy any substance or article that is the cause of imminent danger or serious personal injury.

Inspectors may also take written statements of fact from witnesses and ultimately conduct proceedings in Court even though they are not solicitors or counsel.

The Health and Safety at Work Act also defines the responsibilities and duties of the various parties.

### *Employers*

The duties of the employer include:

- Ensuring, as far as is reasonably practicable, the health, safety and welfare of all employees. This applies particularly to the provision of plant and systems of works that are safe and without risks to health.
- Ensuring that all machinery, equipment and appliances used are safe.
- Ensuring that the handling, transport and storage of materials are safe.

- Providing information, instruction, training and supervision to ensure the health and safety of employees at work.
- Maintaining safe means of access and egress from places of work.
- Provision and maintenance of a safe working environment with adequate facilities for welfare at work.
- The preparation and revision of a written statement explaining the employer's general policy with respect to the health and safety of the employees and the organisation and arrangements made to carry out that policy.

Employers also have a duty with regard for the health and safety of persons who are not employees, such as self-employed or contractors' employees who may be working close to their own employees. This extends to members of the public and employers must ensure that the public are not exposed to health and safety risks.

### Employees

The Act places on the employees the duty to take reasonable care to avoid injury to themselves or to others by their activities at work. Employees must not interfere or misuse anything provided to protect their health and safety and must also co-operate with their employer in respect to health and safety matters.

### Manufacturers and suppliers

The Act places on manufacturers and suppliers the duty to ensure that any article or substance supplied for use at work is safe when properly used.

Thus, a plant hire company has the responsibility placed upon it to ensure that any plant supplied is safe when properly used. The supplier must test any article (i.e. plant item) for safety in use or arrange for a competent authority to test the article. The supplier must also supply information about the use for which an article was designed and include conditions of use regarding its safety.

The general obligations imposed by the Health and Safety at Work Act 1974 are supplemented by the detailed requirements of regulations. The following regulations are specifically of interest to the construction industry:

Construction (General Practices) Regulations 1961;
Construction (Lifting Operations) Regulations 1961;
Construction (Working Places) Regulations 1966.

In addition there are other regulations dealing with specific hazards of which the following are examples relevant to the construction industry:

Asbestos;
Work in compressed air;
Abrasive wheels; and
Woodworking machinery.

Safety statistics

The Health and Safety Executive's report 'Construction — Health and Safety 1978' recorded the following statistics (Table 11.1) which illustrates that construction has a poorer safety record than manufacture in fatal accidents.

**Table 11.1**    Incidence of Accidents for Construction and Manufacture

| Year | Manufacture | | Construction | |
|------|-------------|--------|--------------|--------|
|      | Incidence rate of fatal accidents | Incidence rate of reported accidents | Incidence rate of fatal accidents | Incidence rate of reported accidents |
| 1973 | 4.2 | 3 710 | 21.6 | 3 540 |
| 1974 | 4.5 | 3 520 | 16.0 | 3 460 |
| 1975 | 3.7 | 3 490 | 17.7 | 3 460 |
| 1976 | 3.4 | 3 480 | 15.3 | 3 530 |
| 1977 | 3.4 | 3 590 | 13.1 | 3 300 |

N.B. The incidence rates are per 100 000 at risk.

The fatal accidents were distributed amongst the various causes as shown in Table 11.2, from which it is evident that the most common cause of fatal accidents was falls.

**Table 11.2**    Fatal accidents in construction in 1977 by cause

| Cause | Number | Percentages |
|-------|--------|-------------|
| Machinery | 22 | 16.8% |
| Transport | 12 | 9.2% |
| Fires and explosion | 2 | 1.5% |
| Electrocution | 3 | 2.3% |
| Falls | 74 | 56.5% |
| Stepping on or striking an object | 1 | 0.7% |
| Struck by falling object | 12 | 9.2% |
| Not otherwise specified, including accidental drowning | 5 | 3.8% |
| Total | 131 | 100% |

Safety policy and organisation

Because construction sites are remote from head office and because construction sites have to contend with a widely varying number of factors such as climate, geology, type of work, etc. the role of the company's safety policy and how it is implemented is particularly important. The company's safety policy needs to be supported by realistic organisational arrangements that will make the implementation of the policy effective. There needs to be:

(i) a clear and logical delegation of duties through line management;
(ii) the clear identification of key personnel to carry out the detailed arrangements such as the repair, maintenance and inspection of plant including the keeping of the required records;
(iii) clear job descriptions and organisation charts which show the relationship between line managers and functional managers (such as safety officers), demonstrating the responsibility each manager has for safety;
(iv) a well-defined mechanism to ensure that the safety officer monitors the health and safety aspects of the company operations and reports back to senior managers in a manner in which a clear statement of the health and safety at each site is given.

The company's policy and organisational arrangements must be such that safe systems of work are developed and used. In most construction companies the method or system of work is devised by the site management team. These are generally called method statements. The personnel responsible for developing these method statements must be aware of the safety requirements.

The company also has a duty to train personnel. This means not only operatives who have to be trained in the correct use of plant and equipment but also the supervisors and site managers who are responsible for devising safe methods of work.

*Safety representatives*
Where two or more members of a recognised trade union request an employer to form a joint Health and Safety Committee the employer is required to do so by the regulations on Safety Representatives and Safety Committees, S.I. 1977 No. 500.

The elected Safety Representative is entitled to:

(i) investigate accidents, hazards and complaints and make representations to the employer;
(ii) conduct health and safety inspections;
(iii) receive information from Health and Safety Inspectors;
(iv) attend meetings of the Health and Safety Committee;
(v) receive information from the employer in respect of health and safety issues and inspect statutory documents.

The Safety Representative is also permitted time off with pay to perform the above tasks and also to receive adequate training.

### Notification of accidents and dangerous occurrences

The regulations for the notification of accidents and dangerous occurrences are defined in S.I. 1980 No. 804 and have been effective since 1 January 1981. The previous requirements were revoked.

The notification of accidents and dangerous occurrences can be classified as:

(i) minor injuries;
(ii) major injuries;
(iii) fatal accidents;
(iv) road vehicle accidents;
(v) dangerous occurrences.

The notification requirements of each of these classifications is described below.

*Minor injuries*
Minor injuries are defined as injuries which keep the employee from work for more than three consecutive days. The employer is required to notify the Department of Health and Social Security on Form BI76, when it is received, after a claim by the employee for industrial injury benefit. The D.H.S.S. will then send particulars of the accident to the Health and Safety Executive. If there is no claim for benefit the employer need not report the accident but must keep a record of the accident.

*Major injuries*
A major injury is defined as a fracture of skull, shin, pelvis or any bone, amputation, loss of sight or any injury which results in hospitalisation for more than 24 hours.

The employer is required to notify the enforcing authority by the quickest means possible, usually by telephone. The employer must send a report on Form 2548 to the enforcing authority within seven days and the same notification procedure is required for persons other than the company's employees, such as members of the public, involved in a major accident.

*Fatal accident*
The notification procedures for an accident resulting in the death of a person are the same as for major injuries. Form 2508 should be used for reporting to the authorities.

*Road vehicle accidents*
Accidents involving road vehicles adjacent to the public highway are notifiable only if the person was engaged at the time in work on or alongside a road.

*Dangerous occurrences*
Specified dangerous occurrences which have the potential for causing serious accidents even though physical injuries may not have occurred are notifiable in the

same way as major injuries and fatalities. Examples of dangerous occurrences are scaffold collapse, overturning of a crane, explosions or collapses of structures and buildings under construction.

## Records

Employers are required to keep written records of all notifiable accidents and dangerous occurrences. The details required in these records, which should be kept for three years, are:

(i) the date of accident or dangerous occurrences;
(ii) in the case of accidents, the name, age, sex, occupation of the victim and nature of injury;
(iii) the place where the accident or dangerous occurrence took place;
(iv) a brief description of the circumstances.

## Safety check list

The Health and Safety Executive's report 'Construction – Health and Safety 1978' produced a basic checklist for on site. This list of safety points was produced by the Inspectorate in the light of their experience. The list was intended as an aid to safety supervisors, safety representatives and site managers. This check list is reproduced here with the kind permission of the Controller of Her Majesty's Stationary Office.

## Construction site basic safety checklist

### Is it safe?

One sure way to reduce accidents is to pinpoint unsafe situations or practices, so that steps can be taken to correct them before anyone gets hurt. An attempt has been made to identify some of the most elementary hazards found on sites, which frequently lead to accidents. This check list, as its title says, is basic and it should therefore be modified to suit local needs.

### Safe access

More than 50% of the accidents that keep men away from work involve falls or collisions, of men, materials and vehicles. It is therefore vital that access from place to place be made safe.

### Checkpoints:

1. Is safe access provided for all on site to reach their places of work, i.e. good roads, gangways, passageways, passenger hoists, staircases, ladders and scaffolds?
2. Are all walkways level and free from obstruction?
3. Is edge protection provided or other preventive measures taken where men are likely to fall from an open side?

4. Are holes or openings covered over with securely fixed covers or, alternatively, fenced off?
5. Is adequate artificial lighting available for when work has to continue after dark?
6. Is the site tidy and are materials stored in safe positions?
7. Are there proper arrangements for the gathering and disposal of scrap?
8. Are nails in timber hammered down or removed?

### Ladders
More accidents arise each year from the use and/or misuse of ladders than from any other single piece of equipment.

*Checkpoints:*
1. Is every ladder in good condition and free from obvious defects?
2. Are all ladders secured near the top, including those used for short periods?
3. If the ladder cannot be secured near the top, is it secured near the bottom, weighted, or footed?
4. Does the ladder rise at least 1.07 m (3 ft 6 in) above the place of landing? If not, is there adequate handhold at the place of landing?
5. Are ladders properly positioned for access?

### Tubular scaffolds
The law requires that scaffolding work be done with a competent and experienced supervision. All scaffolders except trainees should be experienced and competent in their work. The loading for which a scaffold has been provided should be known. The loading should be evenly distributed. The scaffold should not be overloaded. Scaffolds are required to be inspected at least once a week and after bad weather.

*Checkpoints:*
1. Has proper access been provided to the scaffold platform?
2. Are all uprights provided with base plates or prevented in some other way from slipping or sinking?
3. Have any uprights, ledgers, braces or struts been removed?
4. Is the scaffold secured to the building in enough places to prevent collapse? Have any ties been removed since the scaffold was erected?
5. Are there sufficient boards at all working platforms in use?
6. Are all boards free from obvious defects and are they arranged to avoid traps?
7. Are there warning notices to prohibit the use of any scaffold that is incomplete e.g. not fully boarded?
8. At every side where a person can fall more than 1.98 m (6 ft 6 in) are the platforms, gangways and runs provided with guardrails and toeboards?
9. Who is responsible for the inspections, and are they carried out and recorded?

### Excavations
The digging of an excavation on a site may be a man's first and last job. If the sides collapse, there may be no escape. There is almost no ground which will not collapse

under certain conditions. If there is any doubt whatsoever about the safety of the sides, they should be timbered or battered. Timbering materials should always be provided on site.

Is the excavation more than 1.21 m (4 ft) deep?

*Checkpoints:*
1. Is the timber provided strong enough to support the sides of the excavation?
2. Is the method of putting in timbering a safe one?
3. Is the angle of batter appropriate?
4. Is the excavation inspected daily, and the timbering weekly?
5. Is there safe access to the excavation?
6. Is there a barrier to prevent persons falling in?
7. Is the stability of the excavation being affected by vehicles which come too near?
8. If vehicles tip into an excavation, are properly secured stop blocks provided?

*Roof work*
*Checkpoints:*
1. Is work being done on a sloping roof of more than 30° or less than 30° but which is slippery? If so, are there crawling ladders or crawling boards? Are these being used? If crawling boards or ladders are not being provided does the roof structure itself provide a safe handhold and foothold?
2. For sloping roofs or work near the edge of flat roofs, is there sufficient edge protection to prevent falls of materials and persons?
3. Are any men working near or on fragile materials such as asbestos cement sheets or glass? If so, are crawling boards provided and used and warning notices posted?
4. Have all rooflights been properly covered or provided with barriers?
5. During sheeting operations are precautions taken to prevent men falling from the edge of the sheet?
6. Where other men are working under roofwork are precautions taken to prevent debris falling onto them?

*Transport*
*Checkpoints:*
1. Are vehicles kept in good repair?
2. Is the steering satisfactory and are the handbrake and footbrake working properly?
3. Are vehicles driven in a safe way?
4. Do the vehicles have any parts likely to cause injury in the normal circumstances of their use?
5. Are vehicles badly loaded so that there is danger from falling loads?
6. Do persons ride in dangerous positions?
7. Are there any tipping lorries? If so, are the dangers of reaching under the raised body understood?

*Machinery*
Some dangerous parts, like gears, chain drives, and rotating shafts with projecting keys and set-screws, are easy to recognise. Others are not so obvious, like projecting engine shafts.

*Checkpoints:*
1. Are there any dangerous parts?
2. Are they guarded?
3. Is the guard secured and in good repair?

*Hoists*
A platform hoist must be protected by a substantial enclosure and the enclosure must be fitted with gates where access is needed. A platform hoist can be dangerous if the gates are not kept shut. Hoists are required to be inspected weekly, and thoroughly examined every six months by a competent person.

*Checkpoints:*
1. Who is responsible for these inspections, and are they carried out and recorded?
2. Is there an enclosure where necessary to prevent people being struck by any moving part of the hoist or materials on it?
3. Are gates provided at all landings?
4. Are the gates kept shut except when the platform is at the landing?
5. Is the control rope so arranged that the hoist can be operated from one position only?
6. Is the safe working load clearly marked on the hoist?
7. Is there a proper signalling system?
8. If the hoist is for materials only, is there a notice on the platform or cage prohibiting persons from riding on it? Is this notice obeyed?

*Cranes and lifting appliances*
The collapse and overturning of a crane can injure other people as well as the crane driver, especially on a crowded site or where the crane is working near a public thoroughfare. Cranes are required to be inspected weekly, and thoroughly examined every 14 months by a competent person.

*Checkpoints:*
1. Who is responsible for these inspections, and are they carried out and recorded?
2. Has the test certificate been seen?
3. Is the driver trained and competent and over 18 years old?
4. Are the controls (levers, handles, switches, etc.) clearly marked?
5. Has the weight of the load been ascertained?
6. Is the crane of more than 1 ton capacity? If so, and it is a jib crane, is it fitted with an automatic safe load indicator in efficient working order, and which is being inspected weekly?

7. Is the crane sited on a hard level base?
8. Has the slinger been trained to give signals and to attach loads correctly?
9. If the crane can vary its operating radius are the safe working loads and corresponding radii plainly marked?
10. Is the crane regularly maintained?

### Electricity

The main causes of electrical accidents on sites are from electrical equipment or lighting, from overhead electric power lines and from underground cables. Treat all electric equipment with respect.

### Checkpoints:

1. Signs of damage to apparatus — especially portable equipment.
2. Signs of damage to outer covering of wires and cables.
3. Are all connections to power points by proper plugs etc. and not bare ends of cables?
4. Are there signs of interference with equipment, damaged or otherwise?
5. Are there any overhead electric lines? If so, is there anything (a crane, forklift truck, tipper lorry, excavator or scaffolding) which might touch these lines? If so, has the electricity supply to these lines been cut off?
6. If not, what other precautions have been taken?
7. If there is an electric underground cable in the vicinity of work being carried out, is the line of the cable known, has it been located and marked and have precautions been taken to prevent contact?

### Manual handling

Ignorance of the best way of lifting a load is a common cause of accidents. Lift with the legs bent, and the back straight. Get a good grip; use gloves if there are any sharp edges; do not lift if the weight is too great.

### Trespassers

Sites should always be made as secure as possible against trespass by children, especially at times when no one is on the site.

### Checkpoints:

1. Are all ladders removed at the end of each working period or made incapable of use by boarding the rungs?
2. Is all plant immobilised at the end of each working period?
3. Are bricks and materials safely stacked?
4. If there is perimeter fencing, is it undamaged and are the gates secured?

### Health risks

Risks to health, which may not show themselves immediately, can arise from some materials. Examples are asbestos, spraying of certain types of plastic paints, burning or cutting lead painted materials, cleaning of sandstone buildings and the use of sand for cleaning buildings. Confined spaces such as manholes and sewers can be dangerous because of lack of oxygen or the presence of fumes and dust.

*Checkpoints:*
1. Have harmful materials been identified?
2. What precautions are needed?
3. Is the necessary safety equipment provided and properly used?
4. Are other workers, who are not protected, kept out of danger areas?
5. In confined spaces has the atmosphere been tested and an air supply provided if necessary?

### Protective clothing
The head, eyes, hands and feet are all very vulnerable to injury. Equipment to prevent accidents can be made available and eye protection for certain dust or particle-creating processes is required by law.

*Checkpoints:*
1. Is protective equipment provided at least to the minimum standard required by law?
2. Do persons employed wear their protective equipment?

### Fire
Fires on construction sites can occur from the ignition of highly flammable liquids used on site e.g. adhesives, floor and wall coatings. The misuse of compressed gases has also been the cause of fire and explosions on sites, and rules for storage and use of cylinders should be strictly observed. Other causes of fire are accidental ignition of waste material, wood shavings, and cellular plastic materials used as insulation or cavity fill material.

*Checkpoints:*
General:
1. Are there any fire extinguishers?
2. Is there a secondary way out if fire blocks the normal route?
Highly flammable liquids:
3. Is there a properly constructed and sited store area?
4. Is the amount of flammable liquid present at the workplace kept to the minimum for the day's work?
5. Is smoking prohibited, and are other ignition sources excluded from the areas where the liquids are present?
6. Are properly constructed safety containers in use?
Compressed gases such as LPG and acetylene:
7. Are the cylinders properly stored?
8. Is the cylinder valve fully closed when the cylinder is not in use?

9. Are cylinders sited outside huts with a piped supply into the hut?
Other combustible material:
10. Are proper waste receptacles provided?
11. Is provision made for regular removal of waste material?

### Explosives
A competent person with knowledge of the dangers should have charge of the storage, handling and use of explosives.

### Cartridge-operated tools
The maker's instructions should always be carefully followed.

### Checkpoints:
1. Has the man using the gun been properly trained and told about the dangers?
2. Is he wearing goggles?
3. Does he know how to deal with misfires?
4. Is the gun being cleaned regularly?
5. Is the gun kept in a secure place when not in use?
6. Are cartridges kept in a secure place?

### Noise
Noise can affect men's hearing if they are exposed to it for long periods.

### Checkpoints:
1. Is there any uncomfortably noisy plant or machinery?
2. Are breakers fitted with muffs and other plant or machinery fitted with silencers?
3. In very noisy surroundings are ear defenders supplied to the men.
4. Do people have to work in places where they must shout to be clearly audible to someone 1 to 2 metres away?

### Falsework/formwork
Temporary works can be a source of danger if not properly constructed.

### Checkpoints:
1. Has anyone checked the design and supports for the shuttering and formwork?
2. Are the props plumb and properly set out?
3. Are the bases and ground conditions adequate for the loads?
4. Are the proper pins used in the props?
5. Are the timbers in good condition?

### Welfare
### Checkpoints:
1. Are the lavatories and washbasins kept clean?
2. Is the mess hut kept clean and free from storage?

3. Is there a hut where wet clothes can be dried?
4. Is there a supply of drinking water?
5. Is there a first aid box?

### Guide to statutory tests, examinations and inspections

In fulfilling the requirements of the Health and Safety at Work Act and the derived regulations there are a number of statutory tests, examinations and inspections that are required. These are summarised in Table 11.3 which was prepared by Geo. Wimpey & Co. Ltd. and originally published in *Building Technology and Management* in March 1974 but the requirements have been checked for current accuracy. The statutory tests, examinations and inspections are particularly relevant to users of plant on site.

This guide is reproduced by the kind permission of the Editor of *Building Technology and Management* and Geo. Wimpey & Co. Ltd.

### Legislation encompassed in Health and Safety relevant to construction

Health and Safety at Work etc. Act 1974.
Factories Act 1961.
Building (Safety, Health and Welfare) Regulations 1948 (SI 1948 No 1145) (Regs 1 to 4 and 99).
Construction (General Provisions) Regulations 1961 (SI 1961 No 1580).
Construction (Lifting Operations) 1961 (SI 1961 No 1581).
Construction (Working Places) Regulations 1966 (SI 1966 No 94).
Construction (Health and Welfare) Regulations 1966 (SI 1966 No 95 as amended by SI 1974 No 209).
Engineering Construction (Extension of Definition) Regulations 1960 (SI 1960 No 421).
Engineering Construction (Extension of Definition) Regulations 1968 (SI 1968 No 1530).
Diving Operations Special Regulations 1960 (SI 1960 No 688) as amended by SI 1973 No 36.
Work in Compressed Air Special Regulations 1958 (SI 1958 No 61) as amended by SI 1960 No 1307 and SI 1973 No 36.
Electricity Regulations 1908 (SR & O 1908 No 1312) as amended by Electricity (Factories Act) Special Regulations 1944 (SR & O 1944 No 739).
Woodworking Machines Regulations 1974 (SI 1974 No 903).
Protection of Eyes Regulations 1974 (SI 1974 No 1681) as amended by SI 1975 No 303.
Lead Paint Regulations 1927 (SR & O 1927 No 847).
Ionising Radiations (Sealed Sources) Regulations 1969 (SI 1969 No 808) as amended by SI 1973 No 36.
Ionising Radiation (Unsealed Radioactive Substances) Regulations 1968 (SI 1968

**Table 11.3** Guide to Statutory Tests, Examinations and Inspections

CONSTRUCTION OPERATIONS

| Type of plant equipment or job involved | A Testing and thorough examination | | | B Thorough examination | | | C Inspection | | | D References |
|---|---|---|---|---|---|---|---|---|---|---|
| | Testing and thorough examination work | Who carries out this work | Results to be recorded on Form No | Thorough examination | Who carries out this work | Results to be recorded on Form No | Inspection to be carried out | Who carries out this work | Results to be recorded on Form No | Legal reference |
| SCAFFOLDING | | | | | | | weekly or more often in bad weather | competent person | form 91 (pt 1) A | W.P. regn 22 |
| EXCAVATIONS EARTHWORKS TRENCHES SHAFTS AND TUNNELS | | | | weekly or more often if part has been affected, e.g. explosives collapse | competent person | form 91 (pt1)B entry to be made day of examination | at least every day or at start of shift | competent person | | G.P. regn 9 |
| MATERIALS OR TIMBER USED TO CONSTRUCT OR SUPPORT TRENCHES EXCAVATIONS COFFER DAMS CAISSONS | | | | | | | on each occasion before use | competent person | | G.P. regn 10 (1) G.P. regn 17 (2) |
| COFFER DAMS CAISSONS | | | | before men are employed therein and at least weekly or more often if explosives are used or any part is damaged | competent person | form 91 (pt1)B | daily and before men are employed therein | competent person | | G.P. regn 18 |
| DANGEROUS ATMOSPHERES | | | | before men are employed therein and as frequently as necessary | competent person Instrument may be necessary | in any convenient way to show how examination was done | | | | G.P. regn (21) (c) |
| CRANES (all types) CRABS WINCHES | once every four years and after substantial alteration or repair | competent person, normally by insurance co. engineer, manufacturer or erector | crane: form 96 crab: form 80 winch: form 80 | at least every 14 months | competent person e.g. insurance co. engineer | form 91 (ptII) J or on a special filing card containing the prescribed particulars | weekly | competent person e.g. crane driver | form 91 (pt1) C-F | L.O. regn 10 (1) (c) L.O. regn 28 (1) (2) and (3) |
| PULLEY BLOCKS GIN WHEELS SHEER LEGS | before first use and after alteration or substantial repair unless used only for loads under 1 ton | competent person, normally the manufacturer or insurance co. engineer | form 80 | at least every 14 months | competent person, e.g. insurance co. engineer | form 91 (ptII)J or on special filing card containing the prescribed particulars | weekly | competent person | form 91 (pt1) C-F | L.O. regn 10 (1) (2) L.O. regn 28 (1) and (2) |

**Table 11.3**  Guide to Statutory Tests, Examinations and Inspections (contd.)

| Type of plant equipment or job involved | A Testing and thorough examination | | | B Thorough examination | | | C Inspection | | | D References |
|---|---|---|---|---|---|---|---|---|---|---|
| | Testing and thorough examination work | Who carries out this work | Results to be recorded on Form No | Thorough examination | Who carries out this work | Results to be recorded on Form No | Inspection to be carried out | Who carries out this work | Results to be recorded on Form No | Legal reference |
| **CRANES** appliances for anchorage or ballasting | | | | on each occasion before crane is erected | competent person, e.g. crane erector of fitter | | | | | L.O. regn 19 (3) |
| **CRANES** test of anchorage or ballasting | before crane is taken into use, i.e. after each erection or re-erection on a site or whenever anchorage or ballasting arrang. changed | competent person, normally crane erector in presence of insurance co. engineer | form 91 (pt I) D | has to be done after exposure of crane to weather conditions likely to have affected its stability. A re-test might be necessary | competent person, e.g. insurance co. engineer | | | | | L.O. regn 19 (4) |
| **CRANES** test of automatic safe load indicator (jib cranes) | after erection or installation of crane and before it is taken into use | crane erector or insurance co. engineer; must be a competent person with knowledge of the working arrangements of indicator | form 91 (pt I) E | | | | weekly | competent person, e.g. crane driver or fitter | form 91 (pt I) E NOTE: this will be part of normal weekly inspection | L.O. regn 30 |
| **CRANES** mobile jib test of automatic safe load indicator | before crane is taken into use, after it has been dismantled or after anything has been done which is likely to affect the proper operation of indicator. e.g. change in jib length | competent person, e.g. erector, manufacturer, engineer, insurance co. | form 91 (pt I) | | | | weekly | competent person, e.g. crane driver | form 91 (pt I) E NOTE: this will be part of normal weekly inspection | L.O. regn 30 |
| **LIFTING** other **APPLIANCES** i.e. excavator dragline piling frame, aerial cableway or ropeway, overhead runway | | | | at least every 14 months or after substantial alteration or repair | competent person | form 91 (pt II) G-K or on a special filing card containing the prescribed particulars | weekly | competent person, e.g. driver | form 91 (pt I) C | L.O. regn 28 L.O. regn 10 |
| **HOISTS** (goods) made altered or repaired after 1st of March 1962 | before first use and after substantial alteration or repair | competent person, manufacturer or insurance co. engineer | form 75 | at least every 6 months | competent person, e.g. insurance co. engineer | form 91 (pt II) G-K or on special filing card containing the prescribed particulars | weekly | competent person, e.g. fitter | form 91 (pt I) H | L.O. regn 46 |
| **HOISTS** passenger | before first use, after re-erection, alterations in height of travel after repair or alterations | competent person, e.g. manufacturer, insurance co. engineer or erector | form 75 or form 91 (pt I) F following alterations to height of travel | at least every 6 months | competent person, e.g. insurance co. engineer | form 91 (pt II) G-K or on special filing card containing the prescribed particulars | weekly | competent person, e.g. fitter | form 91 (pt I) F | L.O. regn 46 |

**Table 11.3**  Guide to Statutory Tests, Examinations and Inspections (contd.)

| Type of plant equipment or job involved | A Testing and thorough examination | | | B Thorough examination | | | C Inspection | | | D References |
|---|---|---|---|---|---|---|---|---|---|---|
| | Testing and thorough examination | Who carries out this work | Results to be recorded on Form No | Thorough examination | Who carries out this work | Results to be recorded on Form No | Inspection to be carried out | Who carries out work | Results to be recorded on Form No | Legal reference |
| CHAINS ROPE SLINGS AND LIFTING GEAR | before first use and after alterations or repair | competent person, normally manufacturer | form 97 | at least every 6 months, except when used only occasionally | competent person, e.g. insurance co. engineer or at a testing house | form 91 (pt I) J or on a special filing card containing the prescribed particulars | SPECIAL NOTE: chains or lifting gear which have to be annealed, see form 91 (pt I) for detail and L.O. 41 | | form 91 (pt I) or form 1946 containing the prescribed particulars | L.O. regn 34 L.O. regn 40 L.O. regn 41 |
| WIRE ROPE | before first use | manufacturer | form 87 | at least every 6 months except when used only occasionally | competent person, e.g. insurance co. engineer | form 91 (pt I) J | | | | L.O. regn 34 |
| STEAM BOILER (new) | before use | manufacturer or boiler inspecting co. | no special form | | | | | | | F.A. 1961 s. 33 |
| STEAM BOILER (cold) | | | | every 14 months and after extensive repairs | competent person, e.g. insurance co. engineer | form 55 | | | | F.A. 1961 s. 33 (4) |
| STEAM BOILER UNDER PRESSURE | | | | every 14 months and after extensive repairs | competent person, e.g. insurance co. engineer | form 55A | | | | F.A. 1961 s. 33 |
| STEAM RECEIVERS AND CONTAINERS | not required | | a certificate as to the safe working pressure provided by maker | at least every 26 months | competent person, e.g. insurance co. engineer | form 58 | | | | F.A. 1961 s. 35 |
| AIR RECEIVERS | before use | manufacturer or insurance co. engineer | a certificate as to the safe working pressure provided by maker | at least every 26 months (see special conditions) | competent person, e.g. insurance co. engineer | form 59 | | | | F.A. 1961 s. 36 |

NOTE:

**re abbreviations used**
F.A. 1961  Factories Act 1961
W.P. regn  Construction (Working Places) Regulations 1966
G.P. regn  Construction (General Provisions) Regulations 1961
L.O. regn  Construction (Lifting Operations) Regulations 1961

NOTE:

**definition of lifting appliance**
means a crab, winch, pulley-block or gin-wheel for raising or lowering and a hoist, crane, sheer-legs, excavator, dragline, piling-frame, aerial cableway, aerial ropeway or overhead runway.

**definition of lifting gear**
means a chain, sling, rope-sling or similar gear and a ring, hook, plate, clamp, shackle, swivel and eye bolt.
**The forms mentioned for result recording are those prescribed and are available from HMSO**

**competent person**
There is no legal definition. The person who is selected or appointed to act as a competent person must have practical and theoretical knowledge together with actual experience on the type of plant, machinery, equipment or work which he is called upon to examine.
Such knowledge and experience will enable him to detect faults, weakness, defects, etc., which it is the purpose of the examination to discover and assess.

NOTE:

For other tests, examinations and inspections in connection with specialised operations, such as diving, work in compressed air, ionising radiations, etc., expert advice should be sought.

EXEMPTIONS:

**Crawler-tracked shovel or dragline excavators**
Such machines are occasionally used as cranes solely by the attachment of lifting gear to the shovel or bucket for work immediately connected with excavations the machine has been directly engaged on; this is only permissible provided a competent person specifies the maximum load or loads to be lifted. The maximum load or loads and the lengths of jib or boom to which they relate, together with a means of indentification, must be plainly marked upon the excavator. The Certificate—Form 2209—must be completed.

**Legal Reference:**
F.A., 1961: The Construction (Lifting Operations) Regulations 1961—Certificate of Exemption No. 2 (General).

No 780) as amended by SI 1973 No 36.

Asbestos Regulations 1969 (SI 1969 No 690).

Abrasive Wheels Regulations 1970 (SI 1970 No 535).

Highly Flammable Liquids and Liquified Petroleum Gases Regulations 1972 (SI 1972 No 917).

Dangerous Occurrences (Notification) Regulations 1947 (SR & O 1947 No 31).

Offices, Shops and Railway Premises Act 1963 modified by Exemption Order No 1 (SI 1964 No 964).

Offices at Building Operations etc (First Aid) Regulations 1964 (SI 1964 No 1322).

Petroleum (Consolidation) Act 1928.

Explosive Act 1875 amended by Explosives Act 1923.

Employment of Women, Young Persons and Children Act 1920.

Hours of Employment (Conventions) Act 1936.

Employment Medical Advisory Service Act 1972.

Fire Certificates (Special Premises) Regulations 1976 (SI 1976 No 2003).

Safety Representatives and Safety Committees Regulations 1977 (SI 1977 No 500).

## Reading list

1. *Health and Safety at Work Act 1974*. H.M.S.O.
2. Health and Safety Executive. *Construction − Health and Safety*. H.M.S.O., 1976.
3. Health and Safety Executive. *Construction − Health and Safety*. H.M.S.O., 1978.
4. Health and Safety Commission. *Health and Safety at Work Act 1974: The Act Outlined*. H.M.S.O., 1975.
5. *Health and Safety at Work Act 1974. Advice to Employers*. H.M.S.O., 1976.
6. Health and Safety Commission. *Safety Representatives and Safety Committees*. H.M.S.O., 1976.
7. Health and Safety Executive. *Forms and Publications*. H.M.S.O., 1977.
8. Health and Safety Executive. *Health and Safety at Work Series Booklets* − a series of booklets produced by the Health and Safety Executive, published by HMSO, of which the following are relevant to construction work generally and the use of construction plant:

   *No. 6A Safety in Construction Work: General Site Safety Practice.*

   *No. 6B Safety in Construction Work: Roofing.*

   *No. 6C Safety in Construction Work: Excavations.*

   *No. 6D Safety in Construction Work: Scaffolding.*

   *No. 6E Safety in Construction Work: Demolition.*
9. Health and Safety Executive. *Guidance Notes*. A series of guidance notes issued under five main headings: Medical (M.S.), Environmental Hygiene (E.H.), Chemical Safety (C.S.), Plant and Machinery (P.M.), and General (G.S.). The Guidance Notes are produced by the Health and Safety Executive and published by HMSO. The following are relevant to construction work generally and the

use of construction plant:
*G.S. 2 Metrication of Construction Safety Regulations.*
*G.S. 6 Avoidance of Danger from Overhead Electric Lines.*
*G.S. 7 Accidents to Children on Construction Sites.*
*G.S. 10 Roof Work: Prevention of Falls.*
*P.M. 3 Erection and Dismantling of Tower Cranes.*
*P.M. 9 Access to Tower Cranes.*
*P.M. 14 Safety in the use of Cartridge Operated Fixing Tools.*
*P.M. 15 Safety in the use of Timber Pallets.*
*P.M. 16 Eyebolts.*
*P.M. 17 Pneumatic Nailing and Stapling Tools.*
*P.M. 20 Cable-laid Slings and Grommets.*
*P.M. 21 Safety in the use of Woodworking Machines.*
*P.M. 22 Mounting of Abrasive Wheels.*
*E.H. 10 Asbestos.*
*M.S. 13 Asbestos.*

10. British Standards Institution. *Code of Practice: The Use of Safety Nets on Constructional Works, C.P. 93.* B.S.I., 1972.
11. British Standards Institution. *Code of Practice: Demolition, C.P. 94.* B.S.I., 1971.
12. British Standards Institution. *Code of Practice: Metal Scaffolding, C.P. 97, Parts 1-3.* B.S.I., 1972.
13. British Standards Institution. *Code of Practice: Safe Use of Cranes, C.P. 3010.* H.M.S.O., 1979.
14. Health and Safety Executive. *Management's Responsibilities in the Safe Operation of Mobile Cranes.* (A report on three crane accidents). H.M.S.O., 1980.
15. *Tower Crane Tester's Handbook.* Training Department, Richards and Wallington Industries Ltd., 1979.
16. *Tower Crane Practice.* Taylor Woodrow Ltd.
17. *Safe Site Code.* John Deere Ltd.

CHAPTER 12

# INSURANCE AND LICENSING LEGALITIES

## Insurance

Construction companies and plant hire companies require a variety of insurance policies and cover. The need for insurance cover could arise because (a) it may be required by law and therefore compulsory, (b) it may be required by a contractual arrangement entered into by the company and another party, and (c) it is sensible to minimise the company's risks although it may not be a requirement placed on the company either by law or by contract.

Examples of compulsory insurances are the insurance of vehicles as required by the Road Traffic Act 1972, the insurance against claims from employees as required by the Employers' Liability Act 1969, and the insurance against claims from the public as required by the Finance (No. 2) Act 1975.

Examples of insurances required by contractual agreements are the responsibilities of contractors under I.C.E. Conditions of Contract or the J.C.T. Standard Form of Building Contract and the insurance required by certain hiring agreements between plant hire companies and the hirer.

Insurance precautions, of course, can go beyond satisfying legal or contractual requirements. The Road Traffic Act only requires a specified minimum insurance cover but the owner of a vehicle may insure it comprehensively to reduce his risks and ensure adequate compensation in the event of loss or accidental damage. Insurance of buildings and contents are other examples. Some hire agreements between plant companies and contractors do not specify insurance but place the responsibility for loss or damage of the plant with the hirer. In such cases insurance is not a contractual requirement but is clearly a sensible precaution.

The broad classes of insurance that are available are: (a) liability insurance, (b) material damage insurance, (c) pecuniary insurance, and (d) benefit insurance.
(a) *Liability Insurances*, as far as contractors and plant companies are concerned, are:

  (i) Employers' liability;

 (ii) Public liability;

(iii) Motor insurance, third party;

(iv) Liability under contract, such as I.C.E. Conditions of Contract or J.C.T. Standard Form of Contract.

(b) *Material Damage Insurance* covers such items as:

  (i) Insurance of works which may be specified in the contract between the employer (i.e. the promoter of the works) and the contractor;

 (ii) Insurance of buildings and contents;

(iii) Insurance of plant and equipment;

(iv) Engineering insurance;

 (v) Motor insurance covering accidental damage.

(c) *Pecuniary Insurances* cover fidelity risks, credit risks and consequential loss.

(d) *Benefit Insurance* covers personal accident.

### Employers' liability insurance

Employers' liability insurance is required by the Employers' Liability (Compulsory Insurance) Act 1969 which became effective from 1972. This Act requires a company, the employer or master, to take an insurance policy to cover the employer's liability to his employees for bodily injury or disease arising out of and in the course of their employment.

Employers' liability insurance is in addition to the responsibilities placed on the employer by the Health and Safety at Work Act as described in Chapter 11. Two issues of this insurance that are relevant to the construction industry are those of labour only sub-contractors, and hired-in plant. Labour only sub-contractors present a problem of definition as to whether the labourers are, for insurance purposes, to be treated as employees. The custom has been to regard them as such for the purposes of employers' liability insurance and to have the insurance extended to cover this.

The situation with regard to hired-in plant with an operator is that whilst the owner of the plant, the hiring company, remains the operator's employer the contract of hire entered into between the owner and the hirer usually requires the hirer to accept liability for the operator (see Clause 8 of the Contractors Plant Association Conditions for Hiring Plant). Although the law requires the owner to protect his employee, the contract between the owner and the hirer gives the owner indemnity against claims by the operator which would normally be regarded as employer's liability. The custom has developed for the hirer to indemnify the owner, but if the hirer is not a company but a private individual excavating for his garage foundations a different view would prevail and the hirer would not be required to carry this responsibility.

## Public liability insurance

The Finance (No. 2) Act 1975 requires that payments to sub-contractors can be made without deduction of tax only if the sub-contractor has an exemption certificate from the Inland Revenue. One requirement in obtaining an exemption certificate is that the company must have an insurance policy covering public liability. This insurance is required to cover claims from the public for bodily injury or disease. No requirement exists to cover claims from the public with regard to property damage although companies may insure themselves against this also and usually do. Generally a public liability policy will cover claims from the public for bodily injury and disease and for property damage.

The situation regarding hired-in plant is similar to that of employers' liability, in that hire agreements between plant companies and contractors (usually based on the Contractors' Plant Association Conditions for Hiring Plant) contain a clause requiring the hirer to indemnify the owner against claims from the public for injury or damage to property. The common forms of contract found in the construction industry usually require the contractor to indemnify the employer (i.e. the promoter of the works) against claims from the public.

## Contractors' all risk policy (mainly material damage insurance)

A contractors' all risk policy is usually entered into jointly by the promoter of the construction work and the contractor and this policy provides the main protection for the works under construction. Usually the items protected against loss or damage in an 'all risks' policy are:

(i) the permanent and temporary construction works and all the materials connected with the works;
(ii) plant, equipment, tools and temporary buildings; and
(iii) employee's personal effects if not covered by other insurances.

The policy normally includes cover whilst materials or other items are in transit to and from the site. It is also possible to arrange inflation protection cover in respect of the additional cost of reconstruction after some mishap. The contractors' all risks policy can be extended to include consequential loss as well as the material damage aspects listed above. The consequential loss cover would protect the promoter of the construction work against loss of income such as rent from an incomplete building delayed by some mishap. The full value of construction plant would normally be insured within a contractors' all risk policy. The I.C.E. Conditions of Contract require the construction plant to be insured but the J.C.T. form of contract does not.

Hire agreements between plant hire companies and contractors usually require the hirer to indemnify the owner of the plant against loss or damage to the plant. The cover given in a contractors' all risk policy would normally include the full value of the plant and therefore protect the hirer against claims from the owner of the plant.

## Plant and equipment insurance (material damage insurance)

Contractors who own plant and plant hire companies will normally ensure that their plant and equipment is insured even though there may be no legal or contractual requirement. Insurance of plant can be arranged separately or can be arranged as extensions to other policies, mainly the contractors' all risk policy or an engineering policy, which is dealt with in the next section, or as part of a commercial vehicle policy if the plant is mechanically propelled.

A contractor's plant policy would be a material damage policy and would cover loss or damage while insured. The same cover could be obtained in a contractors' all risk policy which also includes the travelling of plant to and from the site. An engineering policy would normally be taken to protect against breakdown and as a means of acquiring an inspection service by a competent person (Chapter 10 also refers to this) but the policy may sometimes be extended to cover loss or damage. Mechanically propelled plant such as dumpers, excavators, graders, etc. may be insured within a contractor's commercial vehicle policy.

In hire agreements between plant hire companies (the owner) and contractors (the hirer) the responsibility for loss or damage of the hired plant normally rests with the hirer. The hirer may be responsible for lost revenue after the hire period has expired whilst the plant is being repaired or replaced. The hirer may not necessarily be required to insure the plant but if he does not do so he will be carrying the risk himself. The Contractors' Plant Association Conditions of Hiring Plant are an example whereby the hirer is required to make good to the owner all loss of or damage to the plant from whatever cause and in these circumstances the hirer would be well advised to insure against such claims from the owner. This insurance may be included under the policies described above.

## Engineering insurance (material damage insurance, breakdown and inspection)

An engineering insurance policy can be taken to cover breakdown and accidental damage risks to lifting machinery, breakdown risks to electrical and mechanical plant and the risk of explosion to boilers and pressure plant. Trucks, tractors and dumpers etc. could be included in an engineering policy but would more likely be included in a motor insurance policy.

If lifting machinery is taken as the main example of interest to the construction industry, the two main risks are mechanical and/or electrical breakdown and accidental damage. Insurance against mechanical or electrical breakdown would include the breaking or burning out of part of the plant, arising from a mechanical or electrical defect, causing the plant to stop and requiring immediate repair or replacement. Frost damage would also be covered but the main exclusion to such policies would be 'wear and tear'. Excavators can be insured under the same policies as cranes and clauses for accidental damage will cover damage to the plant from extraneous causes. The engineering policy can also include insurance against damage to property and to the goods being lifted.

The important feature of an engineering policy is that it includes an inspection service by a competent person. The insurance companies who specialise in engineering policies employ qualified engineers to undertake inspections. The inspection service can be acquired separately without an insurance policy and can be arranged to meet the requirements of the Health and Safety at Work Act (see Chapter 11). The competent person provided by the insurance company can certify that the inspections have taken place.

### Motor insurance (liability and material damage insurance)

The Road Traffic Act of 1972 requires certain minimum insurance for motor vehicles used on the road. A motor vehicle used on the roads must be insured to cover death or bodily injury arising out of the use of the vehicle. The liability is up to an unlimited amount and includes emergency treatment fees. The Act also requires that the policy holder must be issued with a certificate of insurance and that the driver involved in an accident must produce the certificate of insurance.

The motor insurances that are available extend the cover beyond the minimum required by the Road Traffic Act. The four main types are (i) comprehensive, (ii) third party, fire and theft, (iii) third party only and (iv) Road Traffic Act only.

The comprehensive policy provides the greatest cover and includes third party liability for death, bodily injury, emergency treatment fees and damage to property, including other vehicles. The comprehensive policy also provides cover for loss or damage to the insured's vehicle caused by accidental damage, fire or theft.

Third party, fire and theft policies cover the third party liability, as in comprehensive policies, and loss or damage to the insured's vehicle due to fire or theft. Accidental damage to the insured's vehicle, which is covered in a comprehensive policy, is excluded.

Third party only policies cover liabilities to third parties, as in comprehensive policies, but exclude loss or damage to the insured's own vehicle.

Road Traffic Act only policies meet the minimum requirements of the Road Traffic Act, which are third party liabilities for death or bodily injuries to third parties arising out of use of the vehicle on the road and fees for emergency treatment.

### Construction vehicles
Special vehicles or certain items of construction plant can be insured under a commercial motor vehicle policy. Such vehicles or plant items can be grouped as follows:

 (i) digging machines;
 (ii) site clearing and levelling plant;
(iii) mobile cranes;
(iv) mobile plant, e.g. compressors, welding and spraying plant;
 (v) dumpers and road rollers.

A goods carrying vehicle fitted with lifting equipment for the purposes of loading goods onto itself is treated as a goods carrying vehicle for insurance purposes. With respect to mobile cranes, the crane itself requires inspection services that are included in an engineering policy. An engineering policy would also provide for breakdown, accidental damage and third party liability, but excludes the liability protection required by the Road Traffic Act. Thus there is a need for both motor insurance and an engineering insurance on, for example, a mobile crane and there may be a risk of duplication if the insurance cover is not carefully arranged.

If the mobile crane is hired out then the motor insurance cover can be extended to include use while on hire. Dumpers can be included in a motor insurance policy and the cover extended to include use by a hirer. Mobile plant such as excavators and shovels can be insured as part of a motor insurance policy and can include damage to the insured's own plant. The cover can also be extended to the hirer. Protection against third party liabilities can be included, but the third party risk other than those arising under the Road Traffic Act may be covered better by a public liability policy.

Site clearing and levelling plant is grouped separately from mobile plant as this class of plant cannot excavate below the level of the wheel base. Third party risks to property in the ground, such as water, drainage and other services, are much reduced and therefore attract different premiums.

### Contingent liability

A motor contingent liability policy is a policy that protects the insured against liability to third parties resulting from the use of vehicles on behalf of the insured, over which the insured does not have immediate control.

As an example, suppose that a plant hire company believes that the hirer's insurance has been extended to indemnify the owner but that the policy, by oversight, has not been extended, or has lapsed. A contingent liability policy would indemnify the owner in these circumstances. Similarly, a hirer may believe that the owner's motor policy extends its protection to the hirer but if the owner's policy has lapsed, or is not extended to cover the particular circumstances, then the contingent liability policy could provide protection. This policy is important because, under hire agreements based on the Contractors' Plant Association Conditions, it is the *hirer* who is responsible for third party liabilities such as injury or property damage caused by the plant. Thus the *hirer* would bear the costs of such claims if the hire company's policy failed to operate.

### Summary of insurance and plant

This review of insurance policies has described the main areas of insurance cover required by the owners and operators of construction plant. It has also described how insurance can be arranged through a variety of different policies, such as employers' liability insurance, public liability insurance, contractors' all risk insurance, engineering insurance and motor insurance. The dangers to avoid in arranging insurance cover are duplication, which increases costs, and gaps in the cover which leave the potential liability or loss uninsured. It is unlikely that such duplication or gaps will arise when plant is owned and used by the same company because all insurances will probably be arranged with the same company or broker and the insurance needs of the company can be arranged in a co-ordinated manner. The main dangers of duplication and gaps arise when plant is hired out or hired in and it is therefore necessary to check all the insurance arrangements in these circumstances.

All companies require employers' liability insurance and most require public liability insurance. A mobile crane would require motor insurance and engineering insurance to cover breakdowns and inspections. A crane used on site would most likely be covered in part by the contractors' all risks policy but would also require engineering insurance to cover breakdowns and to acquire the inspection service. A field excavator used within a site would most likely be covered within a contractors' all risks policy. Thus, the same policy could cover both an excavator owned by the contractor and an excavator which he hired in.

In general, hire agreements place the responsibility for loss and damage to plant and the liabilities with the hirer.

## Licensing

The use of public roads within the United Kingdom is controlled by extensive legislation broadly called the Road Transport Laws which control the construction and use of vehicles on the public roads. Within this legislation is a system of licensing which controls the use of vehicles and their drivers on the public roads and collects taxes. The three main licensing systems of interest to the construction industry are as follows:

(i) *Vehicle excise licensing* which requires a licence, for which duty is payable, to be in force for all vehicles used on the public roads, unless exempted;
(ii) *Driver's licensing* which requires every driver of a motor vehicle to hold a driving licence. A prescribed driving test is taken before a driving licence is issued;
(iii) *Operator's licensing*, a system of goods vehicle licensing which exercises control over operators to ensure the proper use and road worthiness of the vehicles and observance of the drivers' hours law.

In addition to these three licensing systems there is *public service vehicle licensing* which controls vehicles, operators and drivers of passenger carrying vehicles, such as buses and taxis.

The laws relating to road transport which embody the above licensing systems are mainly the following:

Road Traffic Act 1960, 1972 and 1974;
Transport Act 1962, 1968, 1978 and 1980;

Road Traffic Act (Drivers Ages and Hours of Work) 1976;
European Communities Act 1972;
International Road Haulage Permit Act 1975;
Highway Act 1959;
Vehicle and Driving Licenses Act 1969;
Vehicles (Excise) Act 1971;
Finance Act 1971.

From these and other Acts are derived many regulations, general orders and E.E.C. directives, such as the Motor Vehicles (Construction and Use) Regulations, and the Motor Vehicles (Authorisation of Special Types) General Order No. 1198, 1979.

The road transport laws also require all road users to have a minimum insurance as described earlier. These laws also cover all aspects of road use such as lighting of vehicles, speed limits, weight limits, securing loads, crane hooks etc., and the implications of the Weights and Measures Act 1963 with respect to carrying sand, ballast, ready mix concrete, and the need for a conveyance note. Further explanation of these can be obtained from the Acts listed above and the references given.

### Vehicle excise licensing

*General requirements*

A person who uses or keeps on a public road any mechanically propelled vehicle must have an excise licence in force, unless he is exempted. Excise licences are issued from local vehicle licensing offices and can also be renewed from post offices. A vehicle excise licence can be taken out for six months or twelve months. Applications for a licence or its renewal must be accompanied by a certificate of insurance and a test certificate if the vehicle is subject to a test procedure.

The annual duty for vehicles varies according to the class of vehicle as defined in the Vehicle (Excise) Act 1971. Among the classes defined are:

- Tractors for the purposes of agricultural and forestry work;
- Vehicles designed, constructed and used for trench digging or any kind of excavating or shovelling work, used on the public road for that purpose only or for proceeding to and from such but not carrying any load;
- Mobile cranes used on the public road only either as cranes in connection with work being carried out on a site in the immediate vicinity or for the purposes of proceeding to and from a place where they are to be used as cranes, but not carrying any load;
- Works trucks, being goods vehicles designed for use in private premises and used on public roads for carrying goods between two premises or between premises and a vehicle, or in connection with road works;
- Haulage vehicles of different weight classes of up to 2 tons, 2 to 4 tons, 4 to 6 tons, 6 to 7¼ tons, 7¼ to 8 tons, over 8 tons plus additional duty for each ton or part of a ton the additional duty rate increases over 10 tons;

- Goods vehicles, classified into:
   (i) Agricultural vehicles of different unladen weight classes;
   (ii) Goods vehicles registered in the name of travelling showmen, classified into different unladen weight classes;
   (iii) Tower wagons, classified into different unladen weight classes;
   (iv) Goods vehicles except those in items (i), (ii) and (iii) again classified into different unladen weight classes;
   (v) Trailers to goods vehicles, which attract additional duty, and this is further subdivided into trailers of all weights used by travelling showmen and trailers to other goods vehicles where the duty varies according to the different weight classes.

The unladen weight classes for goods vehicles for the purposes of vehicle excise licence duty is up to 12 cwt, 12 cwt to 16 cwt, 16 cwt to 1 ton, 1 ton to 3 tons, 3 tons to 5 tons, 4 tons to 6 tons, 6 tons to 9 tons and exceeding 9 tons. An articulated vehicle is treated as one vehicle, not a vehicle drawing a trailer.

## Exemptions
Certain vehicles are exempt from paying duty under the Vehicles (Excise) Act 1971. Exemptions of particular interest to the construction industry include:

- Road construction vehicles used on a road to carry built-in road construction machinery;
- A vehicle which is to be used exclusively on roads not repairable at the public expense but details of the vehicle must be declared to the licensing authority;
- Subject to approval, no duty is payable on a vehicle which uses public roads only for passing from land in the owner's occupation to other land in his occupation for distances not exceeding 6 miles in any week. This is allowed by section 7 (1) of the Vehicle (Excise) Act 1971.

## Mobile plant
Vehicles carrying no load other than built-in plant or machinery are taxed as goods vehicles. The weight of the built-in plant or machinery is deducted from the total weight in calculating the unladen weight of the vehicle for the purposes of assessing the duty payable.

## Driver licensing

No person may drive nor permit another person to drive a motor vehicle on a road unless that person holds a driving licence granted under the conditions of the Road Traffic Act 1972.

The minimum age for drivers' licences are 16 to 21 depending on the class of vehicle. In the U.K. the minimum age is 17 for an agricultural tractor, for a medium-sized goods vehicle the minimum age is 18 and for larger vehicles it is 21. The minimum age for a goods vehicle not exceeding 7.5 metric tonnes is 18 within the

E.E.C. and 21 for heavier vehicles although this can be reduced for drivers who have attended goods vehicle training courses and hold certificates of competence. The driver must pass a driving test conducted by examiners appointed by the Licensing Authority to obtain a driving licence. Schedule 4 of the Road Traffic Act 1972 sets out the offences that can lead to the driver's licence being endorsed or disqualified.

The classes of vehicle for which licences can be obtained are given in Table 12.1.

**Table 12.1** Groups of motor vehicles for driving tests

| Group | Class of vehicle in group | Additional groups covered |
|-------|---------------------------|---------------------------|
| A | A vehicle without automatic transmission of any class not included in any other group | B, C, E, F, K and L |
| B | A vehicle with automatic transmission of any class not included in any other group | E, F, K and L |
| C | Motor tricycle weighing not more than 410 kg unladen, but excluding any vehicle included in group E, J, K or L | E, K and L |
| D | Motor bicycle (with or without sidecar) but excluding any vehicle included in group E, K or L | C, E and motor cycles in group L |
| E | Moped | — |
| F | Agricultural tractor, but excluding any vehicle included in group H | K |
| G | Road roller | — |
| H | Track laying vehicle steered by its tracks | — |
| J | Invalid carriage | — |
| K | Mowing machine or vehicle controlled by a pedestrian | — |
| L | Vehicle propelled by electrical power, but excluding any vehicle included in group E, J or K | K |
| M | Trolley vehicle | — |
| N | Vehicle exempt from duty under section 7 (1) of the Vehicles (Excise) Act 1971 | — |

*Heavy goods vehicles*

A person must not drive nor permit another person to drive a vehicle classed as a heavy goods vehicle (H.G.V.) unless the driver holds an H.G.V. licence authorising him to drive vehicles of that class. A heavy goods vehicle is defined as a large goods vehicle which is constructed or adapted to carry goods, the permissible maximum weight of which exceeds 7.5 tonnes, or an articulated goods vehicle. The maximum weight of the goods vehicle or trailer usually will be stated as the maximum gross weight on the Department of Environment plate, if fitted, or the manufacturer's plate.

Drivers of certain classes or types of vehicle are exempted from requiring an H.G.V. licence. Among the exemptions that are relevant to the construction industry are:

- Track laying vehicles;
- Road rollers;
- Road construction vehicles used or kept on the road solely for the conveyance of built-in road construction machinery;
- Engineering plant;
- Works trucks;
- Industrial tractors of less than 3.5 tons;
- Digging machines.

To obtain an H.G.V. licence a driver must pass a test conducted by a Department of the Environment examiner. The classes of vehicle for which H.G.V. licences can be obtained are given in Table 12.2.

### Operators' licensing

*General requirements*
The Operators' Licensing system is a system of goods vehicle licensing introduced by the Transport Act 1968 and modified to comply with the E.E.C. Directive 74/561. All goods vehicles exceeding 3.5 tonnes gross plated weight need to be covered by an operator's licence. Exemptions from an operator's licence are as follows:

1. Agricultural machinery and trailers.
2. Dual purpose vehicles and trailers.
3. Vehicles and their trailers using the road for less than 6 miles per week whilst moving between private premises.
4. Public service vehicles and their trailers.
5. Hackney carriages.
6. Hearses.
7. Police vehicles.
8. Fire engines.
9. Ambulances.
10. Fire fighting and rescue vehicles used in mines and quarries.
11. Uncompleted vehicles on test or trial.
12. Vehicles with limited trade plates.
13. Vehicles hired for military purposes.
14. Visiting forces vehicles.
15. Road rollers and road maintenance trailers including water carts.
16. RNLI and coastguard vehicles.

**Table 12.2**    Classes of heavy goods vehicles

| Class | Definition | Additional classes |
|---|---|---|
| Class 1 | An articulated vehicle combination not with automatic transmission, other than a vehicle combination coming within class 4 | Classes 1A, 2, 2A, 3, 3A, 4 and 4A |
| Class 1A | An articulated vehicle combination with automatic transmission, other than a vehicle combination coming within class 4A | Classes 2A, 3A and 4A |
| Class 2 | A heavy goods vehicle not with automatic transmission, other than an articulated vehicle combination, designed and constructed to have more than four wheels in contact with the road surface | Classes 2A, 3 and 3A |
| Class 2A | A heavy goods vehicle with automatic transmission, other than an articulated vehicle combination, designed and constructed to have more than four wheels in contact with the road surface | Class 3A |
| Class 3 | A heavy goods vehicle not with automatic transmission, other than an articulated vehicle combination, designed and constructed to have not more than four wheels in contact with the road surface | Class 3A |
| Class 3A | A heavy goods vehicle with automatic transmission, other than an articulated vehicle combination, designed and constructed to have not more than four wheels in contact with the road surface | |
| Class 4 | An articulated vehicle combination not with automatic transmission, the tractive unit of which does not exceed 2 tons unladen weight | Class 4A |
| Class 4A | An articulated vehicle combination with automatic transmission, the tractive unit of which does not exceed 2 tons unladen weight | |

Note: 'Vehicle with automatic transmission' means a vehicle in which the driver is not provided with any means whereby he may, independently of the use of the accelerator or the brake, vary gradually the proportion of the power being produced by the engine which is transmitted to the road wheels of the vehicle. For the purpose of the above definitions, where a vehicle is fitted with two wheels in line transversely and the distance between the centres of their respective areas of contact with the road is less than 18 inches they shall be regarded as only one wheel.

17. Vehicles used solely on aerodromes.
18. Local authority vehicles of special types.
19. Vehicles with special fixed equipment.
20. Electric vehicles.
21. Travelling showmen's vehicles and trailers.
22. Pre-1979 vehicles not over 1525 kg unladen, plated between 3.5 tonne and 3½ tons.

Vehicles which must be used under an operator's licence include all goods vehicles belonging to the licence holder or in his possession by virtue of a hire purchase agreement, hire or loan i.e. all vehicles used by the licence holder, not simply owned by him. An operator's licence is required for each operating centre, i.e. yard or base for vehicles, in different Traffic Areas. Only one licence is required per Traffic Area, irrespective of the number of operating centres in the Traffic Area.

Application for an Operator's Licence is made to the local Traffic Area Office. Application may be made for additional vehicles not yet acquired and, if authorised, this simplifies the procedures of adding additional vehicles to the operator's fleet. The Licensing Authority, in deciding whether to grant a licence, will consider:

1. Whether the operator is a fit person to hold a licence, bearing in mind past convictions relating to the roadworthiness of the operator's vehicles;
2. Facilities for satisfactory maintenance;
3. Arrangements for ensuring that the law relating to drivers' hours and records will be complied with;
4. Arrangements for checking that vehicles are not overloaded;
5. The suitability of the proposed operating centre;
6. The financial resources for the proper operation of the business;
7. The professional competence of the operator or his manager.

In deciding whether to grant a licence the Licensing Authority may hold a public enquiry or take objections from a specified group of interested parties including the police, the local authorities, certain trade associations and certain trade unions. A licence would normally be granted for five years, and additional vehicles may be applied for at the time of licence application or individually when acquired. Arrangements also exist for permanent one-for-one substitution of vehicles.

The Licensing Authority has disciplinary powers to curtail or revoke the licence if a material change in circumstances occurs, or for certain offences relating to roadworthiness of vehicles, drivers' hours and records, or plating and testing.

An annual fee is charged for each vehicle specified on the licence and a separate identity disc is issued for each vehicle on payment of the fee. The disc must be displayed on the windscreen of the vehicle.

### Maintenance

An applicant for an Operator's Licence must satisfy the Licensing Authority that the maintenance facilities are such that the vehicles are kept in a safe and roadworthy condition at all times. Licensing Authorities expect more than the minimum routine maintenance specified by the manufacturers and more than the daily running checks made by drivers: they look for a convincing system of inspection and preventative maintenance. The Department of Transport Goods Vehicle Tester's Manual lists the inspection items for roadworthiness. Readers are advised to refer to this but a satisfactory preventative maintenance inspection system requires:

- Competent staff capable of recognising the significance of defects;
- A system of recording inspections, detailing what was inspected and the action taken, such as the remedial work done and who undertook the remedial work;
- Adequate facilities for such inspections including means of under-vehicle inspection;
- A schedule of inspections whose frequency is chosen to match the work load and work type of the vehicles;
- A drivers' reporting system whereby the driver can report vehicle defects.

The Licensing Authority requires that maintenance reports are kept for a minimum of 15 months. Even if operators contract out inspections and maintenance to service companies they remain the users of the vehicle and are held responsible to the Licensing Authority for the condition of their vehicles.

### Drivers' hours

The rules defining the permitted driving and working hours of drivers of goods vehicles are divided into four parts:

(i) National rules,
(ii) International rules,
(iii) Domestic rules,
(iv) Mixed-driving rules.

The main exemptions from these rules are drivers whose driving is done completely off the public roads.

*National rules* apply to drivers of laden or unladen goods vehicles greater than 3.5 tonnes maximum weight on journeys within Great Britain. EEC Regulation 543/69 and the Transport Act of 1968 apply to these drivers.

*International rules* apply to drivers of laden or unladen goods vehicles greater than 3.5 tonnes leaving or entering Great Britain. The EEC regulation applies but is sometimes replaced by AETR, an international agreement which includes EEC states together with Austria, Czechoslovakia, German Democratic Republic, Norway, Portugal, Spain, Sweden, Yugoslavia and the Soviet Union.

*Domestic rules* apply to vehicles exempted from national and international rules which are mainly goods vehicles up to 3.5 tonnes maximum weight to which the Transport Act of 1968 applies.

*Mixed-driving rules* apply to drivers who work under both national and domestic rules. When driving under national conditions the national rules apply, and when driving under domestic conditions the mixed driving rules apply. When the hours are added together the mixed driving rules must not be exceeded.

Table 12.3 summarises the basic limits of each of the four sets of rules. However, most limits are qualified in some way and these qualifications are detailed in reference 13.

**Table 12.3**   Basic limits to drivers' working and driving hours

| | Hours | | | |
|---|---|---|---|---|
| Limit | National rules | International rules | Domestic rules | Mixed-driving rules |
| Daily driving | 8 | 8 | 10 | 10 |
| Weekly driving | 48 | 48 | | |
| Fortnightly driving | 92 | 92 | | |
| Continuous driving | 4 | 4 | | 4 |
| Weekly rest | 29 | 29 | 24 | 29 |
| Daily rest | 11 | 11 | 11 | 11 |
| Daily duty | 11 | | 11 | 11 |
| Daily spreadover | 12½ | | 12½ | 12½ |
| Weekly duty | 60 | | 60 | 60 |
| Continuous duty | 5½ | | 5½ | 5½ |
| Breaks | ½ | ½ | ½ | ½ |

National and international rules allow the daily driving limit to be increased to 9 hours twice a week. This extension is not allowed for drivers of vehicles with more than one trailer or exceeding 20 tonnes. For such vehicles second drivers and longer breaks may apply.

### Drivers' records
E.E.C. Regulation 1463/70 requires a tachograph to be fitted and used for goods vehicles on international journeys. For vehicles on national transport operations within the U.K. various dates are prescribed for the fitting and using of a tachograph. At the time of writing the latest of these dates was December 31st 1981, by which time the use of a tachograph in goods vehicles will be compulsory. The driver is responsible for returning the tachograph record sheets to his employer within 21 days of its completion.

When tachographs are used the keeping of a record book is not required. If a tachograph is not in use a driver must be issued with a record book for the purpose of recording the daily and weekly working records which are returned to the employer.

### Plating and testing
Heavy goods vehicles require a first examination at a Department of Environment goods vehicle testing station not more than 12 months after first being registered.

The first examination includes assessing the vehicle's axle and gross weights. These weights are recorded on a plate which must be prominently displayed in the cab of the vehicle: hence these weights are known as the 'plated weights'. The assessment of the weights is followed by a test of roadworthiness and, if satisfactory, the vehicle is issued with a plating certificate and a roadworthiness test certificate. The roadworthiness test must be repeated every 12 months.

Light goods vehicles are subject to a first roadworthiness test after 3 years and every 12 months thereafter.

### Construction and use of vehicles

The law governing the construction and use of vehicles on the road is the Motor Vehicles (Construction and Use) Regulations 1978. If some vehicles do not conform to these regulations its use can be authorised under the Motor Vehicles (Authorisation of Special Types) General Order 1979. This General Order is important to the construction industry in that it covers the movement of abnormal indivisible loads, wide loads, and engineering plant, such as mobile cranes and outsized dumpers.

### Reading list

1. Eaglestone, F.N. *Insurance for the Construction Industry*. George Godwin, 1979.
2. Insurance Committee of the National Federation of Building Trades Employers. *Contractors' Insurance Compendium*. N.F.B.T.E., 1972.
3. Abrahamson, Max W. *Engineering Law and the I.C.E. Contracts*. 4th Edition. Applied Science Publishers, 1979.
4. Uff, J. *Construction Law: An outline of the law and practice in relation to the construction industry*. Sweet and Maxwell, 1978.
5. Joint Contracts Tribunal. *JCT Guide to the Standard Form of Building Contract*. 1980 Edition. J.C.T., 1980.
6. Hibbitt, A.J. Insurances for Hirers of Plant. *Building Trades Journal*, 23 March, 1973.
7. Vann, J.C. Insurance – Why run the risk? *Contract Journal*, 24 January 1974.
8. Duckworth, J. (Ed). *Kitchin's Road Transport Law*. Butterworths, 1981.
9. Department of Transport. *A Guide to Operators' Licensing*. 4th Edition. HMSO, 1977.
10. *Heavy Goods Vehicle Driver Licensing: Notes for Drivers*. Available from local Traffic Area Officers, June 1979.
11. Department of Transport. *Goods Vehicles Testers' Manual*. HMSO, 1976.
12. Department of Transport. *Vehicle Testing: A Guide to the Operation of the M.O.T. Test*. HMSO, 1976.
13. Department of Transport. *Vehicle Testing: The M.O.T. Tester's Manual*. HMSO, 1976.

14. Department of Transport. *Guide to Goods Vehicle Drivers' Hours.* HMSO, 1979.

15. Department of Transport. *A Consolidated Version of Regulation (E.E.C.) No. 543/69 on Road Transport Drivers' Hours and Records.* HMSO, 1978.

16. Department of Transport. *Tachographs: E.E.C. Legislation on the Introduction of Recording Equipment in Road Transport. A consolidated version of Regulations (E.E.C.) Nos 1463/70, 1787/73 and 2828/77.* HMSO, 1980.

17. Department of Transport. *Tachographs: A question and answer guide.* HMSO, 1980.

**Section Four**

# FINANCIAL AND BUDGETARY CONTROL

# CHAPTER 13

## BUDGETARY CONTROL AND COSTING

### Introduction

A budget acts as a standard of measure against which actual performance may be compared. The Institute of Cost and Management Accountants defines budgetary control as 'the establishment of budgets, relating the responsibility of executives to the requirements of a policy and the continuous comparison of actual with budgeted results, either to secure by individual action the objective of that policy, or to provide a basis for its revision'. Budgetary control therefore involves:

- Setting targets
- Monitoring progress
- Taking corrective action when necessary.

Within a system of budgetary control, budgets are established to relate the financial requirements for the component parts of the firm over the forthcoming period of twelve months to the overall policy of the company. Budgets may be forward estimates of costs or revenues and as such are usually derived from records of past performance adjusted for future expectations.

### Preparation of budgets

The budgetary system comprises many individual budgets which are ultimately integrated into a master budget. The master budget (Table 13.4) is similar in form to a profit and loss account but unlike the latter it is based on forward estimates of costs and revenues and is therefore only a forecast of the anticipated profit to be earned. From such an estimate other factors related to future expectations may be projected, such as the rate of return on capital employed, dividends to shareholders, capital to be retained in the business for reinvestment in assets and similar items related to profitability.

At the start of any attempt to prepare budgets for business activity during the coming year it is necessary to prepare a budget for the investments to be made in plant and equipment, since it is through these assets that a plant company's revenues and costs are generated. Subsequently a sales and an operating budget may be synthesised and the cash flow requirements determined. By a gradual process budgets may be adjusted to keep within the constraints on financial resources available to the company, to culminate finally in the Master Budget as shown in Figure 13.1.

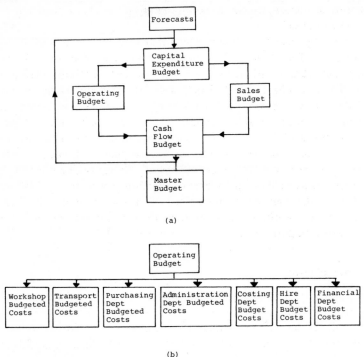

(a)

(b)

**Fig. 13.1**   Budgetary control procedure.

### Types of budget

The *capital investment* budget is determined by the availability of capital to the company and is thus a schedule of available loan capital, equity, leasing and retained profits. These sources of funds are treated more fully in Chapter 15, and the preparation of such a budget is covered in detail in Chapters 5 and 6.

The *cash flow* budget shows the short term cash available period by period and is broadly determined by subtracting costs from revenues after taking into account payment delays. The preparation of a cash flow budget is described in detail in Chapter 14.

The *sales budget* for a plant hire firm is simply the forecast of revenues from plant hire. This will be made up of the expected income from the hire of individual plant items, which may fluctuate on a seasonal basis. Consequently the budget should be prepared showing the anticipated annual and weekly incomes.

The *operating budget* is prepared from estimated costs of the planned requirements for materials such as fuel, lubricants, spare parts; staff and labour; equipment such as small tools, and depreciation of workshop equipment; and the business facilities, rent, rates, electricity, etc.

The difference in value between the sales and operating budgets is the anticipated profit before deduction of depreciation of the firm's assets of plant and buildings etc. for the year ahead.

The operating budget is subsequently subdivided into separate functions (see Figure 13.1(b)). These will include budgets for departments such as transport, workshop and administration. In the larger concerns the latter may be broken down further into hiring, sales, costing, accounts, and purchasing. By providing each department with a separate financial budget, a target is available against which subsequent performance may be monitored. Examples of the form of the annual budgets for the workshop, transport and administration functions are shown in Tables 13.1–13.3. It can be seen that the budgets consist of cost forecasts of the requirements for materials, labour and expenses. A coding system is used to allocate the resources to particular departments or functions concerned and like items are collected under the same alpha-numeric code. It is usual to present both an annual budget and a weekly budget, as short term fluctuations may be the more usual pattern of expected performance.

## Classification of costs

For the preparation and monitoring of budgets, costs are collected and classified into the major functions hiring, purchasing, workshop, transport, costing, administration/personnel, accounting. Within these functions the costs may be further collected into cost centres. For example, each item of plant maintained by the workshop may be given a code number which may represent the cost centre of one or more similar items. The costs recorded for each cost function or centre may be subdivided into elements such as materials, labour and expenses:

(i) Material cost: consumables and spares;
(ii) Labour cost: wages and salaries of the employees;
(iii) Expenses: depreciation of plant and equipment, repairs, administration, services provided, water and electricity.

The costs of materials, labour and expenses which can be clearly allocated to a cost centre are called direct costs, and usually vary with the volume of production. Indirect costs are those materials, labour and expenses which cannot be directly identified to the cost centre, but which provide some function or service, such as a computer or the rent of the firm's offices and works. Indirect costs are thus apportioned between the cost centres, and are usually referred to as overhead costs.

Indirect costs are mostly fixed costs such as staff salaries, rent and rates, insurances, office equipment, maintenance tools and machines, which remain constant irrespective of the volume of work done. A direct or variable overhead is one which varies in cost with the volume of production, such as electricity.

**Table 13.1**  Workshop budget

| Code (W) | Item | Annual £ | Week £ |
|---|---|---|---|
| Direct repair material and stock of spares | | | |
| 10.0 | Crawler cranes | 6 000 | 120 |
| 20.0 | Tower cranes | 8 000 | 160 |
| 30.0 | Trucks | 4 000 | 80 |
| 40.0 | Bulldozers | 5 000 | 100 |
| 50.0 | Loaders | 7 000 | 140 |
| 60.0 | Excavators | 10 000 | 200 |
| Cost | | 40 000 | 800 |
| Direct labour costs | | | |
| 10.1 | Crawler cranes | 7 000 | 140 |
| 20.1 | Tower cranes | 7 000 | 140 |
| 30.1 | Trucks | 5 000 | 100 |
| 40.1 | Bulldozers | 5 000 | 100 |
| 50.1 | Loaders | 8 000 | 160 |
| 60.1 | Excavators | 8 000 | 160 |
| Cost | | 40 000 | 800 |
| Indirect costs | | | |
| 90.1 | Storeman | 6 000 | 120 |
| 90.2 | Staff salaries | 8 000 | 160 |
| 90.3 | Rent | 3 000 | 60 |
| 90.4 | Rates | 2 000 | 40 |
| 90.5 | Electricity | 500 | 10 |
| 90.6 | Depreciation of tools and equipment | 500 | 10 |
| Cost | | 20 000 | 400 |
| Total cost | | 100 000 | 2 000 |

*Note*: In practice the indirect costs may be separated into variable and fixed costs.

**Costing**

While budgets are prepared from predetermined costs, because of short term changes in company performance it is essential that the actual costs incurred are continuously monitored and compared with budgeted costs in order that changes may be implemented. The difference between the actual and predetermined cost is called a variance. A costing system should be updated regularly on a weekly basis and the variances calculated for each function, department or cost centre. The procedure may also include analysis of the variances incurred by the individual items of plant in the fleet.

**Table 13.2**    Transport budget

| Code (T) | Item | Annual £ | Week £ |
|---|---|---|---|
| Direct materials costs | | | |
| 100.0 | Vans | 4 000 | 80 |
| 110.0 | 8-ton lorries | 5 000 | 100 |
| 120.0 | 16-ton lorries | 5 000 | 100 |
| 130.0 | 32-ton lorries | 3 000 | 60 |
| 140.0 | Cars | 3 000 | 60 |
| Cost | | 20 000 | 400 |
| Direct labour costs | | | |
| 100.1 | Vans | 3 000 | 60 |
| 110.1 | 8-ton lorries | 6 000 | 120 |
| 120.1 | 16-ton lorries | 5 000 | 100 |
| 130.1 | 32-ton lorries | 4 000 | 80 |
| 140.1 | Cars | 2 000 | 40 |
| Cost | | 20 000 | 400 |
| Indirect costs | | | |
| 190.1 | Staff salaries | 11 000 | 200 |
| 190.2 | Electricity | 500 | 10 |
| 190.3 | Rates | 1 000 | 20 |
| 190.4 | Rent | 1 000 | 20 |
| 190.5 | Vehicle depreciation | 2 000 | 40 |
| 190.6 | Tools & equipment | 100 | 2 |
| 190.7 | Telephone, etc. | 400 | 8 |
| Cost | | 15 000 | 300 |
| Total cost | | 55 000 | 1 100 |

A note of caution with regard to the budgets, particularly departmental budgets, is advised. It is useful to compare the actual result with the value for the same month or week of the previous year. Astute managers can be adept at 'hiding' behind a 'stuffed' budget.

**Table 13.3** Administration budget

| Code (A) | Item | Annual £ | Week £ |
|---|---|---|---|
| Direct employment costs | | | |
| 300.0 | Staff salaries | 9 500 | 190 |
| Direct material costs | | | |
| 310.0 | Stationery | 200 | 4 |
| Direct expenses | | | |
| 320.0 | Photocopying | 100 | 2 |
| Indirect costs | | | |
| 330.1 | Telephone | 1 000 | 20 |
| 330.2 | Postage | 700 | 14 |
| 330.3 | Electricity | 1 000 | 20 |
| 340.1 | Rates | 500 | 10 |
| 340.2 | Rent | 1 000 | 20 |
| 340.3 | Office equipment | 400 | 8 |
| 340.4 | Insurances | 600 | 12 |
| Total cost | | 15 000 | 300 |

**Table 13.4** Master budget

| Code | Item | Annual £ | Week £ |
|---|---|---|---|
| Budgeted sales | | | |
| (R) | Plant hire | 400 000 | 8 000 |
| Total budgeted sales | | 400 000 | 8 000 |
| Budgeted costs | | | |
| (W) | Workshop Dept costs | 100 000 | 2 000 |
| (T) | Transport Dept costs | 55 000 | 1 100 |
| (H) | Hire Dept costs | 20 000 | 400 |
| (C) | Costing Dept costs | 25 000 | 500 |
| (A) | Administration Dept costs | 15 000 | 300 |
| (B) | Buying Dept costs | 25 000 | 500 |
| (F) | Accounts Dept costs | 20 000 | 400 |
| Total budgeted costs | | 260 000 | 5 200 |
| Budgeted trading profit (Sales minus costs) | | 140 000 | 2 800 |
| Budgeted depreciation on plant and premises | | 100 000 | 2 000 |
| Budgeted net profit before interest and tax | | 40 000 | 800 |

A budget may be 'stuffed' due to changed circumstances, e.g. reduction in the assumed rate of inflation, manipulation of the figures, etc. Managers' performance should therefore be measured against both the budget and previous year results.

### Control of the workshop budget

*Example*

The annual budget for a plant workshop is £100 000 (see Table 13.1). This figure is based upon the size of the plant fleet and the estimated hours that the fleet will be operated during the year.

The budgeted direct costs of the department consist of the purchase of consumable materials and spare parts, labour such as fitters, mechanics, etc. and these total £80 000. Budgeted indirect costs include staff salaries, rent, rates, insurances, general administration charges, depreciation of workshop equipment and power. These amount to £20 000 and are a fixed charge.

At the end of the year the firm's business activity had been lower than expected and the hours operated by the plant fleet were 10% fewer than initial estimates. The actual direct costs of the workshop over this period were £70 000 and the actual cost of overheads was £21 000. The position was:

|  | Planned budgeted costs for this date (£) | Adjusted budgeted costs of work done (£) | Actual cost (£) | Variance (£) |
|---|---|---|---|---|
| Direct costs | 80 000 | 72 000 | 70 000 | +2 000 |
| Overheads | 20 000 | 20 000 | 21 000 | −1 000 |
| Total | 100 000 | 92 000 | 91 000 | +1 000 |

Thus, although the level of activity anticipated at the beginning had not been realised, the works department had managed to maintain a favourable variance on direct costs. In this example only overheads produced an unfavourable variance and a more detailed analysis of costs should reveal the reasons, such as excess secretarial staff. However because the volume of business had not reached the level anticipated, the *budgeted profit* for the company also would not be fully recovered and the costs of the fixed overhead would have to be met from the reduced profits. For a plant hire company such consequences could be particularly severe as much of the business costs are generated as fixed overheads. For a comprehensive review of performance, therefore, the sales variance should be included in the analysis.

## Sales variance

*Example*
The budgeted hire revenue for a plant division over the forthcoming twelve months is £400 000. Profit and overheads (including depreciation) are set at 5% each respectively of revenue. However, the actual revenue was only £300 000. The variances recorded for direct and indirect costs (overheads) were respectively +£3 000 and +£1 000. In addition, several items were written off prematurely, leading to a negative variance on plant depreciation of £1 000.

*Analysis of variance*

| | |
|---|---|
| Sales variance | = −£10 000 (i.e. 10% of £400 000 − £300 000) |
| Direct costs variance | = +£3 000 |
| Indirect costs variance | = +£1 000 |
| Depreciation variance | = −£1 000 |
| Actual shortfall on profits | £7 000 (i.e. £13 000 profit as compared to £20 000 budgeted profit) |

It can be seen that the profit and overhead is under-recovered by £10 000 and only the collective economies made by the various departments reduced the magnitude of the shortfall to £7 000.

## Other useful management information

*Plant utilisation reports*
The sales variance may also be calculated for each group or item of plant to provide management with a regular update of the effects of changes in the levels of plant utilisation and hire rates. The utilisation report is produced monthly and is divided into two sections representing plant for hire, and non-operated plant which contributes to the cost of sales. Each division is subdivided into individual cost centres or like machines, e.g. scrapers, bulldozers, crawler cranes etc., and the utilisation and price variance *on sales* for each plant item in a cost centre is produced in the final report as shown below.

*Analysis of variance*

(a) *Utilisation variance* is the financial effect of using the plant either more or less than those hours budgeted.
Thus:
Utilisation variance = (actual hours × budgeted hire rate) − (budgeted hours × budgeted hire rate)

(b) *Price variance* is the financial effect of charging more or less than the budgeted hire rate.
Thus:

Price variance = (actual hours X actual hire rate) − (actual hours X budgeted hire rate)

The sum of the utilisation and price variances multiplied by the profit and overhead margin is the true sales variance on that item.

## Example

During the month an item of plant was hired out for 280 hours at a hire rate of £2.40 per hour. The budget anticipated only 200 hours of work at a hire rate of £2.50 per hour. Calculate the utilisation and price variances. The profit (and overhead) is set at 10% of the hire rate.

1. Utilisation variance on sales = $(280 \times 2.5) - (200 \times 2.5) = 80 \times 2.5 = +£200$
$$\text{(favourable)}$$

2. Price variance on sales = $(280 \times 2.4) - (280 \times 2.5) = 280 \times -0.1 = -£28$
$$\text{(unfavourable)}$$

Sales variance = (actual revenue − budgeted revenue) X profit and overhead margin = $(280 \times 2.4 - 200 \times 2.5) \times 0.1 = +£17.2$

The effect of operating the plant 80 hours more than planned increased the revenue by £200, reduced to £17.2 because the hire rate was less favourable than budgeted. The variances should be cumulatively totalled for each month to present a comprehensive record, which together with records collected of the hours operated for the machine provide an indication of the competitiveness and excessive use or otherwise of the item.

These two variances signify to management the popular and competitive plant items to operate and the information is therefore valuable in deciding upon purchases and disposals.

## Plant cost report

A positive utilisation variance would usually be associated with increased maintenance, affecting direct costs and possibly indirect costs also. Therefore the budgetary and cost control system recommended for departments should be installed for individual plant items and actual costs and revenues recorded on a regular basis. In this way all the variances may be monitored and the consequences on profitability quickly recognised.

## Example

During a six month period £4 000 revenue was received for a plant item. The budget anticipated £5 000. Direct costs and indirect costs (overheads) from operating the various company departments were budgeted to the plant item respectively at £1 500 and £2 000 with profit at 10% of turnover and £1 000 were provided for depreciation. Actual direct costs recorded during the period were £1 250 and the actual overhead incurred was £1 950. Calculate the variances and percentage return on sales.

*Analysis of variance*

| | | |
|---|---|---|
| Budgeted profit (10% of £5 000) | = | £500 |
| Sales variance (£1 000 × 70%) | = | −£700 |

Direct cost variance

$$\left(£1\,500 \times \frac{4\,000}{5\,000} - £1\,250\right) \quad = \quad -£50$$

| | | |
|---|---|---|
| Overhead variance | = | +£50 |
| Depreciation variance | = | £0 |
| Total variance | = | −£700 |

$$\text{Actual profit on turnover} \quad = \quad \frac{-200}{4000} = -5.0\% \text{ (loss)}$$

A comprehensive record of costs, current written down value, revenue and profitability for each item may be used in conjunction with the utilisation report to purchase and dispose of items at prices which are economic for the company. For many firms this type of information is monitored on an asset register of the plant holdings.

## Marginal costing

Marginal costs are those costs arising directly from the production process, which for a plant hire company would be largely those costs connected with maintenance and servicing of the equipment. They therefore vary directly with the hiring activity. Fixed costs, arising from the establishment charges, fluctuate very little with hiring levels. The purpose of the marginal costing method is to calculate the contribution made by each item of plant for hire towards the fixed costs and profit of the business.

*Example*

| | Plant item £00's (weekly) | | | | |
|---|---|---|---|---|---|
| | A | B | C | D | E |
| Hire revenue | 10 | 9 | 5 | 15 | 10 |
| Labour costs ⎞ | 3 | 2 | 2 | 5 | 2 |
| Material costs ⎬ marginal costs | 3 | 2 | 1 | 5 | 3 |
| Expenses ⎠ | 2 | 2 | 1 | 3 | 2 |
| Contribution* | 2 | 3 | 1 | 2 | 3 |
| Contribution per £1 revenue | 20p | 33p | 20p | 13p | 30p |

*Contribution = Overheads + profit

This technique can be used to advantage during a short term period when the market demand is low and hire rates need to be keen to attract custom, the contention being that any hire rate revenue which exceeds the marginal costs makes a contribution towards the fixed costs. Such a pricing policy, however, should be considered only during a short and difficult period, since the endeavour must be to realise the budgeted profit for each item over the twelve months period. Thus for plant item C, for example, a hire rate exceeding £400 per week will contribute to the fixed overhead, which may be a better alternative than leaving the machine idle.

Conversely, the method gives a clear indication that the firm should be directing its sales effort on items B and E, as these machines can obtain favourable hire rates and give the best contribution towards fixed costs.

### Reading list

1. Cole, D.O. Costing – a realistic approach. *Proceedings 2nd Contractors' Plant Association Conference*. London, 1973.
2. Plant Costing. *Contractor*. May, 1968.
3. Gates, M. and Scarpa, A. Criteria for the selection of construction equipment. *Journal of the Construction Division*. ASCE. June, 1980.
4. Neale, R.H. and Cole, D.O. Shake up for plant hire. *Construction News Magazine*. 4 April 1978.
5. Sizer, J. *An insight into management accounting*. Penguin Books. London, 1973.
6. Cooke, B. and Jepson, W.B. *Cost and financial control for construction firms*. MacMillan. London, 1979.

# CHAPTER 14

## CASH FLOW

### Introduction

Bankruptcy or voluntary liquidation is caused not only by a lack of cash but also an inability to raise cash in the forms of loans or credit to meet immediate commitments because creditors, investors and possible lenders of money – usually the banks – have lost confidence in the business and are unconvinced that the company can continue to trade in a profitable and viable way. This loss of confidence is important because it is the existence of such confidence that permits overdrafts to be obtained and normal trade credit to be received, and a loss in confidence would result in existing creditors pressing harder for payment. Trade credit is an important factor in determining most companies' short term cash requirements and should trade credit be withheld the short term cash requirements increase significantly. The withholding of trade credit simply means that the suppliers to a company demand cash on delivery rather than invoicing, say, at the end of the month and requiring payment by one month later.

Most of Chapter 6 was concerned with profitability measured in terms of return on capital and much of chapter 15, dealing with financial management, will be concerned with determining the company's profit and distributing that profit. Profit seen simply as the difference between revenue and cost is a common measure of a company's well-being and the derived ratios of profit/turnover and profit/capital employed are useful indicators of the company's performance, but these are derived from measuring profit. Undoubtedly a company with a good profit is likely also to have good profitability (i.e. profit as a proportion of capital employed) and, in turn, be in a good state to avoid liquidity problems. But the company's liquidity needs to be monitored and managed also. Although a company may be profitable it may have liquidity difficulties. An unexpected demand for payment may not be able to be met and cause significant difficulties, if not bankruptcy.

The more detailed monitoring and managing of a company's cash flow can be seen as two related and integrated but different aspects. One is the cash required for normal trading operations and the other is the cash required for acquisitions less disposals.

The cash required for normal trading operations is controlled by sales fluctuations, trade credit (creditors less debtors), stocks, work in progress and perhaps value added tax. In plant hire, sales fluctuations are manifest by the utilisation of plant. Plant is idle in a sales slump but all plant is highly utilised and more new plant is required in a sales boom. Stocks in plant hire are less important than in manufacturing and normally only represent spares, repair materials, fuel and oil. Also plant hire companies differ from manufacturing companies in that there is no manufacturing process absorbing manpower and materials and locking up cash. The nearest equivalent to 'work in progress' in plant hire is plant on hire for which the invoices have not been issued, or perhaps plant under repair.

The other aspect is the cash required for the provision of the company's capital assets. This is particularly important to plant hire companies since as much as 50% of sales turnover may be used in meeting the costs of asset ownership. The variables that control this are the purchase and disposal of capital assets, method of acquisition which in turn controls the methods of payment (e.g. purchase, hire purchase, or lease) and the company's ability to utilise capital allowances. In addition to these factors the company's cash flow is also affected by interest and other bank charges, corporation tax and dividends. Corporation tax is important to the cash flow as, at the time of writing, capital allowances of 100% of the purchase price are allowed in the first year of acquiring an asset, such as an item of construction plant. Therefore the disposal and acquisition of plant are significant when determining the corporation tax due and, in turn, the acquisition of plant and payment of corporation tax are significant to the company's cash requirements. Dividends are also significant to the company's cash position but within the control of the company's directors.

The following description of cash flow problems reflect the two main aspects of cash flow: (a) the cash flow resulting from the normal month to month trading operations and (b) the cash flows resulting from the acquisition and disposal of capital assets and these will be considered separately.

## Cash flows from normal trading operations

### Trade Credit, Sales Fluctuations and Stocks

The factors that affect the short term cash requirements in plant hire are trade credit, sales fluctuations and stocks. The effects of these are best illustrated by considering an example which illustrates the effects of these factors one at a time. In manufacturing the additional factor of 'work in progress' is important, but as there is no process in plant hire that can be classed as work in progress it is not significant and is not included in this example.

The monthly net cash flow stated in this example is the difference between the cash outgoings and incomings in that month. The monthly contribution is the revenue that will be derived from the sales (hired out plant) during the month, less the direct costs in supporting the sales for labour, spare parts and consumables. The word contribution is used because this money will be used to meet overhead costs and ownership costs and therefore cannot yet be described as 'profit'. All transactions in this example are exclusive of value added tax which is referred to separately.

### Cash flow example

A plant hire company initially holds 5 items of plant which are hired out at the rate of £1 000 per month. Each month's maintenance on each item of plant uses £200 in spare parts and £100 in consumables such as fuel, oil and grease. The fuel costs for running the plant are the responsibility of the hirer. The workshop providing the maintenance support has sufficient labour to maintain 5 plant items in working order each month. The labour cost of the workshop is £750 per month. If all the five plant items were on hire and all the transactions were in cash the monthly cash flow would be as follows:

*Month 1* (with all transactions in cash)

|  | Cash out | Cash in |
|---|---|---|
| Sales (5 plant items on hire) |  | £5 000 |
| Workshop labour | £750 |  |
| Purchases: |  |  |
|    Spares for 5 plant items for one month | £1 000 |  |
|    Consumables for 5 plant items for one month | £500 |  |
|                Totals | £2 250 | £5 000 |
| Net cash flow for month 1: | +£2 750 |  |
| Contribution to company for month 1: | +£2 750 |  |

The contribution is defined as the revenue derived from the hire sales less the direct costs incurred in supporting these sales, such as labour, spares and consumables. The company profit will be the contribution less the ownership and overhead costs. If the hirers were given trade credit of one month to pay then the cash flow for month 1 would be:

*Month 1* (with trade credit for hirers)

|  | Cash out | Cash in |
|---|---|---|
| Sales (5 plant items on hire) |  | nil |
| Workshop labour | £750 |  |
| Purchases: |  |  |
|    Spares for 5 plant items for one month | £1 000 |  |
|    Consumables for 5 plant items for one month | £500 |  |
|                Totals | £2 250 | nil |
| Net cash flow for month 1: | −£2 250 |  |
| Contribution to company for month 1: | +£2 750 |  |

The company has the same contribution but the effect of trade credit to the hirers produces a net cash flow of −£2 250. If the suppliers of spares and consumables also offered one month trade credit but the labour was paid weekly the cash flows would be as follows:

*Month 1* (with trade credit for hirers and from suppliers)

|  | Cash out | Cash in |
|---|---|---|
| Sales (5 plant items on hire) |  | nil |
| Workshop labour | £750 |  |
| Purchases: |  |  |
| Spares for 5 plant items for one month | nil |  |
| Consumables for 5 plant items for one month | nil |  |
| Totals | £750 | nil |
| Net cash flow for month 1: | −£750 |  |
| Contribution to company for month 1: | +£2 750 |  |

Thus, although the contribution generated in this month was again £2 750 the cash resources required were reduced to −£750 by the availability of trade credit from suppliers. Assuming that this is the normal trading experience, the cash flows in the following month, month 2, will be different from those in month 1 even though the same level of sales (i.e. hired out plant) are achieved. This is because the cash flows from month 1's sales and purchases will be present.

*Month 2*

|  | Cash out | Cash in |
|---|---|---|
| Sales (5 plant items on hire) |  | nil |
| Workshop labour | £750 |  |
| Purchases: |  |  |
| Spares for 5 plant items for one month | nil |  |
| Consumables for 5 plant items for one month | nil |  |
| Revenue from previous month's sales |  | £5 000 |
| Payments for previous month's purchases: |  |  |
| Spares | £1 000 |  |
| Consumables | £500 |  |
| Totals | £2 250 | £5 000 |
| Net cash flow for month 2: | +£2 750 |  |
| Contribution to company for month 2: | +£2 750 |  |

In month 2 the cash flow is a net inflow of +£2 750 arising from the revenue from month 1 sales. The contribution earned in month 2 was again £2 750 and the cash flows and contributions for the two months are:

|  | Cash Flow | Contribution |
|---|---|---|
| Month 1 | −£750 | +£2 750 |
| Month 2 | +£2 750 | +£2 750 |

Provided the 5 items of plant are hired out and maintained each month the cash flows and contributions will continue as in month 2. If in months 3 and 4 only two items of plant are hired out the pattern is disturbed as follows:

*Month 3*

|  | Cash out | Cash in |
|---|---|---|
| Sales (2 items of plant on hire) |  | nil |
| Workshop labour | £750 |  |
| Purchases: |  |  |
| Spares for 2 plant items for one month | nil |  |
| Consumables for 2 plant items for one month | nil |  |
| Revenue from previous month's sales |  | £5 000 |
| Payments for previous month's purchases: |  |  |
| Spares | £1 000 |  |
| Consumables | £500 |  |
| Totals | £2 250 | £5 000 |

| Net cash flow for month 3: | +£2 750 |
|---|---|
| Contribution to company for month 3: | +£650 |
| Number of idle plant items: | 3 |

(The contribution is calculated as the revenue from two plant items of £2 000 less the workshop labour of £750 and the spares for two plant items of £400 and consumables for two plant items of £200).

Although the sales in month 3 were reduced the effect was not shown immediately on the cash flow because of the trade credit. The reduction in contribution generated in the month is aggravated by the fact that the labour costs could not be reduced in a similar way as the purchases were reduced to levels compatible with the reduced sales. A serious problem of reduced sales not shown here but which will be dealt with later is that the ownership costs of the idle plant still have to be met from the reduced contribution. The effects of reduced sales revenue come through in month 4.

*Month 4*

|  | Cash out | Cash in |
|---|---|---|
| Sales (2 plant items on hire) |  | nil |
| Workshop labour | £750 |  |
| Purchases: |  |  |
| Spares for 2 plant items for one month | nil |  |
| Consumables for 2 plant items for one month | nil |  |
| Revenue from previous month's sales |  | £2 000 |
| Payments for previous month's purchases |  |  |
| Spares | £400 |  |
| Consumables | £200 |  |
| Totals | £1 350 | £2 000 |

| | | |
|---|---|---|
| Net cash flow for month 4: | +£650 | |
| Contribution to company for month 4: | +£650 | |
| Number of idle plant items: | 3 | |

Thus the smaller sales revenue from month 3 has reduced the net cash inflow from £2 750 to £650.

If in month 5 the sales improve to four items of plant on hire the improved cash flows again take a further month to come through, as months 5 and 6 illustrate:

*Month 5*

| | Cash out | Cash in |
|---|---|---|
| Sales (4 plant items on hire) | | nil |
| Workshop labour | £750 | |
| Purchases: | | |
|    Spares for 4 plant items for one month | nil | |
|    Consumables for 4 plant items for one month | nil | |
| Revenue from previous month's sales | | £2 000 |
| Payments for previous month's purchases: | | |
|    Spares | £400 | |
|    Consumables | £200 | |
|                 Totals | £1 350 | £2 000 |

| | | |
|---|---|---|
| Net cash flow for month 5: | +£650 | |
| Contribution to company for month 5: | +£2 050 | |
| (Contribution = sales − workshop labour − spares − consumables) | | |
| Number of idle plant items: | 1 | |

*Month 6*

| | Cash out | Cash in |
|---|---|---|
| Sales (4 plant items on hire) | | nil |
| Workshop labour | £750 | |
| Purchases: | | |
|    Spares for 4 plant items for one month | nil | |
|    Consumables for 4 plant items for one month | nil | |
| Revenue from previous month's sales | | £4 000 |
| Payment for previous month's purchases: | | |
|    Spares | £800 | |
|    Consumables | £400 | |
|                 Totals | £1 950 | £4 000 |

| | | |
|---|---|---|
| Net cash flow for month 6: | +£2 050 | |
| Contribution to company for month 6: | +£2 050 | |
| Number of idle plant items: | 1 | |

The cash flow in month 6 reflects the increase in sales experienced in month 5.
The cash flow and contribution for the first six months of this venture are therefore:

| Month | 1 | 2 | 3 | 4 | 5 | 6 |
|---|---|---|---|---|---|---|
| Net cash flows | −£750 | +£2 750 | +£2 750 | +£650 | +£650 | +£2 050 |
| Contribution | +£2 750 | +£2 750 | +£650 | +£650 | +£2 050 | +£2 050 |

It is seen from this that the contribution more closely reflects the fluctuating
sales whereas the effects of trade credit produce different cash flows.

So far the company has been purchasing just enough spares and consumables for
each month's operations but if it wished to build up stocks of spares and consumables then the cash flows would be reduced in order to fund the stocks. Months
7 and 8 are examples of building up stocks to meet a future sales boom.

*Month 7*

| | Cash out | Cash in |
|---|---|---|
| Sales (4 items of plant on hire) | | nil |
| Workshop labour | £750 | |
| Purchases: | | |
| Spares for 8 plant items for one month | nil | |
| Consumables for 8 plant items for one month | nil | |
| Revenue from previous month's sales | | £4 000 |
| Payment for previous month's supplies: | | |
| Spares | £800 | |
| Consumables | £400 | |
| Totals | £1 950 | £4 000 |

| | |
|---|---|
| Net cash flow for month 7: | +£2 050 |
| Contribution to company for month 7: | +£2 050 |
| Number of idle plant items: | 1 |
| Stocks: Spares for 4 plant items for one month: | £800 |
| Consumables for 4 plant items for one month: | £400 |

*Month 8*

| | Cash out | Cash in |
|---|---|---|
| Sales (4 plant items on hire) | | nil |
| Workshop labour | £750 | |
| Purchases: | | |
| Spares for 8 plant items for one month | nil | |
| Consumables for 8 plant items for one month | nil | |
| Revenue from previous months sales | | £4 000 |
| Payment for previous month's supplies: | | |

|  |  | Cash out | Cash in |
|---|---|---|---|
| Spares |  | £1 600 |  |
| Consumables |  | £800 |  |
|  | Totals | £3 150 | £4 000 |

| | |
|---|---|
| Net cash flow for month 8: | +£850 |
| Contribution to company for month 8: | +£2 050 |
| Number of idle plant items: | 1 |

Stocks:

| | |
|---|---|
| Spares for 8 plant items for one month: | £1 600 |
| Consumables for 8 plant items for one month: | £800 |

Thus the build up of stocks has reduced the cash flow to +£850.

To meet the expected sales boom the company increases the total holding to 8 plant items. In order to service this, additional labour is required which brings the workshop labour cost to £1 800.

*Month 9*

|  |  | Cash out | Cash in |
|---|---|---|---|
| Sales (8 items of plant on hire) |  |  | nil |
| Workshop labour |  | £1 800 |  |
| Purchases: |  |  |  |
| Spares for 8 plant items for one month |  | nil |  |
| Consumables for 8 plant items for one month |  | nil |  |
| Revenue from previous month's sales |  |  | £4 000 |
| Payment for previous month's purchases: |  |  |  |
| Spares |  | £1 600 |  |
| Consumables |  | £800 |  |
|  | Totals | £4 200 | £4 000 |

| | |
|---|---|
| Net cash flow for month 9: | −£200 |
| Contribution to company for month 9: | +£3 800 |
| Number of idle plant items: | nil |

Stocks:

| | |
|---|---|
| Spares for 8 plant items for one month: | £1 600 |
| Consumables for 8 plant items for one month: | £800 |

The increase in sales has lead to a negative cash flow because the sales have led to increased trade credit which will not show as cash inflows until next month and the increased workshop costs had to be met immediately. Also the level of purchases of spares and consumables was high in month 8 and cash must be found to fund the stocks. Month 10's cash flow will improve as the increased revenues come through. Such rapid expansion could, if continued, lead to overtrading in which the company's cash resources would not be sufficient to support the expansion.

*Month 10*

|  | Cash out | Cash in |
|---|---|---|
| Sales (8 plant items on hire) |  | nil |
| Workshop labour | £1 800 |  |
| Purchases: |  |  |
| Spares for 8 plant items for one month | nil |  |
| Consumables for 8 plant items for one month | nil |  |
| Revenue from previous month's sales |  | £8 000 |
| Payment for previous month's purchases: |  |  |
| Spares | £1 600 |  |
| Consumables | £800 |  |
| Totals | £4 200 | £8 000 |

| Net cash flow for month 10: | +£3 800 |
|---|---|
| Contribution to company for month 10: | +£3 800 |
| Number of idle plant items: | nil |
| Stocks: |  |
| Spares for 8 plant items for one month: | £1 600 |
| Consumables for 8 plant items for one month: | £800 |

The cash flow in month 10 now reflects the higher sales in month 9. If in month 11 some of the stock held is used to maintain the plant rather than buying new spares and consumables the cash flow will be improved in month 12.

*Month 11*

|  | Cash out | Cash in |
|---|---|---|
| Sales (8 plant items on hire) |  | nil |
| Workshop labour | £1 800 |  |
| Purchases: |  |  |
| Spares for 4 plant items for one month | nil |  |
| Consumables for 4 plant items for one month | nil |  |
| Revenue from previous month's sales |  | £8 000 |
| Payment for previous month's purchases: |  |  |
| Spares | £1 600 |  |
| Consumables | £800 |  |
| Totals | £4 200 | £8 000 |

| Net cash flow for month 11: | +£3 800 |
|---|---|
| Contribution to company for month 11: | +£3 800 |
| Number of idle plant items: | nil |
| Stocks: |  |
| Spares for 4 plant items for one month: | £800 |
| Consumables for 4 plant items for one month: | £400 |

*Month 12*

|  | Cash out | Cash in |
|---|---|---|
| Sales (4 plant items on hire) |  | nil |
| Workshop labour | £1 800 |  |
| Purchases: |  |  |
|     Spares for 4 plant items for one month | nil |  |
|     Consumables for 4 plant items for one month | nil |  |
| Revenue from previous month's sales |  | £8 000 |
| Payment for previous month's purchases: |  |  |
|     Spares | £800 |  |
|     Consumables | £400 |  |
|                 Totals | £3 000 | £8 000 |

| | |
|---|---|
| Net cash flow for month 12: | +£5 000 |
| Contribution to company for month 12: | +£1 000 |
| Number of idle plant items: | 4 |
| Stocks: | |
|     Spares for 4 plant items for one month: | £800 |
|     Consumables for 4 plant items for one month: | £400 |

The cash flow increases to £5 000 in month 12 when the revenues are £8 000 due
to the high sales in month 11 and payments for purchases are only £1 200 because
half the spares and consumables used in month 11 were drawn from stock rather
than purchased. This is known as de-stocking. The cash flows and contributions are
summarised in Table 14.1.

*Summary* of the difference between cash and contribution in Table 14.1:

- The cumulative contribution for the twelve months is £27 400.
- The cumulative cash flow for the twelve months is £23 400.
- The difference between these is due to the trade credit and stocks.

    *Trade credit:*

    *Creditors:*

| Credit received from suppliers | |
|---|---|
|     Spares | £800 |
|     Consumables | £400 |
| | £1 200 |

    *Debtors:*

| Credit given to hirers | |
|---|---|
|     4 plant items on hire | £4 000 |
| Difference between debtors and creditors | £2 800 |

    *Stocks:*

| | |
|---|---|
|     Spares | £800 |
|     Consumables | £400 |
| Total | £1 200 |

Thus the summary of trade credit and stocks is:

**Table 14.1** Summary of cash flows and contributions for 12 months

| Month | 1 | 2 | 3 | 4 | 5 | 6 | 7 | 8 | 9 | 10 | 11 | 12 |
|---|---|---|---|---|---|---|---|---|---|---|---|---|
| Contribution (£) | 2 750 | 2 750 | 650 | 650 | 2 050 | 2 050 | 2 050 | 2 050 | 3 800 | 3 800 | 3 800 | 1 000 |
| Net cash flow (£) | −750 | 2 750 | 2 750 | 650 | 650 | 2 050 | 2 050 | 850 | −200 | 3 800 | 3 800 | 5 000 |
| Reasons for cash flow fluctuations | Trade credit given to hirers and received from suppliers. | | | Falling sales in month 3. | | Increased sales in month 5. | | Increase in stocks in month 7. | Increase in sales leading to increasing trade credit and increase in workshop labour costs to support new sales and stocking in month 8. | | | Destocking in month 11 while sustaining high sales levels in month 11. |

| | |
|---|---|
| Trade Credit | £2 800 |
| Stocks | £1 200 |
| Total | £4 000 |

Of the £27 400 of contribution earned the company has:
   £23 400 in cash (less overheads and ownership costs etc.)
    £2 800 in debtors less creditors
    and £1 200 in stocks.

The cash flows calculated in Table 14.1 were calculated on the basis of trading operations and require further adjustment before they represent the company cash flow. These other adjustments are head office or overhead expenses, the acquiring and disposal of capital assets, value added tax, corporation tax and dividends.

Overheads

Adjusting the cash flows and profits for overheads requires a projection of the head office overheads. Some of these expenses such as salaries will be monthly: others such as telephone, electricity and rentals may be monthly or quarterly, while rates may be half-yearly. Table 14.2 shows the original contribution and cash flows from Table 14.1 with the overhead adjustment included.

**Table 14.2**    Summary of profit and cash flows for 12 months with overheads included

| Month | Contribution before overheads deducted (Table 14.1) £ | Cash flow before overheads deducted (Table 14.1) £ | Overheads £ | Contribution less overheads £ | Cash flow less overheads £ |
|---|---|---|---|---|---|
| 1 | 2 750 | −750 | 150 | 2 600 | −900 |
| 2 | 2 750 | 2 750 | 10 | 2 740 | 2 740 |
| 3 | 650 | 2 750 | 40 | 610 | 2 710 |
| 4 | 650 | 650 | 10 | 640 | 640 |
| 5 | 2 050 | 650 | 10 | 2 040 | 640 |
| 6 | 2 050 | 2 050 | 190 | 1 860 | 1 860 |
| 7 | 2 050 | 2 050 | 10 | 2 040 | 2 040 |
| 8 | 2 050 | 850 | 10 | 2 040 | 840 |
| 9 | 3 800 | −200 | 40 | 3 760 | −240 |
| 10 | 3 800 | 3 800 | 10 | 3 790 | 3 790 |
| 11 | 3 800 | 3 800 | 10 | 3 790 | 3 790 |
| 12 | 1 000 | 5 000 | 40 | 960 | 4 960 |
| Cumulative values | 27 400 | 23 400 | 530 | 26 870 | 22 870 |

The overhead projections in Table 14.2 are as shown. These have been stated in the month in which they occur and the same figure in any month has been deducted from the contribution as well as the cash flow. The difference between the cumulative contribution of £27 400 and the cumulative cash of £23 400 is due to stocks and the difference between debtors and creditors as previously explained. The effect of overheads is simply to reduce the contribution and cash available.

### Value Added Tax

A company collects value added tax on receipt of payment from customers. The company also pays value added tax on the payment of suppliers for goods received. The difference is calculated and either paid to or received from the custom and excise office quarterly. Depending on the difference in value between the amount of goods bought and sold in a quarter the V.A.T. can result in an outflow or an inflow. If the V.A.T. is owed by the company then the collection of V.A.T. has been acting as a source of short term funds. If a V.A.T. refund is due to the company then the company has been funding the difference, and the effect of V.A.T. on the company's cash flow should be calculated.

Although new construction is generally zero-rated the hire of plant is positive-rated. If plant is supplied with an operator the transaction is regarded as providing a service and becomes zero-rated. A company that supplies operators will be paying V.A.T. on goods and supplies received and will be due for refunds because no V.A.T. would have been collected on the sale of services. In this case the company is providing funds for the V.A.T. exercise. V.A.T. should be calculated and included in cash flow considerations.

### Cash flow forecasts for trading operations in plant hire

### Trade credit

Plant hire companies give and receive credit. The credit given to customers is typically one month so that any plant hired this month will have an invoice issued at the time of supply and payment will be expected in, say, thirty days. In preparing a cash flow forecast from the sales forecast the cash in, or revenue, can be derived by inserting the appropriate time shifts between the month in which the sales occur and the month in which the cash is received. In deriving revenue it is usual to assume that not all the customers will pay on the due date and some will default. An analysis of the timing of receipts from customers will indicate which assumed time shifts are appropriate. Representative figures would show that 70% of customers pay within one month, 25% within two months and 5% within three months. It may be that payment is never received on some invoices and this should be taken into account in the cash forecast if this proportion is significant. Thus, a sales forecast and derived cash in or revenue would be as illustrated in Table 14.3.

Similarly, credit would be received from suppliers of spare parts and consumables and from the forecast of required spare parts, repair materials and consumables the appropriate time shifts would be used to determine the cash out. Labour and operatives would be paid weekly and the staff monthly.

**Table 14.3**   Sales forecast and Derived Cash Revenue

| Month | 1 | 2 | 3 | 4 | 5 | 6 | 7 |
|---|---|---|---|---|---|---|---|
| Sales forecast (£) | 10 000 | 15 000 | 18 000 | 12 000 | | | |
| 1 month delay (70%) (£) | | 7 000 | 10 500 | 12 600 | 8 400 | | |
| 2 month delay (25%) (£) | | | 2 500 | 3 750 | 4 500 | 3 000 | |
| 3 month delay (5%) (£) | | | | 500 | 750 | 900 | 600 |
| Cash in (£) | | 7 000 | 13 000 | 16 850 | 13 650 | 3 900 | 600 |

### Stocks and work in progress
As a plant hire operation is not involved in manufacture there is no substantial purchase of raw materials leading to stocks, nor is there any substantial work in progress. Stocks are mainly confined to spare parts and repair materials.

### Sales fluctuations and overheads
As with any type of business the plant hire industry is subject to sales fluctuations. These, like the earlier examples, lead to increases in trade credit and can lead to overtrading in a sustained expansion. Stocking and de-stocking of spare parts and consumables takes place within the cycle of sales fluctuations. Figure 14.1 illustrates the variations in demand, as measured by new orders for the U.K. construction industry from 1970 to 1980. Superimposed on this graph of demand is the overall output for the industry.

The buoyancy of the plant hire industry is correlated with the output of the whole construction industry. Major changes in the level of output during the seventies led to problems of overtrading on the rising markets to 1973 and later in the seventies, when lower levels of construction activity occurred, companies with disproportionate overheads were common. The general contractor is faced with cutting overheads as the market shrinks and the company's turnover declines but the plant hire company has another more difficult problem. This problem is that the plant hire company has capital assets in the form of construction plant which, if they become under-utilised or hired out at an uneconomic rate, or both, quickly cease to give a return on capital. In such a situation companies would try to dispose of their plant but in a market slump this may not be possible. This is the basic risk in all plant hire operations.

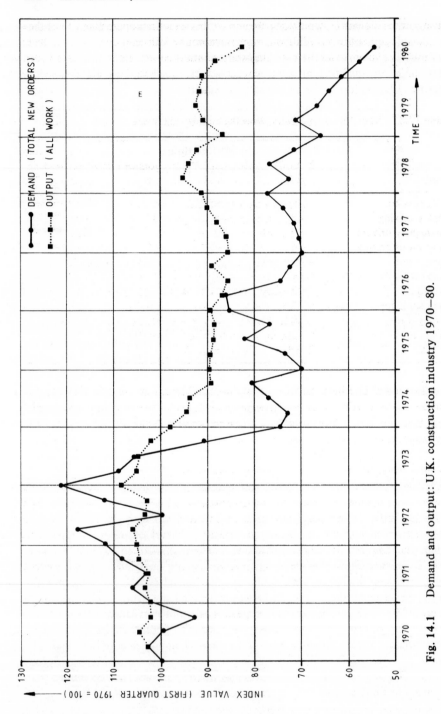

**Fig. 14.1** Demand and output: U.K. construction industry 1970–80.

**Table 14.4**   A tabular form for the construction of a cash flow forecast for trading operations

| Month | 1 | 2 | 3 | 4 | 5 |
|---|---|---|---|---|---|
| Sales forecast | | | | | |
| 1 month delay (70%)<br>2 month delay (25%)<br>3 month delay (5%) | | | | | |
| Revenue or cash in | | | | | |
| Workshop | | | | | |
| Goods purchased<br>    cash out<br>Labour payroll<br>    cash out<br>Staff payroll<br>    cash out<br>overheads (rent, rates, phone, etc.)<br>    cash out | | | | | |
| Total cash out for workshop | | | | | |
| Transport department | | | | | |
| Goods purchased<br>    cash out<br>Labour payroll<br>    cash out<br>Staff payroll<br>    cash out<br>Overheads<br>    cash out | | | | | |
| Total cash out for transport department | | | | | |
| A cash out flow for each section or main head of account in budget would be prepared. | | | | | |
| Total cash out from all sections | | | | | |
| Total cash in from sales | | | | | |
| Net cash flow | | | | | |
| Cumulative cash flow | | | | | |

*Forecasts*

A short term cash flow forecast is derived from the sales forecast and the aggregate cash requirements of all the various heads of account, divided into purchasing supplies, goods, labour, staff and overheads. The heads of account are the same as those used in the budget, namely workshop, transport and the various service departments of purchasing, administration, costing, hiring and finance. A tabular cash flow forecast may be constructed as illustrated in Table 14.4.

## Cash flows for the purchasing and acquisition of capital assets.

One feature of plant hire companies that distinguishes them from general contractors is the high proportion of funds locked up in their capital assets. As much as 40% — 50% of the sales revenue may be dissipated on the ownership costs of the company's assets. The cash flow for the normal month to month trading as in Tables 14.2 and 14.4 should be combined with the company's capital expenditure budget, which includes disposals as well as purchases, to produce the cash flow statement.

As the capital expenditure budget is likely to produce the larger cash flows and will dominate the company cash flow it is not unusual for the capital expenditure budget to be prepared first.

The method of acquisition determines the cash flows for individual items and Chapter 7 reviewed the various methods of acquisition: outright purchase, credit purchase, hire purchase, or lease. All have different cash flow implications, and the cash flows of these various methods of acquisition can be summarised as follows:

| Method of acquisition | Cash flow |
| --- | --- |
| Outright purchase | Single large down payment |
| Credit purchase | Deposit plus regular payments |
| Hire purchase | Deposit plus regular hire charges |
| Lease | No deposit but regular lease payments |

Thus leasing is the least difficult to provide for because it should be paid from revenue. Hire purchase or some credit arrangement is the next easiest since a down payment is required and the remaining charges can be met from revenue. However, the down payment may be borrowed and the loan repayments met from revenue. Similarly outright purchase requires a large single payment of cash but all of this or part of it can be borrowed and payments met from revenue.

Providing a cash flow statement that includes the effects of acquisition and purchasing requires a prediction of the proceeds received from disposals together with a forecast of the expenditure on acquisition divided into down payments, hire purchase or loan repayments, interest charges and lease payments. The following example has been chosen so that it may be included with the cash flow calculated on Table 14.2.

**Table 14.5**  Cash flow for plant acquisition and disposal

| Month | 1 | 2 | 3 | 4 | 5 | 6 | 7 | 8 | 9 | 10 | 11 | 12 |
|---|---|---|---|---|---|---|---|---|---|---|---|---|
| Plant acquisition 5 items, value (£) | 25 000 | | | | | | | | | | | |
| 3 items by lease (£) | 15 000 | | | | | | | | | | | |
| 2 items by h.p. (£) | 10 000 | | | | | | | | | | | |
| Lease payments (£) | | 810 | 810 | 810 | 810 | 810 | 810 | 810 | 810 | 810 | 810 | 810 |
| H.P. deposit (£) | 2 000 | | | | | | | | | | | |
| H.P. payments (£) | | 770 | 770 | 770 | 770 | 770 | 770 | 770 | 385 | 385 | 385 | 385 |
| Plant disposal (£) | | | | | | | | 4 000 | | | | |
| H.P. settlement (£) | | | | | | | | 1 320 | | | | |
| Plant acquisition 4 items, value (£) | | | | | | | | 20 000 | | | | |
| 4 items by lease (£) | | | | | | | | 20 000 | | | | |
| Lease payments (£) | | | | | | | | 1 080 | 1 080 | 1 080 | 1 080 | 1 080 |
| Total cash out (£) | 3 580 | 1 580 | 1 580 | 1 580 | 1 580 | 1 580 | 1 580 | 3 980 | 2 275 | 2 275 | 2 275 | 2 275 |
| Total cash in (£) | | | | | | | | 4 000 | | | | |
| Net cash flow (£) | −3 580 | −1 580 | −1 580 | −1 580 | −1 580 | −1 580 | −1 580 | +20 | −2 275 | −2 275 | −2 275 | −2 275 |

*Example*
Of the five items of plant initially acquired by the company three were leased and two were bought on hire purchase. The outright purchase price of the plant items is £5 000. The lease payments are £270 each per month for 24 months. The h.p. deposit on one plant item is £1 000 and the monthly payments are £385 for 12 months. In month 8, when the plant holding was increased to 8 units, this was done by selling one of the plant items bought by hire purchase for £4 000, paying the h.p. company £1 320 representing the outstanding h.p. payments less the interest that would be charged for the remaining period of four months. The fleet was increased by a further four leased items at a cost of £270 per month each. The cash flows for these acquisitions and disposals are shown in Table 14.5. Cash flow for acquisition and disposal is now added to the cash flows for normal trading from Table 14.2 and is shown in Table 14.6.

**Table 14.6**   Cash flow for normal trading from Table 14.2 plus cash flows associated with plant acquisition and disposal from Table 14.5

| Month | Net cash flow from Table 14.2 (normal trading) £ | Net cash flow from Table 14.5 (acquisition and disposal) £ | Sum or total net cash flow £ | Cumulative cash flow £ | Contribution less overheads from Table 14.2 less net cash flow from acquisition and disposal £ |
|---|---|---|---|---|---|
| 1 | − 900 | −3 580 | −4 480 | −4 480 | − 980 |
| 2 | 2 740 | −1 580 | 1 160 | −3 320 | 1 160 |
| 3 | 2 710 | −1 580 | 1 130 | −2 190 | − 970 |
| 4 | 640 | −1 580 | − 940 | −3 130 | − 940 |
| 5 | 640 | −1 580 | − 940 | −4 070 | 460 |
| 6 | 1 860 | −1 580 | 280 | −3 790 | 280 |
| 7 | 2 040 | −1 580 | 460 | −3 330 | 460 |
| 8 | 840 | +20 | 860 | −2 470 | 2 060 |
| 9 | − 240 | −2 275 | −2 515 | −4 985 | 1 485 |
| 10 | 3 790 | −2 275 | 1 515 | −3 470 | 1 515 |
| 11 | 3 790 | −2 275 | 1 515 | −1 955 | 1 515 |
| 12 | 4 960 | −2 275 | 2 685 | 730 | −1 315 |

*Note*: Adjustments to this cash flow that would render it a true company cash flow would be for V.A.T., interest, corporation tax and dividends.

V.A.T. has been previously described. Interest charges will be due if the negative cash flow is funded from loans or an overdraft and corporation tax will be due after all costs and interest have been deducted from sales revenue. The time lags associated with corporation tax will vary from about 9 months to perhaps 24 months and the payments due would be for previous trading years. Dividends would be paid out on the decision of the board of directors and are determined by the company's cash position amongst other factors.

To complete the plant hire company's cash flow forecast the analysis that was suggested in Table 14.4 needs to be extended as in Table 14.7.

**Table 14.7**    Headings for the cash flow forecast for acquisitions and disposals

| | | | Months | | | |
|---|---|---|---|---|---|---|
| Item | 1 | 2 | 3 | 4 | 5 | etc. |
| Plant disposals | | | | | | |
| Outright purchases | | | | | | |
| Down payments | | | | | | |
| Hire purchase payments | | | | | | |
| Loan repayment | | | | | | |
| Lease repayment | | | | | | |
| Interest | | | | | | |
| Value added tax | | | | | | |
| Corporation tax | | | | | | |
| Dividends | | | | | | |

Aspects that perhaps need further explanation are the recovery of the capital monies invested in plant through hire charges and the implications of corporation tax.

### Sales revenue, depreciation and corporation tax

In a hire company the sales revenue will be exclusively or predominantly made up of hire charges for hired plant. These hire charges will have been set at the current going market rate but will have been chosen not only for market reasons but for economic ones too. The 'economic' hire rate will include four elements; direct costs, indirect costs or overheads, ownership costs and profit. Chapter 9 dealt with such hire rate calculations and a description of the various methods of including the ownership costs. All of these are based on a concept of depreciation. This allowance for depreciation added into the hire rate is intended to ensure that the hire charges are large enough to recover the invested capital and an appropriate return on that invested capital. Thus, the monthly sales revenue includes this depreciation allowance. In the cash flow calculations undertaken in this chapter no attempt has been made to link the depreciation allowance included in the hire charges with the monies to be paid in ownership costs such as h.p., loan repayments or lease payments. Although in calculating hire rates:

sales revenue = direct costs + indirect costs + depreciation + profit,

it is not adequate to say:

profit = sales revenue − direct costs − indirect costs − depreciation

and that the monies available to meet ownership costs are depreciation plus retained profits.

Profit is not calculated in this way for tax purposes as capital allowances are used to offset the cost of acquiring capital assets (see Chapter 15). Furthermore the partitioning of the sales revenue in this way unrealistically suggests that the part of the revenue described as 'depreciation' is unnecessarily limited to be used in meeting ownership costs.

The reason that the sales revenue was left unpartitioned is that the funds can be deployed in any way to suit the company's operations. If the need is to meet the funding of debtors due to increasing sales or stocks or to buy a new item of plant, the surplus of revenue over cost can be deployed in the most advantageous way to suit the company. The company's need for cash is the criterion which dictates the use to which that cash available is put. The original method of calculating the hire charge which made allowances for depreciation was only a method of arriving at a realistic hire charge and has no influence on how the income is used. Thus the cash flow analysis recommended in this chapter does not partition the revenue under the headings used to calculate the original hire charges.

The implications of corporation tax also need to be understood in the context of the depreciation element of sales revenue. If a company buys a capital asset for £1 000, U.K. tax legislation allows 100% of this to be offset against profits in the first year before tax is charged on the remaining profits (at the time of writing). The company's internal depreciation included in the hire charge is unlikely to recover the total capital costs in the first year and may well take say three years to recover the invested capital. Thus, in the first year of purchase, if the company's profits were £1 200 (that is sales revenue less costs) the taxable profit would be £200 less interest charges, which is £1 200 less the capital allowances. If, in the second year, the company's profits (sales revenue less costs) were £1 300 but there were no capital allowances then the taxable profit would be £1 300 less interest charges. As explained in Chapter 7 the method of acquisition influences the capital allowances. The internal depreciation included by the company in their hire charges has no bearing on the calculation of taxable profit.

The corporation tax implications from the three methods of acquisition, outright purchase, hire purchase and leasing can be summarised as follows:

| Method of acquisition | Implications for Corporation Tax |
|---|---|
| Outright purchase | A capital allowance of 100% of the purchase price can be set against profits in the first year. |
| Hire purchase | A capital allowance of 100% of the purchase price can be set against profits in the first year. The interest element of the h.p. charge is deductible from revenue before tax. |
| Leasing | No capital allowance is available but lease payments are deductible from revenue before tax. |
| Interest charges | Interest charges on loans and overdrafts are deductible from revenue before tax. |

Thus the method of acquisition which may be chosen for cash flow reasons has a bearing on the corporation tax due which in turn affects the company's cash flow. The benefit of capital allowances can be derived only if there are adequate profits against which the allowances can be set.

## Cash flow management

This chapter has dealt with explanations of how and why cash flows vary and the need to forecast cash requirements. This has carried with it an implication that the cash flow can be managed, which is so within limits. The variables of sales fluctuations, the amount of credit given, level of stocking, when to dispose of capital assets, when to acquire capital assets and by what method they should be acquired are all subject to some managerial control. However, there are limits.

### Sales fluctuations
It is theoretically easy in an expanding market to control sales growth and hence the increase in debtors. However, increasing sales may be difficult to resist but are likely to be restricted if it means acquiring more capital assets. It is more difficult to improve sales in a declining market: cutting hire charges may be an option but this could lead to unprofitable trading. Thus, if a major slump in the construction industry occurs some plant companies will inevitably cease to trade. A slump in the construction industry is out of the control of plant companies.

### Trade credit
The amount of trade credit is set by the general trading conditions and if a company sets shorter credit periods than competitors the company may lose customers. Thus, trade credit is not wholly within the company's control. However, vigorous credit control can ensure that invoices are not allowed to remain unpaid for long periods beyond the normal credit given. A credit control system is a very important feature of a company's cash flow management. The company's credit controllers

have some control in that credit can always be refused if the customer is deemed unworthy of the risk.

With respect to credit received from suppliers, it is unlikely that a company could extend the normal credit arrangements without losing discount and jeopardising confidence in the company. Confidence is important in obtaining credit, overdrafts and loans.

### Stocking

The level of stocks of spare parts, repair materials and consumables is a matter for plant companies to decide. The equation that is being balanced is the cost of holding such stock against the risk of plant remaining idle while spare parts are sought.

### Disposal of capital assets

The timing of disposals are within the control of company managers but the capital raised by such disposals is controlled more by general market conditions rather than company manager's needs.

### Acquisition of capital assets

The timing and the method of acquisition are both within the control of company managers subject to delivery delays etc.

### Risk

Another need for cash that has not been considered so far is an access to cash to cover risk. It is possible to plan for routine maintenance and, drawing on experience, it is possible to plan for repairs within reason but it is not difficult to imagine situations where expensive repairs are required unexpectedly. The option of delaying repairs until cash becomes available is usually an undesirable situation as this leaves the plant item idle and ownership costs accrue whether the item is idle or not. Consequently, unexpected and expensive repairs often need to be undertaken immediately, and provision for such situations must be made. This implies the ready availability of cash for plant not covered by an engineering insurance policy and the ready availability of cash could suggest that cash may be idle and not working unless invested in short term investments.

### Cash, deficits and surplus

The cash flow illustrated in Table 14.6 showed that the monthly net cash flow in that example varied from −£4 480 to +£2 685. If this example were scaled up to a more realistic size it would show that the company cash flow can swing from considerable deficits to substantial surplus. The company needs a source of funds to cover the deficits and a reasonable use for the surplus that will earn returns without leaving the cash idle. The traditional source of funds in excess of the company's own cash is overdrafts. The use of surplus cash includes short term investments that can be quickly realised to meet cash requirements. In times of high inflation and high interest rates the contribution of such investments can be a source of considerable income to companies.

## Reading list

1. J.E. Smith. *Cash Flow Management*. Second edition, Woodhead Faulkner, 1981.
2. J.M. Samuels and F.M. Wilkes. *Management of Company Finance*. Third Edition. Nelson, 1980.
3. Martin Foreman and John Gilbert. *Factoring and Finance*. Heinemann. London, 1976.
4. J. Sizer. *An Insight into Management Accounting*. Penguin, 1973.
5. H.T. Mead and G.L. Mitchell. *Plant Hire for Building Construction*. Newnes-Butterworths, 1972.
6. W. Coombs. *Construction Accounting and Financial Management*. McGraw-Hill, 1958.
7. Value Added Tax, Construction Industry. *H.M. Customs and Excise Notice No. 708 1975.*
8. F. Harris and R. McCaffer. *Modern Construction Management*. Second Edition. Granada, 1982.

# CHAPTER 15

# FINANCIAL MANAGEMENT

## Introduction

A plant company, like any other, usually has limited liability status, with either private or publicly quoted shares depending upon its ability to secure a quotation on the Stock Exchange. A limited company, irrespective of its size, must file its annual financial accounts with the Registrar of Companies. To ensure that these give a true and fair view of the company's trading position, they are subjected to an annual audit by an independent firm of professional accountants appointed by the Department of Trade. If the company, on the other hand, is a subsidiary or department of a parent company, its trading position need only be included generally in the controlling company's accounts.

Beyond these legal requirements, however, the financial accounts provide a basis for measuring the profit made by the company and its overall financial performance during the year past. In addition the accounts give shareholders information on the investment policy, borrowing and other details of interest to investors and creditors. In the annual report the main items presented are the Profit and Loss Account, the Balance Sheet and notes to the accounts.

## The Profit and Loss Account

The Profit and Loss Account is a statement of the company's total profit or loss resulting from trading during the year. Its main features are the revenues generated from sales together with the costs incurred in producing the sales. The difference between the two values represents the profit or loss. After deducting interest charges on borrowed capital and corporation tax, the resulting surplus is used to provide a dividend to shareholders and/or for reinvestment in the company as retained earnings.

Example: a Profit and Loss Account for 1980

|  | £000's |
|---|---:|
| *Turnover* (Revenue) | |
| Hire of equipment and services | 16 500 |
| *Costs* | |
| Materials, labour, expenses (including depreciation), overheads | 14 500 |
| *Net profit* | 2 000 |
| Add depreciation back in (depreciation value agreed with tax inspector) | (2 000) |
| *Assessable profit* | 4 000 |
| Deduct capital allowances on plant and equipment | |
| (agreed with tax inspector) | 2 500 |
| Add profit from sales of fixed assets | (500) |
| Profit before taxation and interest | 2 000 |
| Deduct interest charges on borrowings (15% p.a.) | 1 500 |
| *Profit before tax* | 500 |
| Deduct corporation tax (say 50%) | 250 |
| Distributable profit after tax | 250 |
| Proposed dividend | 150 |
| *Profits retained in business*, C/F to Balance Sheet | 100 |

### Turnover

The company's turnover is the total value of sales of goods and services during the year, before costs are deducted. For a plant hire company or division this sum represents the total payments invoiced to clients for plant hired.

### Assessable profit for corporation tax with capital allowances

The assessable profit is obtained by subtracting the cost of sales from the turnover value. At present published accounts are not required to reveal details of the operating costs, which comprise the following elements:

Materials used, i.e. opening stock plus purchases minus closing stocks,
Wages, salaries and fees,
Expenses excluding depreciation,
Administration overheads.

### Depreciation and capital allowances

The principles of depreciation are discussed in Chapter 9. However, internal depreciation rates are usually ignored for preparation of the Profit and Loss Account as it is likely that capital allowances[3] (i.e. writing down allowances) offered by current tax legislation would be more favourable. Capital allowances like depreciation are deducted from the trading profit and the resulting sum is the net profit before interest charges on borrowed capital and tax. 100% capital allowances (i.e. the full cost of an item of new or used plant set against profits during the year of purchase), for many firms, has had the net effect of virtually eliminating the need to pay corporation tax.

One effect of capital allowances can be merely to defer payment of taxes rather than avoid them, especially if there is no corresponding upsurge in profitability as a result of the purchase. Such an effect is best illustrated by a simple example of two identical companies having the same gross profit of £400, one favouring the use of capital allowances and the other, not. In both cases they buy an item of plant worth £1 000, which is written off in equal amounts over four years.

*Company 1: Not using capital allowances*

|                            | Year 1 | Year 2 | Year 3 | Year 4 |
|----------------------------|--------|--------|--------|--------|
| Profit before depreciation | 400    | 400    | 400    | 400    |
| Depreciation               | 250    | 250    | 250    | 250    |
| Net Profit                 | 150    | 150    | 150    | 150    |
| Tax @ 50%                  | 75     | 75     | 75     | 75     |
| Profit after tax           | 75     | 75     | 75     | 75     |

Therefore total tax paid by Company 1 = £300.

*Company 2: Using capital allowances*

|                    | Year 1   | Year 2  | Year 3  | Year 4 |
|--------------------|----------|---------|---------|--------|
| Net Profit         | 150      | 150     | 150     | 150    |
| Depreciation       | 250      | 250     | 250     | 250    |
| Assessable Profit  | 400      | 400     | 400     | 400    |
| Capital Allowance  | (1 000)  | (600)*  | (200)*  | —      |
|                    | (600)    | (200)   | 200     | 400    |
| Tax @ 50%          | —        | —       | 100     | 200    |

*Capital allowance carried forward
Therefore total tax paid by Company 2 = £300

In both instances the total tax paid is £300 but with Company 2 this has been deferred.

In practice it is apparent that many hire companies try to avoid paying this deferred tax by continuing to buy new plant: Year 4 in the second example shows what could occur if such continual buying ceased. In this case, the company would be liable to payment of taxes in excess of the net profit earned for the year. Not only, therefore, do capital allowances provide a carrot, they also provide a stick. A company could, in certain circumstances, be effectively trapped in the system by a slow almost undetected, build-up of tax liabilities.

*Interest charges*
Loan capital, other than shareholders' equity, usually incurs an annual interest charge. In effect, this represents an indirect cost on the business and is deducted as such from net profit for the calculation of corporation tax payment.

## Profit before taxation

The income from all the company's activities, including subsidiary and associated companies, is added to its own profit before tax. The total is called the *pre-tax profit* upon which corporation tax is levied. The amount of tax due varies depending upon government policy and also on the size of company turnover. Currently in the U.K., for most medium to large companies 52% of profits are payable in corporation tax. After making provisions for payment of advanced corporation tax the remaining tax liability can be deferred until the following year after declaration of the company report and therefore provides a cheap source of short term funds to aid cash flows.

## Distribution of profits after tax

After the total distributable profits are determined, amounts may be apportioned to the various claimants. The order of priorities is set out in the Articles of Association of the company with preference shareholders having first claim, the remainder of the distributed profits going to the ordinary shareholders. The profits awarded in this way are usually called the *dividend*. The dividend is recommended by the directors of the firm at the Annual General Meeting who then vote to accept it or otherwise. The amount of dividend will naturally depend upon the level of profits and may not be declared when profits are too low. Whenever healthy profits are available for distribution the directors usually aim for an acceptable rate of return on the par (nominal) value of the share price.

Once the dividend has been paid the remaining profit is retained in the business and used to finance further investments in plant and other assets.

## The Balance Sheet

The function of the Balance Sheet is to portray the financial position of the company on a specific date, for example, 31st December 1980. Because time is needed to prepare the balance sheet information, the details could change just before or immediately after publication, e.g. settlement of an account by a debtor. The balance sheet is a 'photograph' of a particular financial position, whereas the Profit and Loss Account shows the record of achievement throughout the year.

The balance sheet is usually presented in tabular format separating capital employed from employment of capital. But alternatively some companies prefer liabilities and assets to be clearly separated on different pages. In either case the two sets of measures must balance exactly. Thus for example, any increase in cash must be counterbalanced by a decrease in some other asset or alternatively by an increase in liabilities. This principle applies throughout.

### Example of a balance sheet

Using information given in the previous example together with the following company details the balance sheet at 31st December 1980 may be prepared as follows:

*Note 1: Information in preparation of the Balance Sheet as at 31st December 1980*

|  | £000's |
|---|---|
| Value of fixed assets (see note 2) | 20 000 |
| Cash at bank | 910 |
| Stock of materials and spares | 1 000 |
| Debtors | 4 000 |
| Bank overdraft | 10 |
| Creditors | 3 000 |
| Taxation (from P. & L. Account) | 250 |
| Proposed Dividend | 150 |
| Profit and Loss Account transferred to General Reserve | 100 |
| Interest paid on loans (15% p.a.) | 1 500 |
| Issued Share Capital | 1 900 |
| Reserves at 31st December 1979 | 10 000 |
| Loan Stock (at 15% interest) at 31st December 1979 | 12 000 |
| Loan Stock repaid during 1980 | 2 000 |
| Capital allowances for plant agreed with Tax Inspector | 2 500 |

*Note 2: Valuation of assets* (buildings and plant)

|  | £000's |  |
|---|---|---|
| Valuation at 1st January 1979 | 21 000 |  |
| Additions in year | 10 000 |  |
| Disposals during year | (3 000) |  |
| Valuation at 31st December 1979 | 28 000 | 28 000 |

Buildings and plant depreciated according to
company policy agreed with the Inspector of
Taxes. (Capital allowances must be determined
separately).

*Depreciation*

|  |  |  |
|---|---|---|
| Cumulative up to 1st January 1979 | 6 000 |  |
| Provided for in 1979 (agreed with Tax Inspector) | 2 000 |  |
|  | 8 000 |  |
| Net book value 31st December 1979 | 20 000 | 20 000 |

*Note 3: Capital allowances*
The book value of the firm's assets shown on the balance sheet is normally calculated
by taking a realistic rate of depreciation. Because capital allowances and not depreciation is used to calculate profit for corporation tax assessment, however, the
difference between capital allowances and depreciation, like unrealised profit,
should therefore be allocated to the reserves. Furthermore, some accountants
prefer to show parts of these net allowances as deferred taxation as it should

be recalled that they will be liquidated when the asset is sold, or gradually eliminated as the asset is fully depreciated over its life.

In the example given, capital allowances on plant purchases for 1980 are £2 500
whereas depreciation has been assessed at only £2 000. The net £500 has therefore
been allocated to reserves.

### Tabulated Balance Sheet as at 31st December 1980

|  | £000's | Depreciation £000's | £000's | £000's |
|---|---|---|---|---|
| *Employment of capital* | | | | |
| Fixed assets | 28 000 | 8 000 | 20 000 | 20 000 |
| Current assets | | | | |
| Cash at bank | | | 910 | |
| Stock of materials | | | 1 000 | |
| Debtors | | | 4 000 | |
| | | | 5 910 | 5 910 |
| Current liabilities | | | | |
| Bank overdraft | | | 10 | |
| Creditors | | | 3 000 | |
| Taxation due | | | 250 | |
| Proposed dividend | | | 150 | |
| | | | 3 410 | 3 410 |
| Net current assets (working capital) | | | 2 500 | |
| | | | 22 500 | 22 500 |
| *Capital employed* | | | | |
| Issued Share Capital | | | 1 900 | |
| Reserves (i) P. & L. Account | | 100 | | |
| (ii) Net capital allowances | | 500 | | |
| (iii) As at 31.12.79 | | 10 000 | | |
| | | 10 500 | 10 600 | |
| Loan stock | | | 10 000 | |
| | | | 22 500 | 22 500 |

N.B. Because the interest paid on loans has been transacted it is not shown as a
liability.

### Loan capital

Short term loans are usually classified with current liabilities, but medium and long
term loans are placed with the capital employed. Loans may take several forms of
which debentures and loan stock form the most important sources. Such lenders of
capital are creditors of the company and not owners as are shareholders.

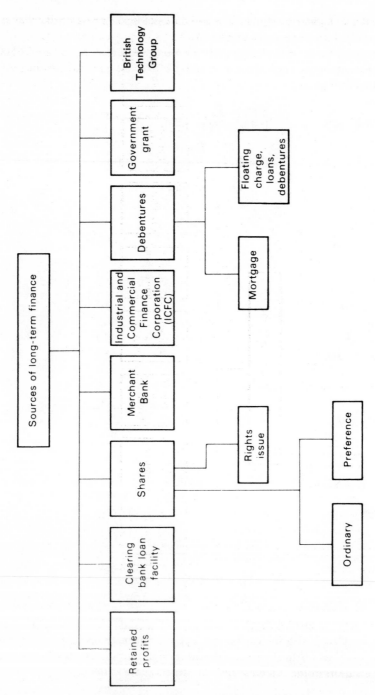

**Fig. 15.1** Sources of long-term finance.

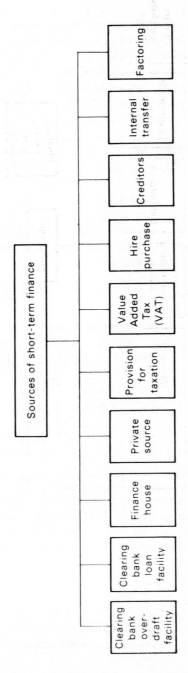

**Fig. 15.2** Sources of short-term finance.

### Long-term/Medium-term Finance

Long-term finance is that capital required for five to ten years, either to start the business or to carry out expansion programmes. Broadly, the capital is used to purchase buildings, plant and equipment and to carry stocks of materials. The risks to the lender are high because of the time scale involved, and consequently only established firms are generally considered by the lending institutions. Some of the more important sources of long-term capital are shown in Figure 15.1.

*Loans* are not easy to obtain. Lenders of such capital often request the borrower to provide a proportion of the finance from internal sources and in addition require convincing evidence that the loan capital can be secured against an asset with profitable expectations. The rate of interest, period of loan and capital repayments vary according to the lenders' request.

*Debentures* are offered for sale by the company, and are requests for loan capital with a fixed annual interest payment and life. Clearly the company must show that it is able to pay the interest, and the capital itself will usually be mortgaged against the company's assets. Loan stock and debentures rank ahead of shareholders in entitlement for payment.

### Short-term Finance

The firm when established often needs short-term capital to overcome immediate cash flow problems. Materials have to be purchased, plant hired, labour and sub-contractors paid and so on before payment is received for the finished product or service. Furthermore, capital may be required to smooth out the strains on cash flow resulting from rapid fluctuations in the market demand for the company's goods. Many sources of short-term finance are available to ease the situation, but naturally the firm must be well managed and profitable before the lending institutions will consider any loan application. The main sources are shown in Figure 15.2, but the clearing bank overdraft facility is the most important source. However, a leasing facility from a finance house is also an important source of either long or short term funding of plant acquisitions. The method is described in Chapter 7 and operates more like a rental payment than a loan.

Sources of most types of capital, their advantages and disadvantages and the costs involved are summarised in Table 15.1. Table 15.2 presents the results of a B.I.M. survey of capital requisition methods used by a sample of construction companies.

### Working capital

Working capital is represented by the difference between current assets and current liabilities and is locked up in a continuous cycle as shown in Figure 15.3.

**Table 15.1** Summary of capital sources

| Source | Finance | Advantages | Disadvantages | Costs |
|---|---|---|---|---|
| Bank | Overdraft | 1. Usually cheapest source<br>2. Quickly arranged<br>3. Flexible<br>4. No minimum<br>5. Renewable<br>6. Interest paid only on usage<br>7. Sometimes available unsecured | 1. Subject to changes in government economic policy<br>2. Repayable on demand<br>3. Subject to changes in bank policy<br>4. Tempting to use for funding long term purchases | 1. Floating interest charge at base rate plus 1–4%<br>2. May incur a commitment fee |
| Bank or finance house | Short term loan | 1. Term commitment by loan institution<br>2. Competition between lending houses especially for hire purchase<br>3. Relatively quickly arranged<br>4. Can be used in conjunction with an overdraft facility<br>5. Sometimes available unsecured | 1. Generally more expensive than an overdraft<br>2. Term commitment and funds may therefore be idle if forecast for funds inaccurate<br>3. Tends to require security against other assets | 1. Floating interest charge at base rate plus 2–5% |
| Finance house | Hire purchase facility | 1. Inexpensive and specially arranged<br>2. Payments fixed over term agreed<br>3. Ideal for short term requirements<br>4. Normally an overdraft facility is not affected<br>5. Capital allowances against corporation tax available immediately<br>6. Not classed as borrowings | 1. Expensive<br>2. Subject to government economic policy changes, but never retrospectively<br>3. Defaults usually rigorously prosecuted<br>4. Interest rate quoted may be misleading due to period of payments and compound interest calculations<br>5. Purchased assets not legally passed over to lender until final payment | 1. Interest fixed at time of negotiations at finance house base rate plus 4–5% |

**Table 15.1 (contd)**

| Source | Finance | Advantages | Disadvantages | Costs |
|---|---|---|---|---|
| Finance house | Lease facility | 1. Similar advantages to hire purchase<br>2. Overgeared firm can acquire resources without affecting the balance sheet | 1. Ownership does not pass to lessee and therefore capital allowances are not available<br>2. Values not reflected in balance sheet assets, and so might give a distorted impression of firm's capabilities | 1. Similar to hire purchase costs, but user must be aware of possible commitments to pay for mandatory maintenance and repairs<br>2. Tax concessions foregone must be compared with H.P. alternative |
| Clearing banks<br>Merchant banks<br>ICFC | Medium term loan | 1. Term commitment by lender<br>2. Capital and interest repayment can be arranged to suit borrowers future cash flow position<br>3. Size of loan may be small or large, especially from clearing banks<br>4. Inflation reduces the real cost over time<br>5. Fixed interest charge can sometimes be negotiated | 1. Usually higher interest charge than shorter term finance<br>2. Long-term commitment which may require short term borrowings to finance interest payment if cash flows became distorted from forecasts<br>3. Negotiation fee likely<br>4. Legal costs also often incurred | 1. Fixed or variable interest charge set at 1½–4% above 6 months inter-bank rate |

**Table 15.2** Summary of British Institute of Management survey of capital requisition methods used by a sample of 200 construction companies (1976).

| Proportion of firms | Up to 1/3 | 1/3 to 2/3 | Over 2/3 | 1 | Total |
|---|---|---|---|---|---|
| Hire purchase | 8% | 1% | 1% | 0.5% | 10.5% |
| Finance lease | 21% | 1% | 0.5% | – | 22.5% |
| Operating lease | 17% | 0.5% | 0.5% | – | 18% |
| Outright purchase | 3% | 4% | 26% | 16% | 49% |
| | | | | | 100% |

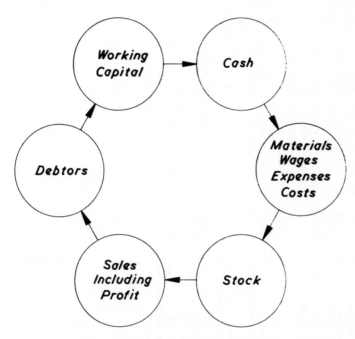

**Fig. 15.3** The working capital cycle.

Example of the working capital requirements

A construction company owns and operates plant. The plant is grouped into a separate division responsible for generating its own turnover in the market place. The turnover of this division is £20 million pounds per year, broken down as 45% plant ownership costs, 15% for materials and 10% for wages for maintenance and transport, 20% for overheads incurred in maintaining the depot establishment and administration facilities and 10% profit. On average, the company keeps three months' material spares in stock and is allowed three months credit by suppliers: wages are paid weekly. Hirers of the company's plant (i.e. debtors) are usually allowed up to two months to pay. Overheads must be met monthly. The ownership costs comprise the capital repayment and interest charges for hire purchase agreements to be paid monthly. Determine the minimum working capital required.

*Working capital calculations*

*Materials* (15% × £20 millions = £3 millions p.a.)

|                           | Time factor |
|---------------------------|-------------|
| Materials held in stock   | 3 months    |
| Credit to customers       | 2 months    |
|                           | 5 months    |
| Less credits from suppliers | 3 months  |
|                           | 2 months    |

$$\therefore \text{Materials} = \frac{2}{12} \times 3\ 000\ 000 = £500\ 000$$

*Labour* (10% × £20 millions = £2 millions p.a.)

|                              | Time factor   |
|------------------------------|---------------|
| Credit to customers          | 2 months      |
| Less one week arrears on wages | 0.25 months |
|                              | 1.75 months   |

$$\therefore \text{Labour} = 2\ 000\ 000 \times \frac{1.75}{12} = £292\ 000 \text{ approx.}$$

*Overheads* (20% × £20 millions = £4 millions p.a.)

|                                                | Time factor |
|------------------------------------------------|-------------|
| Credit to customers                            | 2 months    |
| Less one month arrears on salaries, rents, rates, etc. | 1 month |
|                                                | 1 month     |

$$\therefore \text{Overheads} = 4\ 000\ 000 \times \frac{1}{12} = £330\ 000 \text{ approx.}$$

*Ownership costs* (45% × £20 millions = £9 millions p.a.)

|                                     | Time factor |
|-------------------------------------|-------------|
| Credit to customers                 | 2 months    |
| Less time delay on hire purchase payment | 1 month |
|                                     | 1 month     |

$$\therefore \text{Ownership costs} = 9\ 000\ 000 \times \frac{1}{12} = £750\ 000$$

*Working capital requirements*

The above figures can now be added together to calculate the total working capital requirements:

| Materials | £500 000 |
|---|---|
| Labour | £292 000 |
| Overheads | £330 000 |
| Hire purchase | £750 000 |
| | £1 872 000 |

Such capital needs would usually be financed by means of an overdraft negotiated with a bank or alternatively with private funds. It can be seen however that if plant had been purchased with internal funds rather than by hire purchase, the working capital needs would be £0.75 millions less. The equivalent sum would then remain in the business and offset the working capital needs.

## Aspects of the financial accounts

Ratio analysis

The main short-term techniques for managerial control are cash flow forecasting, budgetary control and costing described in Chapters 13 and 14. Unfortunately, however, they provide absolute figures which are of marginal value in monitoring the long term profitability and short term liquidity of the company. Regular internal ratio analysis using the financial accounts offers a complementary *post mortem* to these standard procedures.

*Working capital ratios*

1. Current ratio $= \dfrac{\text{Current assets}}{\text{Current liabilities}}$

2. Acid test $= \dfrac{\text{Cash and debtors}}{\text{Current liabilities}}$

Most accountants look for ratios of 2:1 and 1:1 respectively. Using the balance sheet given earlier it can be seen that:

$$CR = \frac{5\,910\,000}{3\,410\,000} = 1.73$$

$$AT = \frac{910\,000 + 4\,000\,000}{3\,410\,000} = 1.44$$

In this hypothetical company the current ratio is a little low and the acid test a little high. This situation could be improved by increasing stocks by £½ million and reducing creditors and debtors respectively by £1 and £1½ million to give the following values:

$$CR = \frac{4.91}{2.41} = 2.03$$

$$AT = \frac{3.41}{2.41} = 1.41$$

*Profitability and operating ratios*

1. $\dfrac{\text{Net profit before tax}}{\text{Turnover}} = \dfrac{2\,000\,000}{17\,000\,000} = 11.8\%$

2. $\dfrac{\text{Net profit before tax}}{\text{Capital employed}} = \dfrac{2\,000\,000}{22\,500\,000} = 8.9\% \,(\text{primary ratio})$

3. $\dfrac{\text{Turnover}}{\text{Capital employed}} = \dfrac{17\,000\,000}{22\,500\,000} = 0.76\% \,(\text{turnover ratio})$

The turnover ratio can provide telling information about the capital structure of the company. For example, the plant company is more similar to manufacturing with its turnover ratio approaching one, whereas with most construction companies the ratio is more often nearer to 6, the difference being accounted for by the huge capital investment required in plant. The ratio could, of course, be increased by leasing rather than owning plant.

*Other ratios*

$\dfrac{\text{Debtors}}{\text{Turnover}} \times 12 = \dfrac{4\,000\,000}{17\,000\,000} \times 12 = 2.82 \text{ months}$

This means that customers are given nearly three months to pay.

$\dfrac{\text{Creditors}}{\text{Purchases}} \times 12 = \dfrac{3\,000\,000}{12\,500\,000} \times 12 = 2.88 \text{ months}$

This means that suppliers give nearly three months credit.

The ratios suggest that the company is applying a sensible policy with respect to both suppliers and customers, and a deeper investigation may also yield important details regarding productivity using the following ratios:

(a) $\dfrac{\text{Turnover}}{\text{Number of employees}}$

(b) $\dfrac{\text{Profit}}{\text{Number of employees}}$

(c) $\dfrac{\text{Plant and equipment value}}{\text{Number of employees}}$

(d) $\dfrac{\text{Profit}}{\text{Plant and equipment value}}$

**Capital gearing**

Capital gearing is defined as the ratio of fixed return capital (FRC) to ordinary share capital, FRC being preference shares, debentures and loan stock. A company with a ratio exceeding one is described as a highly geared company.

When a company can expect confidently to make a constant level of high profits over a number of years, then it is wise to raise some of the capital by means of debentures or loan stock and so improve the yield to the ordinary shareholder. Such a technique is known as leverage and the effects are demonstrated in the following example.

## Example

The capital structures for two plant hire companies are given in Table 15.3 and the profits available for interest payments and dividends for a range of company performance levels are given in Table 15.4.

(a) Calculate and comment upon the capital gearing ratios for each of the companies.
(b) Calculate the dividend available to the ordinary shareholders and comment upon the earnings per share at each level of profit. Corporation tax is 50%.

**Table 15.3**   Capital structures

|  | Company A (£'000) | Company B (£'000) |
|---|---|---|
| Ordinary shares (50p) | 155 | 35 |
| 7% Preference shares | 45 | 45 |
| 10% Loan stock (debentures) | – | 120 |

**Table 15.4**   Performance levels

|  | 1 | 2 | 3 | 4 | 5 | 6 |
|---|---|---|---|---|---|---|
| Profit (£) | 10 000 | 12 000 | 18 000 | 20 000 | 25 000 | 30 000 |

*Solution: Part (a)*

|  | Company A | Company B |
|---|---|---|
| 10% Debentures | – | 120 |
| 7% Preference shares | 45 | 45 |
| FRC | 45 | 165 |
| Ordinary shares | 155 | 35 |
| Capital gearing ratio | $\frac{45}{155} \times 100 = 29\%$ | $\frac{165}{35} \times 100 = 470\%$ |
|  | Low geared | High geared |

Company A is low geared and may be able to declare a dividend to ordinary shareholders even at low levels of profit. Company B is highly geared and must therefore ensure that profits are stable and regular and above all sufficient to meet the interest due on debenture holdings. However, the highly geared company should be able to yield a higher rate of return to ordinary shareholders when profits are high.

*Solution: Part (b)*

**Table 15.5** Company A (Low Geared)

| | Performance level | | | | | |
| --- | --- | --- | --- | --- | --- | --- |
| | 1 | 2 | 3 | 4 | 5 | 6 |
| Ordinary shares (50p) | 155 | 155 | 155 | 155 | 155 | 155 |
| Preference shares | 45 | 45 | 45 | 45 | 45 | 45 |
| Debentures | – | – | – | – | – | – |
| Total capital employed (£'000) | 200 | 200 | 200 | 200 | 200 | 200 |
| Profit before tax | 10 | 12 | 18 | 20 | 25 | 30 |
| Corporation tax at 50% | 5 | 6 | 9 | 10 | 12.5 | 15 |
| Profit available as dividend | 5 | 6 | 9 | 10 | 12.5 | 15 |
| Dividend on pref. shares | 3.15 | 3.15 | 3.15 | 3.15 | 3.15 | 3.15 |
| Profit available to ordinary shareholders | 1.85 | 2.85 | 5.85 | 6.85 | 9.35 | 11.85 |
| Profit per ordinary share | 0.6p | 0.92p | 1.89p | 2.2p | 3p | 3.8p |
| Return on ordinary share capital | 1.2% | 1.84% | 2.78% | 4.4% | 6% | 7.6% |
| Return on total share capital | 2.5% | 3% | 4.5% | 5% | 6.25% | 7.5% |

**Table 15.6** Company B (High geared)

| | Performance level | | | | | |
| --- | --- | --- | --- | --- | --- | --- |
| | 1 | 2 | 3 | 4 | 5 | 6 |
| Ordinary shares (50p) | 35 | 35 | 35 | 35 | 35 | 35 |
| 7% preference shares | 45 | 45 | 45 | 45 | 45 | 45 |
| 10% debentures | 120 | 120 | 120 | 120 | 120 | 120 |
| Total capital employed (£'000) | 200 | 200 | 200 | 200 | 200 | 200 |
| Profit before tax | 10 | 12 | 18 | 20 | 25 | 30 |
| Interest on 10% debentures | 12 | 12 | 12 | 12 | 12 | 12 |
| Profit available | −2 | Nil | 6 | 8 | 13 | 18 |
| Corporation tax at 50% | Nil | Nil | 3 | 4 | 6.5 | 9 |
| Profit available as dividend | Nil | Nil | 3 | 4 | 6.5 | 9 |
| Dividend to preference shareholders | Nil | Nil | 3 | 3.15 | 3.15 | 3.15 |
| Profit available to ordinary shareholders | Nil | Nil | Nil | 0.85 | 3.35 | 5.85 |
| Profit per ordinary share | Nil | Nil | Nil | 1.2p | 4.8p | 8.35p |
| Return on ordinary share capital | Nil | Nil | Nil | 2.4% | 9.6% | 16.7% |
| Return on total share capital | Nil | Nil | 3.75% | 5.0% | 8.12% | 11.25% |

Table 15.5 shows that Company A is able to pay the full dividend to preference shareholders at all times, even the ordinary shareholder received payment at all the given levels of profit.

Table 15.6 shows that Company B is in a much more difficult position while profits are poor. In fact, for the first profit period a loan or bank overdraft must be negotiated in order to meet the interest charges on the debenture stock. The full dividend to preference shareholders cannot be met until profit level 4, when there is also a small amount available for distribution to ordinary shareholders. However, the high profits at levels 5 and 6 yield a far better return to the ordinary share-holders than in the low-geared company and this trend will continue for all increased levels of profit.

If the Preference shares were issued as cumulative, then in the case of the highly geared situation additional dividend would be paid out in the good years to make up for the lost years, but at the expense of the ordinary shareholder.

## Plant profitability

It has been argued that it is more advantageous for a plant department to be operated as a profit centre and not on the service principle as is often the case in a construction company. This is best illustrated by the following example using financial data for a plant holding construction company.

### Example

A construction company has an annual turnover of £20 millions of which one fifth is from plant operated by its plant department. The expected profit is 20% of the capital employed and the company is typical for the construction division in that capital is turned over eight times per year whereas for plant the turnover ratio is unity.

| | £ millions | | |
|---|---|---|---|
| | Parent company | Construction division | Plant division |
| Turnover | 20 | 16 | 4 |
| Capital employed | 6 | 2 | 4 |
| 20% profit on capital employed | 1.2 | 0.4 | 0.8 |
| Profit expressed as a percentage on turnover | $\frac{1.2}{20} \times 100 = 6\%$ | $\frac{0.4}{16} \times 100 = 2.5\%$ | $\frac{0.8}{4} \times 100 = 20\%$ |

If the plant division, for instance, had made only £0.5 millions profit, then for the company as a whole, the construction division would have to make £0.7 millions profit or 4.375% on turnover to achieve 6% overall on turnover. Thus any shortfall in plant profitability requires a monumental effort of the construction division to redress the balance.

### Accounting for inflation

During the past ten years or so, the annual level of inflation in the U.K. has exceeded 10%. Consequently results portrayed by the historical method of accounting described earlier in this chapter are not 'true and fair' as required by the Companies Act. The main effects of inflation are as follows:

(i) Assets are undervalued. If, for example, a company purchases an excavator for £10 000 in 1970 then in 1980 the same machine may cost £20 000 because of inflation. The valuation shown in the accounts, however, will be based on £10 000. The company's assets and the shareholders interest are therefore undervalued. Also more importantly, because the depreciation is based on the 1970 figure, profits will consequently be overstated. However, since the introduction of capital allowances into tax legislation (i.e. 100% depreciation during the year of purchase), this latter detrimental effect of inflation is significantly lessened.

(ii) Stocks of materials are undervalued. The change in the value of stocks, between opening and closing dates in the accounts, may have been caused by both a volume difference and a change in prices. This latter aspect is not taken into account in calculating the cost of sales and so, in times of rising prices, the profit is overstated and extra tax paid.

(iii) Companies which finance their operations by loan capital will gain over companies that are self-financing because monetary debts will depreciate in real value. For example, in real terms £1 000 borrowed in 1970 and repayable in 1980, is equivalent to £385 if the rate of inflation is 10% p.a.

In the early 1970s it became obvious that the historical system of accounting was becoming unsatisfactory and disadvantageous to the commercial sector of the economy. Several bodies subsequently put forward proposals for dealing with the problem[2] and in 1980 the Accounting Standards Committee published guidance notes for preparing financial accounts with inflation.[1] However, as yet, these are not mandatory under the Companies Acts and taxation and other government requirements are still largely based on the historical accounts, with some exemptions allowed for stock appreciation. The Accounting Standards Committee has recommended that the traditional historical accounts should be presented with the inflation adjusted accounts side by side. In this way the effects on profits of a combination of inflation and the present requirements for payment of corporation tax can be more clearly monitored. The necessary adjustments to the historical accounts are largely those described under points (i), (ii) and (iii) above and the reader is referred to the Committee's guidance notes for further advice.

**Reading list**

1. The Accounting Standards Committee. *Guidance Notes on SSAP 16: Current Cost Accounting*. London, 1980.
2. The Institute of Chartered Accountants. *Current Cost Accounting: SSAP 16*. London, 1980.
3. Board of Inland Revenue. *Capital Allowances on Machinery or Plant. Leaflet C.A.1*. HMSO, 1973.
4. Goch, D. *Finance and Accounts for Managers*. Pan Books. London, 1971.
5. Nedved, S.C. *Builders Accounting*. Newnes-Butterworths. London, 1973.
6. Rockley, L.E. *The Non-Accountant's Guide to the Balance Sheet*. Business Books. London, 1973.
7. Coombs, W.E. *Construction Accounting and Financial Management*. McGraw-Hill. London, 1958.
8. Phillips, J. *Company financial reports – how to reach and interpret them*. Financial Techniques Ltd. London, 1977.
9. Confederation of British Industry. *The presentation of company accounts*. London, 1974.
10. Berry, K.W. *The use of ratios in the study of business fluctuations and trends*. Institute of Chartered Accountants, London, 1966.
11. *Extel British Company Service*. Extel Statistical Services Ltd., London.
12. HMSO. *The Companies Act*.
13. Smith, T. Plant Finance. *Construction News Magazine*. 2 November 1976.
14. Byrne, P. Today's plant with tomorrow's money. *Contract Journal*. 15 July 1976.
15. Shires, D. Plant: Hire Purchase or Leasing. *National Builder*. November 1974.
16. Glautier, M.W.E. and Underdown, B. *Accounting theory and practice*. Pitman. London, 1976.
17. Glautier, M.W.E., Underdown, B. and Clarke, A.C. *Basic accounting practice*. Pitman. London, 1978.
18. Watts, B.K.R. *Elements of finance for managers*. MacDonald & Evans. Plymouth, 1976.
19. Cousins, D. *Book-keeping*. Teach Yourself Books. London, 1970.

# CHAPTER 16

# COMPUTERS AND PLANT MANAGEMENT

## Introduction

The management of a plant division within a company, a plant company within a group of companies, or an independent plant hire company encompasses all the general management tasks faced by most companies. As in other types of companies, the use of computers has become established in basic bookkeeping or accounting functions such as payroll and ledgers. Some plant companies have extended the use of computers into management accounting and management information systems. Examples of these uses include the maintenance of an asset register which is particularly valuable because of the high value of capital assets represented in a large number of plant items. Other examples include plant location reports, cost and revenue reports and variance analyses which compare income with budgeted income and actual usage with planned usage. Stock control and maintenance record keeping are also examples of management information applications.

Other uses of computers in plant management include financial appraisals where financial modelling systems are used to explore the cash flow and profitability prospects of various proposals.

The larger companies have had access to computers for many years and the applications developed by these companies have naturally developed to suit the larger computers. More recently, the availability of small microcomputers has extended the use of computers to smaller companies and many of the applications referred to above are becoming available on these smaller machines.

This chapter will briefly describe the features of the smaller computer systems and review the computer applications that are particularly relevant to plant management.

**Features of a computer system**

Until the late seventies most computing work of the type undertaken by plant companies employed a large computer system known as a main frame computer. Since then the so-called micro revolution has taken place and many of the applications that were hitherto available on large computers have become available on microcomputers. Many companies still use and will go on using large computers because it suits their operations and management organisation but the arrival of the microcomputer has extended the number of potential users of computers and few companies are now excluded from access to a computer simply on grounds of capital cost. Many of the smaller companies who might otherwise have used bureau services are able to afford to install their own microcomputer which can offer the facilities and services they require. This section will describe the features of a small computer system as a guide to the hardware required. Later sections will describe applications of computers to plant management although not all these applications are available on microcomputers at the time of writing. The development of software (programs) for microcomputers is a very active area and it will only be a matter of time until all applications described in this chapter are fully available on microcomputers.

Microcomputer systems

The components of a microcomputer system are illustrated in Figure 16.1. These components are:

(i) Central processing unit
(ii) Memory
(iii) Mass storage
(iv) Input/output devices namely a visual display unit and keyboard, and a printer
(v) Systems software
(vi) Applications software

The *Central Processing Unit* performs all the calculations and manipulations. It is in fact executing program instructions and fetching data from files or input devices, performing the required calculations or manipulations and returning the resulting data to file or to the output devices.

The *Memory* is the unit that holds data and instructions to which the central processing unit can have access. The size of the memory limits the calculations that can be undertaken at one time. Because the size of the memory in small computer systems is limited, a secondary memory or mass storage system exists that can hold data or program instructions which are not in use at a particular moment.

*Mass storage devices*, which are usually magnetic tapes, floppy discs or hard discs are used to store information, data or program instructions that are not required by the central processing unit at a particular time. The information stored on these devices is not directly accessible by the central processing unit and portions of the information held in mass storage devices are copied to memory which then makes it accessible by the central processing unit.

*Magnetic tapes* on larger computers are usually open reel tapes, and small cassette tapes on microcomputers. The storage of data on cassette tapes on very small machines is generally considered to be slow in transferring data from tape to memory and this can make such systems tedious to use.

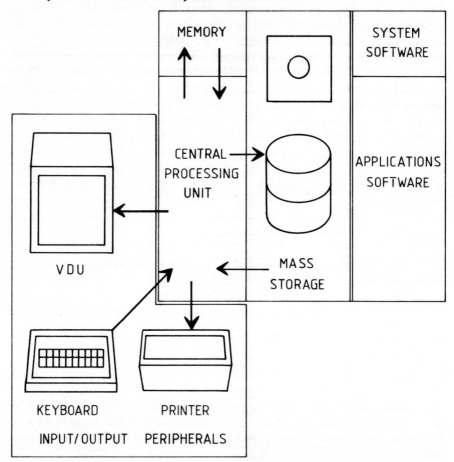

**Fig. 16.1** The components of a microcomputer system.

*Floppy discs* are flexible plastic discs either 5¼ inch or 8 inch in diameter and the signal is recorded on the magnetic coating on both sides of the disc's surface. Floppy discs are loaded via a slot in the disc drive and offer a convenient method of storing data and programs, although each disc can carry only a limited amount of data. If large volumes of data are required then many floppy discs are needed and the tedium of continually re-loading these discs grows. However, for many applications they are adequate.

*Hard discs,* which can be fixed or removable, store more data and are much faster than floppies in accessing the data. Speed of accessing data is reflected in the performance of a computer system, and for applications involving the storage of large amounts of data hard disc systems are preferable. In microcomputer systems it is the more expensive microcomputers that include hard disc systems. These are generally sealed or non-removable hard disc systems supported by back-up systems which are usually floppy discs. Thus a floppy disc system and a hard disc system working together combine the ability to hold large amounts of data on the hard disc with the ability to store other data on floppy discs outside the computer system to provide an element of portability in data storage.

*Input/output devices* enter input data and give out the results. A payroll system, for example, requires that input data is supplied to the computer system in the nature of employee records, including names, work numbers, tax and national insurance information, holiday pay deductions, pay etc. The output required is the printed pay slip and updated records of the employees' pay, tax, national insurance and holiday pay etc. The most common devices now in use are visual display units with keyboards which act as both input and output devices and printers which act only as output devices.

A *visual display unit with a keyboard,* sometimes referred to as a terminal, is a television-type screen with a typewriter-styled keyboard. Data and instructions can be entered on the keyboard and displayed on the screen for a visual check which can be edited before committing to the computer for calculation. The screen also acts as an output device which can receive the results of the calculations for visual inspection. If a printed copy of the output is required then a printer is needed.

*Printers* are available in a wide price range, the main differences being the quality of the printing and the speed. Thus, if large volumes of printed data are required a relatively expensive, high quality, fast printer is needed.

The *systems software* or the operating system performs all the tasks of managing the computer system. The use of the computer's resources and the processes that are performed by the computer system are organised by the operating system, handling all the instructions between the computer's central processing unit and all the input/output devices. The operating system organises the data files and the transfer of data between the mass storage system and the central processing unit: in multi-user computer systems, it shares the available computer resources between each user. It is evident that the operating system is a crucial component in the effective running of a computer system but many users buying a small micro-computer system may be unaware that they are also purchasing an operating system and that more than one operating system may be available. Users are usually more interested instead in the applications software that makes the computer system undertake the tasks required by the user.

*Applications software* comprises the computer programs that perform the user's tasks. Three fundamental facilities of computer systems can be employed through the programs and these are:

(i) A filing system, using the mass storage facilities;

(ii) A calculator, using the central processing unit and memory;

(iii) A report generator, printing information held on file or calculated in any number of predetermined ways.

The applications software employed in plant management fall into three categories: basic bookkeeping or accounting, management accounting and information, and other applications such as financial appraisals. The next section reviews each of these categories of applications.

### Computer applications in plant management

Computers may be applied to plant management in:

1. Basic accounting or book-keeping: (a) payroll, (b) purchase ledger, (c) sales ledger and (d) nominal ledger.
2. Management accounting and information: (a) asset register, (b) purchase and disposal analysis, (c) weekly hire charges reports, (d) period hire charges reports, (e) plant locations, (f) revenue and cost reports, (g) plant utilisation reports, (h) stock control and (i) maintenance records.
3. Financial appraisals.

Basic accounting or book-keeping

*Payroll*

Amongst the labour intensive industries, construction is perhaps the one with the most complicated payroll requirements. Very few firms in construction pay all their employees on the same basis: instead there is a mixture of remuneration by piece-work, hourly, daily or weekly wages, as well as monthly salaries. As a result the computerisation of payroll nearly always produces considerable benefits. Unlike other industries where the sales—purchase—nominal group of ledgers is the first to be computerised, payroll is almost invariably the first in construction. Plant hire companies and plant divisions of construction companies have been influenced by this and payroll has been amongst the first applications for computerisation.

There is a great number of general purpose payroll packages available for practically every computer in the market. As with all commercial software, payroll programs can be bought or leased for implementation on the user's own computer. Payroll and other book-keeping programs can also be used through bureaux which offer a comprehensive service. This service usually involves the user in sending completed data forms to the bureau and receiving the processed results, or information, by post. This can sometimes be the most economical way of using payroll programs, even by organisations which have their own computer. The reason is that different companies' payrolls can be processed in a single 'production line'. Moreover, common data, such as tax tables, are used for all payrolls and the cost of updating them is shared by a large number of clients. Prices offered are therefore very competitive. Payroll programs are also available for the smaller micro-computers.

An important aspect of payroll programs is that they deal with something which is not stable. Taxation changes every year, often more than once; so does national insurance. Pension and bonus schemes also change, and so does the form and the kind of information that the inland revenue, and other authorities, want presented to them at the end of each year. A company's employees often work on different contracts within a single period and the distribution of their time amongst these contracts changes every day. A company contemplating the use of a payroll package has to take this fluidity into serious consideration. If the company has its own data processing department which will write the program from scratch, care should be taken to design the package for flexibility. If the intention is to use a package developed outside its organisation, through straightforward purchase, bureau service, or in any other way, it must be clear whose responsibility it is to update the package when changes occur, as well as the deadlines associated with such updates. Updating a payroll program can be a very expensive task and it accounts for the high cost of maintenance charges imposed by most software houses.

The basic facilities of a payroll system would be:

- Payroll creation, the creation and amendment of fixed details;
- Payroll calculation, calculating the weekly and monthly pay of employees;
- Printing payslips, P35, P11 and non-employees list;
- Amend tax and N.I. rates and pensions;
- Payment by cash, cheque or credit transfer.

Payroll systems based on timesheet information allow labour costs to be allocated to each job thus providing information for job costing. Figure 16.2 shows an example of a file creation document and Figure 16.3 shows an example of a blank payslip on which the pay details would be printed.

*Sales, purchase, nominal ledger and V.A.T.*
The facilities offered in sales and purchase ledger systems are: (a) accounts creation, amendments and deletions, (b) accounts postings, (c) cash postings, (d) period statements and remittance advices. Derived from these basic accounting functions the reports that are available include accounts over credit limit, accounts overdue, accounts turnovers, and customer lists. Linked to the sales and purchase ledgers are V.A.T. maintenance systems. These collect and analyse V.A.T. collected and paid, enabling the total amount due to be calculated. The nominal ledger systems maintain a set of nominal accounts.

Examples of the information available in the forms of documents, reports and accounts are shown in Figures 16.4 and 16.5.

An important aspect of having the basic accounting functions computerised is that the information contained in the accounting system can be made available to other functions such as plant and job costing and stock control. The information contained in the payroll system and in the sales and purchase ledgers are relevant to these other functions and in many accounting systems offer the important facility of feeding information to these other functions. Two important chains can be identified: purchase ledger–payroll–job costing and purchase ledger–order processing–stock control.

```
                    PAYROLL FILE CREATION DOCUMENT

   EMPLOYEE NUMBER  I.....I          I.....I          I.....I          I.....I
                    *                *                *                *
 1 SURNAME          I...........I    I...........I    I...........I    I...........I
 2 INITIALS         I...........I    I...........I    I...........I    I...........I
 3 DEPT/LAB CODE    I...........I    I...........I    I...........I    I...........I
 4 PAYTYPE(C/G/Q)   I...........I    I...........I    I...........I    I...........I
 5 N.I. NUMBER      I...........I    I...........I    I...........I    I...........I
 6 N.I.CODE(ABCDE)  I...........I    I...........I    I...........I    I...........I
 7 TAX CLASS        I...........I    I...........I    I...........I    I...........I
 8 WK/MTH 1 FLAG    I...........I    I...........I    I...........I    I...........I
 9 TAX CODE         I...........I    I...........I    I...........I    I...........I
10 TAX WK/MTH       I...........I    I...........I    I...........I    I...........I
11 FREE PAY         I...........I    I...........I    I...........I    I...........I
12 PEN DED'N        I...........I    I...........I    I...........I    I...........I
13 PENSION T.D      I...........I    I...........I    I...........I    I...........I
14 + UNUSED +       I...........I    I...........I    I...........I    I...........I
15 GROSS PAY TE     I...........I    I...........I    I...........I    I...........I
16 GROSS PAY PE     I...........I    I...........I    I...........I    I...........I
17 GROSS-NTE TE     I...........I    I...........I    I...........I    I...........I
18 GROSS-NTE PE     I...........I    I...........I    I...........I    I...........I
19 TAX TE           I...........I    I...........I    I...........I    I...........I
20 TAX PE           I...........I    I...........I    I...........I    I...........I
21 NI CONT (EE)     I...........I    I...........I    I...........I    I...........I
22 NI CONT (ER)     I...........I    I...........I    I...........I    I...........I
23 BASIC RATE       I...........I    I...........I    I...........I    I...........I
24 OTHER RATE1      I...........I    I...........I    I...........I    I...........I
25 OTHER RATE2      I...........I    I...........I    I...........I    I...........I
26 OTHER RATE3      I...........I    I...........I    I...........I    I...........I
27 BASIC HOURS      I...........I    I...........I    I...........I    I...........I
28 HOURS OTHER1     I...........I    I...........I    I...........I    I...........I
29 HOURS OTHER2     I...........I    I...........I    I...........I    I...........I
30 HOURS OTHER3     I...........I    I...........I    I...........I    I...........I
31 WAGE/SALARY      I...........I    I...........I    I...........I    I...........I
32 OTHER PAY        I...........I    I...........I    I...........I    I...........I
33 EXPENSES         I...........I    I...........I    I...........I    I...........I
34 BONUS            I...........I    I...........I    I...........I    I...........I
35 TOOL MONEY       I...........I    I...........I    I...........I    I...........I
36 EXTRAS 1         I...........I    I...........I    I...........I    I...........I
37 EXTRAS 2         I...........I    I...........I    I...........I    I...........I
38 SICK/PH          I...........I    I...........I    I...........I    I...........I
39 HOL PAY          I...........I    I...........I    I...........I    I...........I
40 *N-T-E           I...........I    I...........I    I─I...........I    I...........I
41 DEDUCTION 1      I...........I    I...........I    I...........I    I...........I
42 DEDUCTION 2      I...........I    I...........I    I...........I    I...........I
43 DEDUCTION 3      I...........I    I...........I    I...........I    I...........I
```

**Fig. 16.2**    Example of a payroll file creation document showing space for the details of four employees. (Reproduced by kind permission of Q-Genesys Ltd. and extracted from the Q-Genesys Accounts System).

### Management accounting and information

The applications of computers in management accounting and information is less standardised than the basic accounting functions. Consequently, there are fewer computer packages available for purchase. Also it is a group of applications that more closely reflects the management and organisation of a company. Consequently this group of applications, more than the basic accounting functions, have

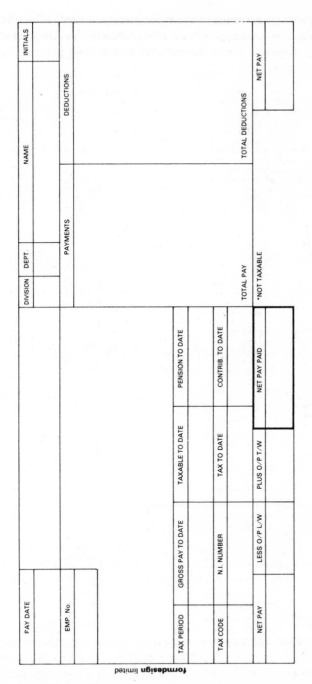

**Fig. 16.3**    Example of a blank payslip on which pay details would be printed. (Reproduced by kind permission of Q-Genesys Ltd.).

been developed within companies for their own use. Nevertheless several software houses do offer systems purposely designed and suitable for plant companies. The applications that come in this group are reviewed as follows.

```
DEMONSTRATION LIMITED      ACCOUNTS - OPENING REPORT AS AT 31.05.81    PAGE    1

ACCOUNT          NAME                          DEBITS              CREDITS

    1            SALES ACCOUNT 1                                 24268.30
    2            SALES ACCOUNT 2                                 20027.00
    3            SALES ACCOUNT 3                                 30000.00
    4            SALES ACCOUNT 4                                 40500.00
   19            DISCOUNTS GIVEN                 87.50
   21            PURCHASES ACCOUNT 1          7500.00
   23            PURCHASES ACCOUNT 3         20000.00
   24            PURCHASES ACCOUNT 4         25000.00
   41            WAGES                        3994.33
   42            SALARIES                     1150.00
   43            NATIONAL INSURANCE            200.00
   45            RENTS                        2500.00
   46            RATES                        1100.00
   47            ELECTRICITY                   300.00
   48            HEAT & LIGHT                  500.00
   49            GAS & FUEL OIL                200.00
   51            INSURANCES                   1100.00
   52            VEHICLE INSURANCE             516.80
   53            VEHICLE LICENCES             1000.00
  131            LAND & BUILDINGS            10000.00
  133            PLANT & MACHINERY            5000.00
  134            DEP'N PROVISION                                  1000.00
  135            OFFICE EQUIPMENT             4000.00
  136            DEP'N PROVISION                                  1000.00
  137            MOTOR VEHICLES               2000.00
  138            DEP'N PROVISION                                  1000.00
  163            DEBTORS CONTROL             43077.05
  164            BANK ACCOUNT                48415.80
  165            CASH IN HAND                  258.20
  166            V.A.T.                                           7177.25
  167            BANK ACCOUNT 2                                  10000.00
  168            BAD DEBTS PROV'N             1300.00
  170            SALARIES CONTROL                                 2628.89
  171            PENSIONS CONTROL                                  100.00
  176            CREDITORS CONTROL                               21840.00
  177            ACCRUALS                                         5000.00
  178            TAX PROVISIONS                                   3000.00
  179            C.I.R. - PAYE                                     692.85
  180            C.I.R. - N.I.                                     570.39
  191            LOAN ACCOUNT 1                205.00
  192            LOAN ACCOUNT 2                                    500.00
  201            ORD. SHARE CAPITAL                               100.00
  202            PREF.SHARE CAPITAL                             10000.00
  205            P & L APPR'N ACCOUNT                           27000.00
  221            STOCK ACCOUNT 1              3000.00
  222            STOCK ACCOUNT 2              7000.00
  223            STOCK ACCOUNT 3              6000.00
  224            STOCK ACCOUNT 4             11000.00

                                           ==========          ==========

                 REPORT TOTALS            206404.68            206404.68

                                           ==========          ==========
```

**Fig. 16.4**    Sample accounts opening report. (Reproduced by kind permission of Q-Genesys Ltd.).

```
                            DEMONSTRATION LIMITED
********           BALANCE SHEET  AS AT  31.05.81        ********

FIXED ASSETS
************
LAND & BUILDINGS                              10000.00

PLANT & MACHINERY                 5000.00
DEP'N PROVISION                   1000.00      4000.00
                                  --------

OFFICE EQUIPMENT                  4000.00
DEP'N PROVISION                   1000.00      3000.00
                                  --------

MOTOR VEHICLES                    2000.00
DEP'N PROVISION                   1000.00      1000.00
                                  --------

                                  ========              18000.00


CURRENT ASSETS
**************
CLOSING STOCK                                 27000.00
DEBTORS CONTROL                               43077.05
BANK ACCOUNT                                  48415.80
CASH IN HAND                                    258.20
BAD DEBTS PROV'N                               1300.00
SALARIES CONTROL                       (       2628.89)
PENSIONS CONTROL                       (        100.00)
                                              ========
                                             117322.16
                                              ========

CURRENT LIABILITIES
*******************
CREDITORS CONTROL                             21840.00
ACCRUALS                                       5000.00
TAX PROVISIONS                                 3000.00
C.I.R. - PAYE                                   692.85
C.I.R. - N.I.                                   570.39
V.A.T.                                         7177.25
BANK 2 OVERDRAWN                              10000.00
                                              ========
                                              48280.49
                                              ========

NET CURRENT ASSETS                                      69041.67
******************                                      ========
                                                        87041.67
LOAN ACCOUNTS
*************
LOAN ACCOUNT 1     OWED                          205.00
LOAN ACCOUNT 2     OWING                (        500.00)
                                              ========       (    295.00)

                                                         ********
                                                         86746.67
                                                         ********
```

```
                            DEMONSTRATION LIMITED
********           BALANCE SHEET  AS AT  31.05.81        ********

REPRESENTED BY
CAPITAL ACCOUNTS
****************

ORD. SHARE CAPITAL                              100.00
PREF.SHARE CAPITAL                            10000.00
P & L APPR'N ACCOUNT TO OPEN      27000.00
                     PROFIT       49646.67    76646.67
                                  ========
                                                        86746.67
                                              ========  ********
                                                        86746.67
                                                        ********
```

**Fig. 16.5** Sample balance sheet. (Reproduced by kind permission of Q-Genesys Ltd.).

*Asset register*

Assets accounting deals with assets which, usually, have a long lifespan, extending over several accounting periods. Computer programs for assets accounting provide, at any one time, (a) an assets register with straightforward information on what assets the contractor has, and where they are, (b) their written down value, and depreciation to date, and (c) their replacement cost.

Information provided on the replacement cost is perhaps the most valuable as it forms the essential test on the wisdom, or otherwise, of the depreciation policy being adopted. Most asset register systems offer a range of depreciation methods including straight line and declining balance. The effects of inflation have complicated this and, following the SSAP 16 recommendations as to standard accounting practice relating to current cost accounting, asset registers now include a depreciation adjustment based on these recommendations.

Thus reports from asset register systems include:

- A list of plant items grouped by type of plant;
- Inventory numbers;
- Value;
- Depreciation to date by usual methods and according to SSAP 16 recommendations;
- Depreciation for this year.

Separate reports will include technical details of each plant item held.

The importance of an asset register for the plant company is that it maintains detailed information relating to the plant items held in a form that supports the production of the company accounts and in a form that allows managers to consider their depreciation and disposal policies. The depreciation policy is particularly important to a plant company because the depreciation element, or capital cost, forms as much as 50% of a hire rate. The purchase and disposal of plant is equally important to the continued well-being of a company.

*Purchase and disposal analysis*

Linked to the asset register is a purchase and disposal analysis which is a maintained record of the plant items bought and sold. This aids the preparation of annual accounts and assists companies in managing the size of their plant fleet.

*Plant reports*

The plant hire company requires its own set of management reports to inform the company managers and allow them to take the various day-to-day decisions.

The management reporting systems dealing with plant include:

- Weekly hire charges;
- Period hire charges;
- Plant locations;
- Revenue and cost reports;
- Plant utilisation reports.

Here the computer systems are being employed in handling relatively large quantities of data regularly, to provide the plant manager with the information he requires.

The two key reports are the 'Plant Utilisation Report' and the 'Plant Cost and Revenue Report'. These two reports provide essential information for the running of any large plant holding. Essentially they are designed for the plant hire company to monitor their costs and revenues and hence their profits. But it is equally essential for the construction company holding plant in order that they may manage the plant subsidiary as a profit centre whose main revenues come from internal charges.

### The Plant Utilisation Report
This information is usually produced monthly and is intended to be a statement of the plant's actual usage in comparison with the budgeted (or planned) usage. Using the principles of management accounting, the plant utilisation report tends to present the information in the form of variances. These variances compare the actual performance with the anticipated performance, the performance being measured in terms of the number of hours on hire, and the 'price' (or revenue) obtained for these hours of hire.

A typical report would be presented in the form of a table. The headings of such a table are shown in Figure 16.6, with a short explanation of the entries that would go under each heading.

### Plant Cost and Revenue Report
This report, also produced at least monthly, is the comparison of costs and revenues. The costs listed in such a report would refer to direct costs associated with the plant item and so the net revenue remaining still has to pay for company overheads before being properly classified as 'profit'.

The headings of a typical report would be as shown in Figure 16.7. Like the plant utilisation report, this report is also in the form of a table.

The other reports that are available include:

### Weekly and period hire charges
This reporting system records the current hire charges for all plant and the dates when hire charges were changed.

### Plant locations
Plant location reports record the current location of plant on hire and the length of time at that location. The location of idle plant is also monitored in reports of this type.

### Stock control
Stock control is described in more detail in Chapter 10. In plant management, stock control relates mainly to the supply of spare parts and consumables. The purpose of keeping stock is to supply the plant fleet with the items it needs but this need must be tempered with economy. Over-stocking causes locked-up capital but under-

stocking may cause a repair to be delayed and involve expensive down time. Good stock control aims at achieving a balance between over-stocking and under-stocking. Stock recording and control systems monitor stock issues and delivery notes, perform stock taking and prompt re-ordering when minimum levels of stock of a particular item are reached.

```
PLANT UTILISATION REPORT                Month ending .......
                                        Weeks in month .....

Description:  A description of each plant item.  Plant items
              are grouped together; all cranes in one group,
              all compressors in another etc.

Planned quantity:  The quantity, or number of items of plant
              planned in the budget.

Actual quantity:  The actual quantity of plant held.

Usage:        The number of hours or days the plant was used
              in the month, and the total for the year to date.

Income:       The income for the month based on the monthly
              usage and the income for the year, based on the
              usage for the year to date.

Utilisation variance:  The effect, in money terms, of the
              usage being more or less than planned for the
              month, and for the year to date.

Price variance: The effect, in money terms, of the hire rate
              being more or less than budgeted for the month,
              and for the year to date.

Utilisation:  The percentage of the planned utilisation
              achieved in the month and the year to date.

External Usage:  The percentage of the utilisation for the
              year to date that was hired externally.
```

Fig. 16.6    Plant Utilisation Report

Stock control systems are generally linked to purchasing systems and hold details of the various suppliers, the purchase order details for the suppliers and the invoices. Stock control systems offer savings by optimising the level of stock held and holding up-to-date information on the stocks and reducing the manpower committed to stock taking.

```
┌─────────────────────────────────────────────────────────────────┐
│ PROFIT AND COST REPORT              Month Ending .......          │
│                                     Weeks in month .....          │
│                                                                   │
│                                                                   │
│ Description:      As before.                                      │
│                                                                   │
│ Actual quantity:  As before.                                      │
│                                                                   │
│ Capital cost:     Self explanatory.                               │
│                                                                   │
│ Current written down value:  Self explanatory.                    │
│                                                                   │
│ Depreciation:     The amount of depreciation in money terms       │
│                                                                   │
│                   this month and the total amount of              │
│                                                                   │
│                   depreciation for the year to date.              │
│                                                                   │
│ Maintenance:      The amount of maintenance this month and        │
│                                                                   │
│                   the total maintenance costs for the year        │
│                                                                   │
│                   to date.                                        │
│                                                                   │
│ Income:           The income for this month and for the           │
│                                                                   │
│                   year to date.                                   │
│                                                                   │
│ Net Profit:       The income less depreciation and main-          │
│                                                                   │
│                   tenance for the month and for the year          │
│                                                                   │
│                   to date.                                        │
│                                                                   │
│ Profit:           Profit as a percentage of income for the        │
│                                                                   │
│                   month and for the year to date.                 │
│                                                                   │
└─────────────────────────────────────────────────────────────────┘
```

**Fig. 16.7**    Profit and Cost Report

*Maintenance records*

The maintenance records described in Chapter 10 can be held on computer file for ease of update and reference.

*Other applications: financial appraisals*

A common application relating to plant management that is not part of day-to-day company management routines are financial appraisals. A number of investment appraisal programs are available to perform such tasks.

These investment appraisal programs provide a range of calculations which enable a proposed investment to be evaluated. The investment in this case is a capital sum from which revenue, or some other form of return, is expected and the evaluation determines whether these returns are enough to justify the capital investment. The adequacy of these investments is measured by profitability, not just simple profit. The most common profitability measures, based on discounting techniques, are net present value and yield or rate of return. Other measures produced by these programs, which do not rely on discounting, are the payback period and the average annual rate of return. All these methods of measuring profitability are described in Chapter 6.

The more sophisticated programs offer facilities which enable the modelling of the estimates and calculations that determine the investment projects' cash flow. Using this modelling facility the estimates can be varied and the sensitivity of the investment project's profitability to certain estimates can be determined. An example of these financial appraisals would be as follows.

Figure 6.1 in Chapter 6 shows a simple model of the relationship between the cash flows that go into calculating a rate of return. The rate of return is defined as the *discounted cash flow yield*. Given estimates, based on historical records, and experienced guesswork for each of the elements in the model, the expected d.c.f. yield can be calculated. However, two of the key elements in this calculation are the hire rate and the utilisation factor. The 'market' controls both the hire rate and the utilisation factor and therefore neither can be readily estimated with accuracy. Using some of the existing software packages it is relatively easy to calculate the rate of return for a range of utilisation factors for a range of hire rates. By way of example this has been done for an actual case and the results are plotted and shown in Figure 6.3 in Chapter 6. The interesting aspect of Figure 6.3 in Chapter 6 is that it tells you that the plant needs to be utilised at 60% for hire rate 1 before it breaks even and if the company specified its minimum rate of return as 10% then this particular item of plant would need to be utilised at 82%. It is now a market judgement as to whether this item of plant can be hired out for the required time to be profitable. The exciting aspect of this type of calculation is that having done it as a means of evaluating whether the plant item should be in the fleet or not, the same data or graph can be used in a management sense to set targets for salesmen.

The other major use made of these evaluation programs arises in the decision whether to purchase outright, to use hire purchase, or to lease. The capital payments of each of these three methods of acquisition are different and occur at different times. Also the implications with respect to corporation tax and capital allowances are different.

The capital allowances for plant are such that all the investment can be allowed against tax in the first year of operation. Outright purchase, therefore, attracts this allowance. However, to take advantage of these substantial allowances the company must be making profits. Thus the method of acquisition is affected by the capital available and the company's current profits. These factors can be 'modelled' in systems, which are essentially programs that permit the manipulation of cash flows.

Thus the method of acquisition that best suits the company at the particular time can be evaluated.

Most of the calculations described in this section are capable of being undertaken manually with calculators. The use of computers, however, serves to make the calculations more thorough in that having set up the exercise for computer analysis it is easy to explore it more thoroughly and to explore more alternatives.

### Reading list

1. *D.O.C. Report No. 4. Evaluation of Computer Programs for Construction Management.* D.O.C. Construction Industry Computing Association. Cambridge, 1979.
2. *Micros in Construction.* C.I.C.A. Cambridge, 1980.
3. *List of Building Application Programs for Members.* D.O.C. Construction Industry Computing Association. Cambridge, 1981.

*Acknowledgement*
Some of the material presented in this chapter was based on the author's contribution to reference no. 1.

## INTEREST AND TIME RELATIONSHIPS AND TABULATIONS FOR INTEREST RATES OF 10% and 15%

### Interest and time relationships

Cash flows are transfers of money. Positive cash flows are transfers into a project or scheme, and negative cash flows are transfers of money out of a project or scheme. If a company purchased an item of plant the purchase price and the running costs would be negative cash flows. The revenue from hire and the resale would be positive cash flows. Cash flows can be individual lump sums or a recurring series, that is the same cash flow recurring each period. The manipulation of both types of cash flow, the lump sum and the recurring series, are achieved by the use of derived relationships between interest and time. The derived relationships are tabulated as factors which can be used to achieve these manipulations. The expressions used to calculate these factors are given later in the example tables for the interest rates 10% and 15%. The expressions are also given in the following six explanation examples which are presented in the same order as they are tabulated. The expressions are easily incorporated into computer programs or programmable calculators and the use of tables is diminishing.

### 1. Compound amounts

If a sum of money, £1 000, is invested for some years, say eight, at an interest rate of 10%, the sum of money that can be withdrawn at the end of that time would be:

$$£1\ 000 \times 2.1435 = £2\ 143.50$$

2.1435 is the compound amount factor taken from the tables or calculated from the expression $(1 + i)^n$, where i is the interest rate 0.1 (for 10%) and n is the number of years, 8. This process is represented in the following diagram, Figure A.1, to illustrate the reward received for money loaned or invested.

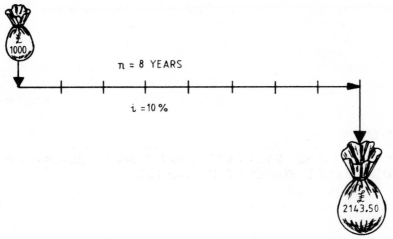

**Fig. A.1**   Compound amount.

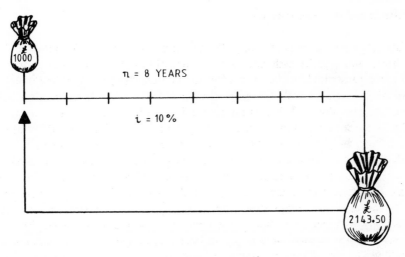

**Fig. A.2**   Present worth.

## 2. Present worth

The inverse of calculating compound amounts is calculating the present worth. If a sum of money, £2 143.50, is required in eight years' time the capital sum that would be required to be invested today to generate this amount, given an interest rate of 10%, would be £1 000:

$$£2\ 143.50 \times 0.46650 = £1\ 000$$

0.46650 is the present worth factor taken from the tables or calculated from the expression:

$$\frac{1}{(1 + i)^n}$$

where i is the interest rate and n is the number of years as before. This expression is the inverse of the expression for the compound amount factor and the process can be represented in Figure A.2 which illustrates that if £2 143.50 is required in eight years £1 000 has to be invested now. The £1 000 is said to be the equivalent of £2 143.50 in eight years given the interest rate of 10%. £1 000 is the present worth of the £2 143.50 in eight years, given the interest rate of 10%.

Thus £1 000 in year 0 is the same as £2 143.50 in year 8 and the difference of £1 143.50 is the interest earned in the intervening eight years. This process of converting the £2 143.50 in year 8 to £1 000 in year 0 is known as discounting. This discounting process is very widely used because it provides a convenient method of converting future cash flows to a common base date and provides a means of comparing cash flows of different magnitude occurring at different times.

It is important to remember that the present worth of a future cash flow is the capital sum that would be required to be invested today to generate that future sum.

### 3. Compound amount of a regular or uniform series

If a sum of money, £100, is invested regularly for, say, six years, the sum available at the end of the six years — given an interest rate of 15% — is £875.30, given by:

$$£100 \times 8.753 = £875.30$$

The 8.753 is the uniform series compound amount factor taken from the tables or calculated from the expression:

$$\frac{(1 + i)^n - 1}{i}$$

where i is the interest rate and n is the number of years.

Each sum is invested for a different period of time and the compound amount could be calculated using the compound amount factor for each of the six individual cash flows and summing the results. The uniform series compound amount factor allows this to be done in one step as illustrated in Figure A.3.

The illustration also shows that the cash flows are included in the calculation at the end of the year or period in which they occur. This is the assumption on which the expression was derived and is known as the 'end of period convention' which states that all cash flows take place at the end of the period.

### 4. Sinking fund deposit

The inverse of the compound amount of the uniform series is to find how much should be deposited each year or period in order to generate a certain sum at the end of the time. If £875.30 is required at the end of year 6 and it is intended to provide this sum by saving or investing a sum for each of the next six years at an interest rate of 15%, the sum to be saved would be £100:

$$£875.30 \times 0.11423 = £100$$

0.11423 is the sinking fund deposit factor taken from tables or calculated from the expression:

$$\frac{i}{(1 + i)^n - 1}$$

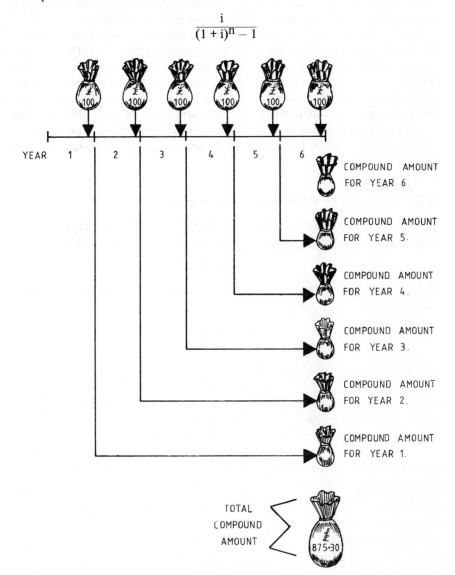

Fig. A.3    Compound amount of a uniform series.

where i is the interest rate and n is the number of years. This expression is the inverse of the uniform series compound amount factor. This factor is used in calculating the monies to be taken from revenue to repay borrowed capital or to replace plant.

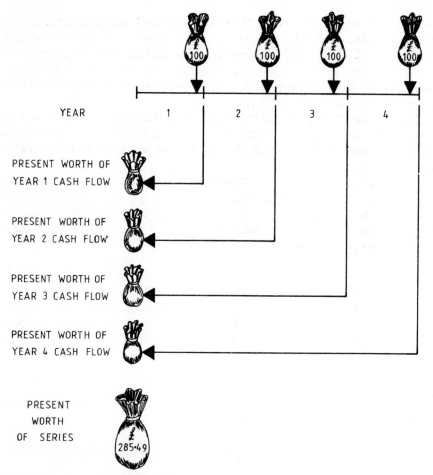

YEAR

PRESENT WORTH OF
YEAR 1 CASH FLOW

PRESENT WORTH OF
YEAR 2 CASH FLOW

PRESENT WORTH OF
YEAR 3 CASH FLOW

PRESENT WORTH OF
YEAR 4 CASH FLOW

PRESENT
WORTH
OF SERIES

**Fig. A.4**   Present worth of a uniform series.

### 5. Present worth of a regular or uniform series

As the present worth factor calculated the present worth for a lump sum, this factor calculates the present worth of a series of cash flows recurring for a number of years or periods.

The present worth of £100 each year for the next four years, given an interest rate of 15%, is £285.49:

$$£100 \times 2.8549 = £285.49$$

2.8549 is the uniform series present worth factor taken from tables or calculated from the expression:

$$\frac{(1 + i)^n - 1}{(1 + i)^n i}$$

where i is the interest rate and n is the number of years. It should be noted that the expression is the uniform series compound amount factor multiplied by the present worth factor. £285.49 could have been found by calculating the present worth of each of the four individual cash flows and summing them. The uniform series present worth factor achieves this in one step, as illustrated in Figure A.4. The use of the end of period convention is also illustrated.

The meaning of the present worth of £285.49 for this series of cash flows is the same as that for the present worth of a single sum i.e. the sum required to be invested in year 0 at 15% that will allow £100 to be withdrawn each year for the next four years.

This process is widely used to discount regular series into lump sums, i.e. to capitalise the regular series. It is important because it permits recurring cash flows to be converted to capital sums and thereby compared to capital sums. It provides the mechanism for comparing invested capital with running costs and thereby evaluating any possible trade-offs between them.

### 6. Capital recovery

The inverse to the uniform series present worth factor is the capital recovery factor. This allows the income that can be taken on a regular basis from an invested capital sum to be calculated. If a sum £285.49 is invested at an interest rate of 15% then the regular income that can be taken each year for the next four years is £100:

$$£285.49 \times 0.35026 = £100$$

0.35026 is the capital recovery factor taken from tables or calculated from the expression:

$$\frac{i (1 + i)^n}{(1 + i)^n - 1}$$

where i is the interest rate and n is the number of years. This expression is the inverse of the uniform series present worth factor.

The importance of this calculation is that it allows the conversion of capital sums into annual sums. This provides an alternative means of comparing capital with running costs. For example, if £285.49 is not invested but used to purchase an item of plant then the cost of that plant item can be regarded as £285.49 or as an annual cost of £100 for four years. The annual cost being set equal to the amount of income that the investor is deprived of because the capital is locked up in the plant. This calculation is useful in comparing hiring with purchasing or in calculating the 'capital' element in hire rates.

**Tabulations of interest and time relationships for interest rates of 10% and 15%**

**Table A.1** Interest factors for 10%

| Year or period (n) | $(1 + i)^n$ Compound amount of a single sum | $\dfrac{1}{(1 + i)^n}$ Present value of a single sum | $\dfrac{(1 + i)^n - 1}{i}$ Compound amount of a uniform series | $\dfrac{i}{(1 + i)^n - 1}$ Sinking fund deposit | $\dfrac{(1 + i)^n - 1}{i(1 + i)^n}$ Present worth of a uniform series | $\dfrac{i(1 + i)^n}{(1 + i)^n - 1}$ Capital recovery |
|---|---|---|---|---|---|---|
| 1 | 1·100 0 | 0·909 09 | 1·000 | 1·000 00 | 0·909 0 | 1·100 00 |
| 2 | 1·209 9 | 0·826 44 | 2·099 | 0·476 19 | 1·735 5 | 0·576 19 |
| 3 | 1·330 9 | 0·751 31 | 3·309 | 0·302 11 | 2·486 8 | 0·402 11 |
| 4 | 1·464 0 | 0·683 01 | 4·640 | 0·215 47 | 3·169 8 | 0·315 47 |
| 5 | 1·610 5 | 0·620 92 | 6·105 | 0·163 79 | 3·790 7 | 0·263 79 |
| 6 | 1·771 5 | 0·564 47 | 7·715 | 0·129 60 | 4·355 2 | 0·229 60 |
| 7 | 1·948 7 | 0·513 15 | 9·487 | 0·105 40 | 4·868 4 | 0·205 40 |
| 8 | 2·143 5 | 0·466 50 | 11·435 | 0·087 44 | 5·334 9 | 0·187 44 |
| 9 | 2·357 9 | 0·424 09 | 13·579 | 0·073 64 | 5·759 0 | 0·173 64 |
| 10 | 2·593 7 | 0·385 54 | 15·937 | 0·062 74 | 6·144 5 | 0·162 74 |
| 11 | 2·853 1 | 0·350 49 | 18·531 | 0·053 96 | 6·495 0 | 0·153 96 |
| 12 | 3·138 4 | 0·318 63 | 21·384 | 0·046 76 | 6·813 6 | 0·146 76 |
| 13 | 3·452 2 | 0·289 66 | 24·522 | 0·040 77 | 7·103 3 | 0·140 77 |
| 14 | 3·797 4 | 0·263 33 | 27·974 | 0·035 74 | 7·366 6 | 0·135 74 |
| 15 | 4·177 2 | 0·239 39 | 31·722 | 0·031 47 | 7·606 0 | 0·131 47 |
| 16 | 4·594 9 | 0·217 62 | 35·949 | 0·027 81 | 7·923 7 | 0·127 81 |
| 17 | 5·054 4 | 0·197 84 | 40·544 | 0·024 66 | 8·021 5 | 0·124 66 |
| 18 | 5·559 9 | 0·179 85 | 45·599 | 0·021 93 | 8·201 4 | 0·121 93 |
| 19 | 6·115 9 | 0·163 50 | 51·159 | 0·019 54 | 8·364 9 | 0·119 54 |
| 20 | 6·727 4 | 0·148 64 | 57·274 | 0·017 45 | 8·513 5 | 0·117 45 |
| 21 | 7·400 2 | 0·135 13 | 64·002 | 0·015 62 | 8·648 6 | 0·115 62 |
| 22 | 8·140 2 | 0·122 84 | 71·402 | 0·014 00 | 8·771 5 | 0·114 00 |
| 23 | 8·954 3 | 0·111 67 | 79·543 | 0·012 57 | 8·883 2 | 0·112 57 |
| 24 | 9·849 7 | 0·101 52 | 88·497 | 0·011 29 | 8·984 7 | 0·111 29 |
| 25 | 10·834 7 | 0·092 29 | 98·347 | 0·010 16 | 9·077 0 | 0·110 16 |
| 26 | 11·918 1 | 0·083 90 | 109·181 | 0·009 15 | 9·160 9 | 0·109 15 |
| 27 | 13·109 9 | 0·076 27 | 121·099 | 0·008 25 | 9·237 2 | 0·108 25 |
| 28 | 14·420 9 | 0·069 34 | 134·209 | 0·007 45 | 9·306 5 | 0·107 45 |
| 29 | 15·863 0 | 0·063 03 | 148·630 | 0·006 72 | 9·369 6 | 0·106 72 |
| 30 | 17·449 4 | 0·057 30 | 164·494 | 0·006 07 | 9·426 9 | 0·106 07 |
| 35 | 28·102 4 | 0·035 58 | 271·024 | 0·003 68 | 9·644 1 | 0·103 68 |
| 40 | 45·259 2 | 0·022 09 | 442·592 | 0·002 25 | 9·779 0 | 0·102 25 |
| 45 | 72·890 4 | 0·013 71 | 718·904 | 0·001 39 | 9·862 8 | 0·101 39 |
| 50 | 117·390 8 | 0·008 51 | 1 163·908 | 0·000 85 | 9·914 8 | 0·100 85 |

Tables are reproduced from the examination tables of Loughborough University of Technology, Department of Civil Engineering.

**Table A.2**   Interest factors for 15%

| Year or period ($n$) | $(1 + i)^n$ Compound amount of a single sum | $\dfrac{1}{(1 + i)^n}$ Present worth of a single sum | $\dfrac{(1 + i)^n - 1}{i}$ Compound amount of a uniform series | $\dfrac{i}{(1 + i)^n - 1}$ Sinking fund deposit | $\dfrac{(1 + i)^n - 1}{i(1 + i)^n}$ Present worth of a uniform series | $\dfrac{i(1 + i)^n}{(1 + i)^n - 1}$ Capital recovery |
|---|---|---|---|---|---|---|
| 1 | 1·150 0 | 0·869 56 | 1·000 | 1·000 00 | 0·869 5 | 1·150 00 |
| 2 | 1·322 4 | 0·756 14 | 2·149 | 0·465 11 | 1·625 7 | 0·615 11 |
| 3 | 1·520 8 | 0·657 51 | 3·472 | 0·287 97 | 2·283 2 | 0·437 97 |
| 4 | 1·749 0 | 0·571 75 | 4·993 | 0·200 26 | 2·854 9 | 0·350 26 |
| 5 | 2·011 3 | 0·497 17 | 6·742 | 0·148 31 | 3·352 1 | 0·298 31 |
| 6 | 2·313 0 | 0·432 32 | 8·753 | 0·114 23 | 3·784 4 | 0·264 23 |
| 7 | 2·660 0 | 0·375 93 | 11·066 | 0·090 36 | 4·160 4 | 0·240 36 |
| 8 | 3·059 0 | 0·326 90 | 13·725 | 0·072 85 | 4·487 3 | 0·222 85 |
| 9 | 3·517 8 | 0·284 26 | 16·785 | 0·059 57 | 4·771 5 | 0·209 57 |
| 10 | 4·045 5 | 0·247 18 | 20·303 | 0·049 25 | 5·018 7 | 0·199 25 |
| 11 | 4·652 3 | 0·214 94 | 24·349 | 0·041 06 | 5·233 7 | 0·191 06 |
| 12 | 5·350 2 | 0·186 90 | 29·001 | 0·034 48 | 5·420 6 | 0·184 48 |
| 13 | 6·152 7 | 0·162 52 | 34·351 | 0·029 11 | 5·583 1 | 0·179 11 |
| 14 | 7·075 7 | 0·141 32 | 40·504 | 0·024 68 | 5·724 4 | 0·174 68 |
| 15 | 8·137 0 | 0·122 89 | 47·580 | 0·021 01 | 5·847 3 | 0·171 01 |
| 16 | 9·357 6 | 0·106 86 | 55·717 | 0·017 94 | 5·954 2 | 0·167 94 |
| 17 | 10·761 2 | 0·092 92 | 65·075 | 0·015 36 | 6·047 1 | 0·165 36 |
| 18 | 12·375 4 | 0·080 80 | 75·836 | 0·013 18 | 6·127 9 | 0·163 18 |
| 19 | 14·231 7 | 0·070 26 | 88·211 | 0·011 33 | 6·198 2 | 0·161 33 |
| 20 | 16·366 5 | 0·061 10 | 102·443 | 0·009 76 | 6·259 3 | 0·159 76 |
| 21 | 18·821 5 | 0·053 13 | 118·810 | 0·008 41 | 6·312 4 | 0·158 41 |
| 22 | 21·644 7 | 0·046 20 | 137·631 | 0·007 26 | 6·358 6 | 0·157 26 |
| 23 | 24·891 4 | 0·040 17 | 159·276 | 0·006 27 | 6·398 8 | 0·156 27 |
| 24 | 28·625 1 | 0·034 93 | 184·167 | 0·005 42 | 6·433 7 | 0·155 42 |
| 25 | 32·918 9 | 0·030 37 | 212·793 | 0·004 69 | 6·464 1 | 0·154 69 |
| 26 | 37·856 7 | 0·026 41 | 245·711 | 0·004 06 | 6·490 5 | 0·154 06 |
| 27 | 43·535 3 | 0·022 96 | 283·568 | 0·003 52 | 6·513 5 | 0·153 52 |
| 28 | 50·065 6 | 0·019 97 | 327·104 | 0·003 05 | 6·533 5 | 0·153 05 |
| 29 | 57·575 4 | 0·017 36 | 377·169 | 0·002 65 | 6·550 8 | 0·152 65 |
| 30 | 66·211 7 | 0·015 10 | 434·745 | 0·002 30 | 6·565 9 | 0·152 30 |
| 35 | 133·175 5 | 0·007 50 | 881·170 | 0·001 13 | 6·616 6 | 0·151 13 |
| 40 | 267·863 5 | 0·003 73 | 1 779·090 | 0·000 56 | 6·641 7 | 0·150 56 |
| 45 | 538·769 2 | 0·001 85 | 3 585·128 | 0·000 27 | 6·654 2 | 0·150 27 |
| 50 | 1 083·657 3 | 0·000 92 | 7 217·715 | 0·000 13 | 6·660 5 | 0·150 13 |

# INDEX